## *Enthusiastic Praise for Spice for Life*

"Ed and Shiela open a door to this fascinating world of herbs and spices and show how they can be delightfully integrated into our mainstream diet. For our spiritual progress as much as anything else, it is mandatory to find nourishment in a well-balanced way. This is more than a recipe book: it is an essential guide to holistic eating."

— James Anderson, Coordinating Editor NAMAH, the *Journal for Integral Health,* Pondicherry, India

"Have you ever visited an old and treasured friend and discovered something bright and new? *Spice for Life* does just that. It brings me back to earlier years when exploring herbs for healing brought purpose and pleasure — and refreshes the feast. Ed Bauman and Shiela Moorthy offer you the art and the science, the taste and aromas. From recipes to remedies, you'll find spices you probably already know (like basil and ginger) as well as those you'll want to explore or repurpose (saffron, say). I am especially delighted to see Ashwagandha get its due!"

— Michael Anne Conley, MA, LMFT, Integrative Health Consultant, Director at *Stillpoint Integrative Health Center*

"Incredible health, healing, happiness and harmony emanates from the *Spice for Life.* I am excited to refer friends, family, clients and doctors to this wonderful book. Dr. Bauman mentored myself and countless others to apply holistic nutrition and culinary alchemy in their very own kitchen. YAYA!"

— Cathy Crystal, NC, Nutrition Consultant & Herbalist, Vibrational Sound & Attunement *SoulCollage*® Facilitator

"I had the incredible fortune to be a taste-tester for the recipes in this book. What heaven! I never knew what delights would await me at day's end. Everything is SO delicious (with the added benefit of being healthy and nutritious). After experiencing explosions of flavors, I would look over the recipe and be amazed that the words could transform into such culinary masterpieces. Please give yourself the gift of trying all these recipes."

— Ann Dannelly, Iyengar Yoga & Zen Awareness Practitioner

"*Spice for Lif*
This easy-to-
look at a variety of spices. More than a cookbook, it provides an engaging and comprehensive resource for traditional uses, health benefits, clinical applications, as well as mouthwatering nourishing recipes. *Spice for Life* is a resource that belongs in every kitchen."

— Mira Dessy, Nutrition Educator, Author of *The Ingredient Guru*

"The one (and perhaps only) good thing we can say about the breakdown of the conventional health-care system is that it's causing more and more of us to seek out and discover the profound power of healing foods. Ed Bauman has been a true pioneer in bringing this ageless knowledge to contemporary audiences for decades; and I know that *Spice for Life* will be one of those books that will never leave my kitchen counter. The beauty, information, and recipes contained here make it a must-have volume for anyone who truly wants to take their health and gustatory pleasure into their own hands."

— Marcella Friel, Author of *Tap, Taste, Heal: Use Emotional Freedom Techniques (EFT) to Eat Joyfully and Love Your Body*

"Ed Bauman has been sharing the good word of nutrition long before it became fashionable. This book is yet another example of his ability to weave together the science of whole foods, in this case spices, with delicious recipes that will spice up your life. This book deserves a spot in the kitchen and confirms what the research tells us, and traditional cultures have shared with us, that food is our best medicine."

— Mary Sheila Gonnella, NC, BCHN, Health and Wellness teacher, speaker, practitioner at *Occidental Nutrition*

"Dr. Ed Bauman and I have been colleagues and friends for many decades. He is an excellent nutrition teacher and great chef with a Masters in Spice. *Spice for Life* is superlative! Any great chef knows that spices are the key to add flavor and health to our diet and to our life."

— Elson Haas, MD, Family Medicine Practitioner, Author of many books, including *Staying Healthy with Nutrition*

"*Spice for Life: Self-Healing Recipes, Remedies and Research* combines just the right mix of Ed's passion for evidence based nutrition education and years of recipe creation with Shiela's fragrant Indian kitchen and scientific mindset. Their delicious recipes are accessible and beautifully photographed by Christine Bauman."

— Patty James, MS, NC Founder, *Patty James Cooking School and Nutrition Center,* Author of *More Vegetables, Please!*

"To fully understand *Food as Medicine,* we must open the apothecary's chest, filled with herbs, resins, and spices. The warm smell of clove, allspice, coriander, celery, and black pepper used in corned-beef or chi permeates the air. These powerful anti-viral spices date to the time of the crusades for those of northern European ancestry, far longer for others. The traditional and creative recipes included in *Spice for Life: Self-Healing Recipes,Remedies, and Research* once again awakens our hunger for food as medicine. Spices have been in use as flavorings and medicine from the dawn of time. As a third-generation wildcrafter and lover of herbs and spices, this book will hold a place of honor and use in my kitchen library."

— Tammera J. Karr, Ph.D., BCHN, Food Historian and Author of *Our Journey with Food Cookery Book*

"In *Spice for Life,* Dr. Ed and Shiela take us on a wonderful adventure though the fascinating world of spices and their life-affirming and healing properties. Their beautifully illustrated book is not only an antidote to processed food and resultant metabolic syndrome disease but a path for those seeking the zest-filled life."

— Todd Knobel, Founder and CEO, *Foogal, Inc.*

"Using food as medicine just got easier! *Spice for Life: Self-Healing Recipes, Remedies and Research* take the reader on a journey that will not only awaken their senses but also their understanding of how to use the healing power of spices in their daily lives. With recipes and detailed descriptions of the flavors, health benefits and research behind a range of herbs and spices, readers will be empowered to get into the kitchen and explore their newfound love for these flavor-bombs!"

— Sally Lamont, Naturopathic Doctor, Acupuncturist, Cook and Founder of **www.drsallyskitchen.com**

"If there is a Michael Jordan of nutrition education, it is Dr. Ed Bauman, founder of Bauman College. *Spice for Life* showcases an abundance of vivid illustrations, self-healing recipes, remedies and scientific research that bring life to the world of nature's medicine. This one of a kind manual will empower and provide an understanding of the vast world of spices, and how they can be used in everyday life. I highly recommend this book, a remarkable encyclopedia of wisdom."

— Rob Liakos, NC, *True Earth Farmacy,* Savannah, GA

"I find myself returning to *Spice for Life* regularly for directions on usage, herbal lore, and a variety of delicious recipes. I love these spices! As Ed and Sheila introduce you to memory-enhancing basil, the warmth of ginger, the pungency of peppers, and ashwaganda, an herb that calms and energizes at the same time. These 10 plant personalities will fill your teacup, your garden, your plate and your heart."

— Erin Livers, Nutrition Therapist, *Food As Nourishment Revitalize Digestion*

"I have had the good fortune to know and work with Ed Bauman for more than 20 years. In that time we have collaborated on numerous nutrition and health-related projects that were always inspirational and transformative. Ed and I have also seen a lot of great jazz here in the Bay Area. Already, I digress... Dr. Bauman and his co-author Shiela Moorthy has given us an enormously valuable resource for delving into the world of herbs and spices. *Spice for Life* is truly a "one-stop shopping" work that provides an abundance of information for the clinician, chef or food enthusiast alike. I love the format because you get a balance of history, research, clinical pearls and of course, delicious recipes. This is one of those books you'll wish you had years ago because it is so thorough and has all the excellent, diverse and well laid out content you want at your fingertips. Get this book. Read this book. Read it again... and the next time someone asks you why you think turmeric is "such a big deal," you can say with confidence (and say it with your best Arnold Schwarzenegger impression), "I've read *Spice for Life.*"

— Geoffrey Marx, linical Nutrition Consultant, Chef, *Marx Culinary*

"I couldn't be more impressed with the the *Spice for Life* book written by my mentor, collaborator on all things nutrition and culinary and dear friend, Ed Bauman and his co-author, Shiela Moorthy. I saw the seedling of this creation starting with Ed's spice blend, '*Spice of Life.*' Now that spice blend has been unfolded into an incredible book that is part research manual, part cookbook and part user manual for the gardener, herbalist or healing foods chef. It's not only a treasure tome of well-researched nutritional wisdom, gardening tips and delicious recipes but a heartening travel guide to what is clearly a passion for both authors; the connection between powerful healing spices and a mutual love for cooking and community. As a culinary nutrition instructor, I would strongly recommend this book as a valuable resource and as a chef I would gladly gift this book to anyone interested in deepening their knowledge about herbs and spices."

— Lizette Marx, NC, Chef Instructor, Culinary Nutritionist, Yoga Teacher and Author, *Marx Culinary*

"Wow, *Spice for Life* is a humdinger, a real gem! It is a compendium of everything that's sexy, practical, clinical, and exciting about spices. In my 30 years working in the natural lifestyle industry, *Spice for Life* is the first book on herbs and spices that's hit my hot button when it comes to culinary use. It's the ultimate bedside read."

— James McDonald, BSc Dip ION, *JM Nutrition Services,* Reading, United Kingdom

"*Spice for Life* asks and answers the question of why use herbs and spices in your daily life. It adeptly provides examples of how to use them, when they should be avoided, and how to grow and cook with spices to add flavor and zest. Wonderful information is provided for practitioners wanting a deep-dive into clinical research as well as treasures for self-help nutrition consumers searching for spice nutrition lore. This book belongs on everyone's shelf, or better yet, in their kitchen. I know it will be in mine."

— Barbara Rodgers, NC, BCHN®, Author of *Baby Maker: A complete guide to holistic nutrition for fertility, conception and pregnancy*

"*Spice for Life* is a great title and book by Dr. Bauman. I have had the good fortune of meeting Dr. Bauman and love this great book on spices with recipes. He has been able to intertwine and narrate traditional and scientific knowledge of these herbs with authority. Herbs and spices have been used all over the world for their culinary and healing properties. My grandma used herbs and spices for almost every ailment humans suffer with greater success. I wish Dr. Bauman great success with his book. With best wishes."

— Dr. Virender Sodhi and Rekha Sodhi, *Ayush Herbs, Ayurvedic and Naturopathic Clinic,* Seattle, WA

"In this book, Ed and Shiela have blended a mastery of nutrition with a delicious treasury of spice lore. *Spice for Life* is a great resource on how spices and seasonal herbs enhance the flavor of vegetable, chicken, fish and meat dishes. Spices and herbs have long been revered for their health attributes. This book is a remarkable transformational resource."

— Karen Weaver, MBA, NC, Owner of *Flour Chylde Bakery and Café*

"Food is medicine and medicine is food, especially when we include culinary herbs and spices, of which Ed has so elegantly captured in this treasure of a book *Spice for Life.* The combination of wonderful recipes, with in-depth information on the health benefits, and the beautiful photography, it pulls you in, and soon you will be in the kitchen creating one of these dishes or running to the store to pick up a spice you may not have ever used before."

— Donnie Yance, Clinical Herbalist, Founder and President of *Mederi Centre for Natural Medicine*

# Spice for Life

## SELF-HEALING RECIPES, REMEDIES AND RESEARCH

Dear Tom and Linda,
I know you will enjoy
lots of family time reading
and creating in your kitchen.

Much Love

Shiela Moorthy

9/5/21

Ed Bauman, M.Ed., PhD & Shiela Moorthy, MA, MBA, NC

© 2020, **Spice for Life: Self-Healing Recipes, Remedies and Research**

ISBN: 978-0-578-67069-0

Authors: Dr. Ed Bauman and Shiela Moorthy

Editor: Francesca Fifis

Photographs: Christine Bauman, B.S. — cover, pages 9, 17, 19-21, 23, 25, 26, 29 top and middle, 37-39, 42-45, 47 top, 57-60, 63 middle and bottom, 70-73, 76-78, 81, 83, 89, 91-97, 99, 108-109, 115, 122-127, 129-131, 138-141, 143-145, 155, 157-159, 162, 163 bottom, 169-175, 194

ShutterStock.com — pages 8, 27, 28, 29 bottom, 46, 47 middle and bottom, 62, 63 top, 75, 79, 80, 81 top, 82, 90, 98, 106-107, 111-114, 128, 146-147, 153, 160-161, 163 top, 168, 176

Book Design: Phyllis Peterson, MagnoliaStudio.com

**Notice of Rights**
All rights reserved. No part of this book may be reproduced or transmitted in any form by any means, electronic, mechanical, photocopying, recording, or otherwise, without the prior written permission of the publisher. For more information on getting permission for reprints and excerpts, use contact information below.

**Notice of Liability**
The information in this book is distributed on an "As Is" basis without warranty. While every precaution has been taken in the preparation of the book, neither the authors nor Bauman College shall have any liability to any person or entity with respect to any loss or damage caused or alleged to be caused directly or indirectly by the instructions contained in this book.

**Trademarks**
Many of the designations used by manufacturers and sellers to distinguish their products are claimed as trademarks. Where those designations appear in this book, and Bauman College was aware of a trademark claim, the designations appear as requested by the owner of the trademark. All other product names and services identified throughout this book are used in editorial fashion only and for the benefit of such companies with no intention of infringement of the trademark. No such use, or the use of any trade name, is intended to convey endorsement or other affiliation with this book.

BAUMANWELLNESS.COM

# Dedications

This book is dedicated to my mother, Pramila Murthy (and all mothers) whose energy sees no bounds. She is forever positive, a born healer. Her tasty home cooking has nourished our families and friends for as long as I can remember. Whether in Bangalore, India caring for her mother, or in the United States visiting her beloved children and grandchildren, Pramila is ever ready to cook, care for others and share her deep faith and love.

— Shiela Moorthy

My wife, Chris and I share this dedication with Shiela to her mom. We had the honor and pleasure to visit her in India recently. Pramila changed our life with her warm and lasting embrace. We had so much fun cooking with her, picking up tips and tricks she intuitively used in preparing the best tasting food we have ever tasted. You are an inspiration to us.

Shiela and I offer the blessing of *Spice for Life* to families everywhere as they renew their relationship with traditional food and healing spices prepared with love. May all of our relations and Mother Earth be cherished and well-nourished. Namaste.

— Ed Bauman

# Acknowledgments

I am deeply grateful to every member of the *Spice for Life* team for their tireless effort to create a book that will be read and enjoyed by many across the globe for years to come. Shiela Moorthy, thanks for accepting my challenge to "show me the research" that spices heal and how they do so. Chris Bauman, thanks for the images you styled and shot that adorn our book. Your photos captured the light within and around each special spice and recipe. Linda Ford, thanks for testing recipes with us and adding your love to the project. Francesca Fifis, thank for being our editor, for checking the authenticity of the work, polishing language, and creating a consistent recipe format. And finally, thanks to Phyllis Peterson, book designer and project coordinator. You laid out the brilliant template, and lovingly held us accountable to produce every piece of our spice puzzle, that you then carefully laid into place. Huge high five to Jennifer and Donnie Yance for crafting a great preface to be the perfect hors d'oeuvre for a main course of *Spice for Life.*

I honor my teachers and mentors for the past fifty years, beginning with my mother, Jane Bauman, who taught me to smell the cantaloupes before picking the best one. Shout out to my daughter, Jessica Bauman, who may still be the best chef in our family, though that will always be up for debate. Blessings and love to friends and colleagues who share our love of healing spices, education, and co-creating a world of well-being for all.

— Ed Bauman

I am eternally grateful to Dr. Bauman, for trusting me on this very important journey to document proof and relevance of how spices do more than make food pleasing to our palates. You are a wonderful human being, generous, kind, and always taking care of the community. I am grateful to Phyllis Peterson for a blow out job in designing *Spice for Life,* Francesca Fifis for patiently editing the text, and Chris Bauman for her artistry in photography and placement.

I am very grateful to my grandmother Jaiakka, for her unconditional love and affection, who at 97 years old, is an amazing role model. I am grateful to our neighbor Eileen Winchell for celebrating every milestone we have reached with numerous cups of tea and warm hugs. Thanks to Judy and David Deardorff for your invaluable help with food preparation and recipe testing. Thank you to Dave and Dawn Lindberg, and Kurshid Kazim for taste-testing and providing candid feedback. I am grateful to my husband Girish Moorthy for standing by me as I dedicated so much time and rigor to this epic project. You are a great cook and make the greatest tea. Thanks to Nikhil Moorthy, our son, for your love, affection and humor. Your refined palette affords you a great potential to carry on our family lineage of preparing beautifully spiced homemade meals.

— Shiela Moorthy

# Table of Contents

# Preface

Donald R. Yance, CN, MH, RH (AHG)

Ed and I have been close colleagues and friends in the field of health for well over two decades. In watching trendy diets come (and often go), we have both stayed true to our whole-food balanced, approach. We believe in the importance of what tradition and culture teaches, as well as what we continue to learn through modern science.

As Hippocrates said: "Let food be thy medicine and medicine be thy food." This is especially true when we include culinary herbs and spices. In *Spice for Life,* the combination of wonderful recipes, with in-depth information on health benefits, and beautiful photography will entice and draw you in. Soon you will be in the kitchen cooking up one of these dishes or running to the store to pick up a spice you never knew or used before.

Besides being an herbalist, nutritionist and jazz musician, I am a chef as well. I have an intense passion for food preparation and cooking. It is no different than mixing synergistic herbs for medicine or composing music. Studying the medicinal value of common spices is like studying theology to me. There isn't a finite end. The deeper we go in uncovering their endless health benefits, the closer we get to see the face of the Master at work, in a most humble way.

One of the reasons spices such as turmeric and cumin were added to dishes was to reduce rancidity and oxidation, thus extending their shelf life, often without refrigeration. When we consume these same herbs, they preserve our cellular health, protecting us from damage, and even aging. They are not anti-aging; for they aren't against aging, but rather they enable us to age gracefully.

Recently I have been fascinated by a human-to-plant concept called "xenohormesis." The notion that plants make substances of benefit to human health has been known for millennia. Did you ever think that all those wonderful aromas (I love the smell of fresh basil and rosemary) that add the taste we love from the herbs and spices are nature's healing pharmacy (farm-acy)?

Many of the known active compounds in spices are referred to as secondary compounds. They evolve within the plant, through the plants life-force intelligence for stress protection. Their synthesis coincides with environmental stresses — UV light, lack of nutrients, disease, and predation. An example of members of one broad chemical class in plants that confer human health benefits are the phenols. Curcumin is a phenolic compound in the well-known curry spice turmeric. The content of phenols provides a chemical signature within the plant that adapts to the state of the environment. Stress-induced plant compounds tend to upregulate pathways that provide stress resistance. People who consume non-pampered plants develop mechanisms to become attuned to chemical cues and respond like a cellular Tai Chi master, or when seriously provoked, like a kick boxer.

The health benefits from phytochemical compounds in spices are not simply from responses to mild cellular damage or from their antioxidant properties, but rather from the evolutionarily adaptive modulation of the enzymes and receptors of the stress-response. You see what I am talking about when I say theological, and let's add profoundly beautiful!

The science of epigenetics is turning what we've long held true about biological destiny upside down. Although it remains true that our DNA — our genetic code — provides the blueprint for our physiological makeup, researchers have discovered that there's something extra controlling our genes — and culinary herbs, spices and food may in fact be the most important factors in our genetic well-being.

**A Look Forward**

As several metabolic diseases and age-related degenerative disorders are closely associated with oxidative and inflammatory processes in the body, the use of culinary herbs and spices offer a sensible, easy and tasty way to combat disease. *Spice for Life* is the bible to help guide you in your daily quest to become a co-creator with nature to live long and well. I will be recommending *Spice for Life* to all of my patients and students.

---

Donald R. Yance is a Certified Nutritionist and Master Herbalist. He is the President and Founder of *Mederi Center and Natura Health Products* in Ashland, Oregon.

# Introduction

Herbs and spices are a key component of healing foods, imparting taste, texture, aroma and nutrition. These plants, originally found in the wilds, and now cultivated for worldwide consumption, contain the most concentrated amounts of vitamins, minerals, protective and restorative phyto (plant) nutrient compounds of all the foods known to man. Yes, spices are more nutrient dense per ounce than meats, dairy, grains, legumes, nuts, seeds, vegetables or fruits! Spices enable us to optimally digest and assimilate our daily foods, which is especially important to an aging or ailing population.

For those who did not grow up in a household with traditional homemade food, spices may appear to be exotic, and taste rather strong, even off putting. Pungent spices are often savory, bitter and astringent. These tastes are not common in standard bland, *one taste fits all,* commercial cuisine that is familiar to an unseasoned palate. Herbs and spices, when properly used by a skillful chef, give simple food a remarkable aroma, taste and "wow" factor. Spices provide the eater with a synergistic effect of hundreds and in some cases thousands of phytonutrients, that gives the plants and the dishes and beverages that contain them, their bright color, complex flavor, and powerful medicinal effect.

Ethnic cooking from every part of the globe features locally grown herbs and spices to give foods their distinctive aroma and flavor profile. Sadly, modern American cuisine is one of the least spice-centric of all world cuisines. Burgers and fries, meat and potatoes, cereal, cookies and milk, ice cream, diet soda and energy drinks, typically lack aromatic herbs and savory spices. Salt, pepper, fat and sugar predominate in conventional restaurant or processed, prepared foods, rather than green tea, ginger, garlic, chili, saffron, cumin, oregano, and thyme that liven up Asian, Mid-Eastern and Latin American dishes.

Renowned ethnobotanist James Duke examined 4,500 recipes from 100 cookbooks. They found that 93% contained at least one spice, with the average amount of spices per dish to be four. That average is a minimum in the healing cuisines of India, Thailand, China, European and Mediterranean countries. It is the combination of fresh, whole foods plus distinctive local herbs and spices that define the elegance and signature of these beloved international cuisines. (*CRC Handbook of Medicinal Spices,* 2002)

## Why Use Herbs and Spices?

- Give food a mouthwatering aroma that stimulates the appetite
- Blend in new taste sensations
- Impart layers of flavor, such as sweet, salty, savory, sour, hot
- Serve as natural tenderizer for meats and gluten-free grains
- Add body and texture to dishes, acting as thickeners and binders for sauces
- Color a dish, making it a feast for the eyes
- Promote a robust digestive process
- Improve liver detoxification, immune function and tissue healing

## A Life and Health Changing Book

*Spice for Life* is a handbook to educate people who never received vital nutrition, culinary, botanical or self-care information to wake up and smell the garlic, taste the spicy chai, and savor the pesto. Our experience has been that when people eating regular, somewhat healthy foods, elevate their eating experience as they learn to prepare and enjoy what we call S.O.U.L. (seasonal, organic, unprocessed, local) food, with herbs and spices, they awaken an innate food intelligence that has been muted by a lifetime of poor eating habits and choices. Herbs and spices are nature's way of reminding us that it's thyme to wake up and *Eat for Health*™.

*Spice for Life* will provide the reader with a blend of reliable, non-commercial information, not found in any one book, journal, or online website. This includes information on herbs and spices, history and use, constituents, health benefits, medicinal use and synergies, supplement use and dosage range, culinary blends and sauces, easy to make gourmet recipes, self-care remedies, home cultivation, and online ordering resources.

## Health Benefit of Herbs and Spices

When herbs and spices are added to fresh, whole foods, they impart a salutary benefit that contributes to strengthening of all body systems, cooling inflammation, balancing sensitive neurometabolic, hormonal signals and building cellular resilience. Eating this way can slow the onset of premature aging and illness and complement modern medicine to manage and in some cases reverse disease. This is the most exciting research we are witnessing today in the field of nutrition and integrative medicine. As our grandparents were taught by their parents and grandparents, learning how to cook is crucial to holding a family together and building their health. Knowing how and when to use flavorful herbs and spices not only protected our forebears, but warded off infection and illness that could have wiped them out.

Now, as in times gone by, the cure can be in the kitchen, if the kitchen, garden and pantry are properly stocked. Fortunately, dried herbs and spices have the same, and often more potency than their fresh counterparts, so one can stock up, once it is known what to have on hand.

## Diet-Disease Connection

Many Americans and people around the world eating modern convenience foods, have lost interest in cooking and rely on takeout or pre-packaged foods with numerous additives and preservatives, high in calories and low in nutrients and flavor. Eating this way is unsatisfying and unhealthy. Lifelong poor eating habits and choices can be directly correlated with premature chronic illness as evidenced by the precipitous rise in food and chemical sensitivities, obesity, allergies, blood sugar and hormonal imbalances, depression, anxiety and insomnia. These conditions can often be resolved with a change in diet, lifestyle and attitude, greatly enhanced by the addition of herbs and spices enjoyed at each meal as part of well prepared, nutritionally concentrated foods.

When the health syndromes and conditions mentioned above are not addressed properly and in a timely fashion, more serious disease progression tends to follow. This is evidenced by the alarming rise of diabetes, cardiovascular disease, autoimmune disease, such as Hashimoto's thyroiditis, multiple sclerosis, lupus, rheumatoid arthritis, neurodegenerative conditions such as Parkinson's, Alzheimer's and dementia, as well as the most challenging illness of all, cancer, that can affect any system of the body. While modern medicine has an impressive array of diagnostic techniques, pharmaceutical and surgical options to manage disease and expand the lifespan, the quality of one's life can be compromised due to treatment complications and side effects.

Statistics for 2014 indicate that heart disease causes almost one third of all U.S. deaths. More than 68% of American adults over the age of 20 are overweight or obese; 8.3% of our adult population have been diagnosed with type-2 diabetes, while about half that many are thought to be afflicted with it but undiagnosed; and another 38.2% of adults have pre-diabetes (1), an almost equally dangerous condition of high blood sugar. (Go, et al., 2014)

Herbs and spices, with their high density of protective phytonutrients and antioxidants, when consumed daily as part of one's diet, or as a therapeutic supplement at an appropriate dose, are powerful and reliable ways to cool inflammation and detox from environmental chemicals.

## How Taste Influences Metabolism

According to traditional Ayurvedic, Chinese and Naturopathic medicine, the flavor of a food or spice has a profound influence on the physiology, endocrinology and neurochemistry of the body. Strong, clear tastes set our digestion in motion, and at some point, send signals to the brain that we have eaten enough. The most predominant flavor of many plant medicines, is bitter, one the average person only experiences when eating dark chocolate, black coffee or perhaps bitter greens, such as arugula. In truly excellent cooking all six tastes are present, in balanced amounts, giving food a bright flavor, and dynamic healing effect.

Widening one's flavor palate is key to enjoying more tastes that spices can bring to a dish.

**Bitter** — Detoxifies the body, cleanses the liver, controls skin ailments, aids lymph flow and protein digestion

**Astringent** — Causes constriction of blood vessels, reduces secretions such as sweating and bleeding

**Pungent** — Stimulates appetite, maintains metabolism, improves blood circulation

**Salty** — Cleanses tissues, makes the system limber, activates digestion, supports adrenal glands and kidneys

**Sour** — Aids in digestion and elimination of waste from the body, assists in liver detox and fat metabolism

**Sweet** — Promotes tissue growth, comforts the body, relieves hunger

## Spices in Action

- **Turmeric** adds a bitter flavor, brilliant orange color, promotes digestion, healing of inflamed tissues and improved liver and immune functions.
- **Coriander**, the seed of the cilantro plant, can be used as a sweet spice with cereal, yogurt and fruit, as well as a thickener, imparting a nutty, aromatic flavor. It can be chewed as a breath freshener.
- The chlorophyll-rich **cilantro** leaf, combined in formulas with chlorella, marine algae, has been used to safely detoxify mercury from body and nerve tissues.
- **Ginger** root makes a delicious tea, spice for stir-fry dishes, flavor for cookies, tonic for sluggish digestion and to alleviate nausea

## Specific Examples of Healing Herbs and Spices

Herbs and spices play a significant role in the prevention and management of heart disease, cancer, diabetes, allergies, asthma, obesity, depression and cognitive decline. International research is released on a regular basis confirming the health benefits of a plant based diet, supplemented with an array of herbs and spices. Little of this comes from the U.S., where pharmacology is the dominant paradigm. For example:

- Herbs, such as **rosemary, sage, oregano, thyme, cilantro** and **parsley** have significant amounts of flavonoids which can act as antioxidants to protect LDL cholesterol from being oxidized. They can inhibit the formation of blood clots providing anti-inflammatory and anti-tumor benefits. A study published in 2002 in the *American Journal of Clinical Nutrition* (Knekt, et al.) showed that consuming more plant bioflavonoids is linked to lower incidence of heart disease and stroke, and is more protective than statin drugs.
- **Lemongrass** and **mint** help block the production of cholesterol. **Fenugreek** is high in saponins and soluble fiber which helps decrease the absorption of cholesterol from food and can help lower blood glucose levels in people with diabetes (Kumar, et al., 2011).
- **Ginger** contains several natural terpenoid and phenolic phytochemicals that inhibit the formation of blood clots. Ginger has been used in medicine to assist pregnant women with managing morning sickness. Ginger combined with turmeric, which contains curcuminoids, have been reported to prevent cancer development.
- **Cinnamon**: A study published in *Diabetes Care* in 2003 has shown that small amounts of cinnamon in humans can lower blood glucose, cholesterol and triglycerides. Sixty Pakistani men and women were divided into 6 groups and given 1, 3 or 6 grams of cinnamon or similar amounts of placebo for 40 days. Blood glucose and lipids dropped on average by 20% and remained low for 20 days after intake was stopped. The impact on blood levels was the same at all doses i.e. there was no dose response — so 1g was as effective as 6g. Cinnamon has also been found to enhance insulin activity (Sahib, 2016).

## Cooking with Herbs and Spices

In India and Indonesia, spices such as garlic, ginger, turmeric and chili added to hot oil at the beginning of a recipe infuse meats and vegetables sautéed in them with a savory flavor. Then, later in the cooking process, the more delicate flavors from herbs such as basil, cilantro and dill are added to finish the dish, or as a garnish to balance and cool the hot spices used earlier in the preparation. The contrast and blending of flavors is what creates a rich and enjoyable experience for the eater and his or her metabolism, which responds to the symphony of taste, texture and nutrition of the culinary composition.

## How to Spice Up Your Life

Culinary herbs and spices can be used in a variety of creative ways. You can add them to any recipe including soups, stews, breads, mustards, marinades, butters, sauces, salad dressings, stocks, vinegars, desserts and beverages. To be an excellent home chef, it is important to maintain dry good products that are fresh and not rancid. Flours, grains, seeds, nuts, herbs and spices oxidize and become rancid when exposed to heat and light. A kitchen makeover is the first step in wanting and being able to prepare exciting, healing foods at home. Here are some suggestions on getting stocked up:

- Utensils for preparing fresh herbs include scissors, a sharp knife and a cutting board.
- Utensils for preparing dried herbs include a grinding mill, or a mortar and pestle.
- Use wooden utensils when mixing prepared herbs.
- Dried herbs are more concentrated than fresh. One teaspoon dried herb equals three teaspoons of fresh.
- If you regularly use herbs in your cooking, it may save you time to prepare your own *"bouquet garni"* stash. Parcel your chopped and mixed herbs in little muslin bags. Add a bouquet garni during the last stages of cooking.
- Unlike other herbs, parsley retains its flavor during the cooking process and can be added at the start.
- Fresh herbs can have a more pungent flavor due to the higher content of fragrant essential oils and antioxidants. During the herb drying process there is a loss of oils and nutrients.
- The flavor of herbs diminishes with time; discard if they become rancid.
- Dried whole herbs i.e. where the leaves are still attached to their stalk tend to be "fresher" and have a stronger flavor than loose leaves sold in packets/bottles. Dried whole herbs such as oregano and sage can be purchased from shops specializing in Mediterranean or Middle Eastern products.

## Wonderful Herb and Food Combinations

Try combining herbs as follows to enliven the flavor, and boost the nutritional value of the foods you enjoy. Something as simple as popcorn can be quite tasty, and much more nourishing when adding any of your favorite herbs and spices mentioned below:

**Basil** — pesto, tomato sauce, tomato soup, tomato juice, potato dishes, prawns, meat, chicken and poultry, pasta, rice, egg dishes

**Bay leaf** — soups, stews, casseroles, meat and poultry marinades, stocks

**Chili** — meat, chicken and poultry, prawns, shellfish, tomato dishes, curries

**Chives** — salads, chicken, soups, cheese dishes, egg dishes, mayonnaise, vinaigrettes

**Coriander** — Asian dishes, stir-fries, curries, soups, salads, seafood

**Dill** — salads, sauces, fish, salad, sour cream, cheese and potato dishes

**Fennel** — stuffing, sauces, seafood, mouth freshener

**Garlic** — soups, sauces, pasta, meat, chicken, shellfish, pesto, salad dressings, bread

**Ginger** — cakes, biscuits, tea, Asian dishes

**Lemongrass** — Asian dishes, stir-fries, curries, seafood, soups, tea

**Marjoram** — meat, fish, egg dishes, cheese dishes, pizza

**Mint** — drinks, confectionary, meat, chicken, yogurt, desserts, sauces, vegetable dishes

**Oregano** — cheese dishes, egg dishes, tomato sauce, pizza, meat, stuffing, bread, pasta

**Parsley** — pesto, egg dishes, pasta, rice dishes, salads, butter, sauces, seafood, vegetable dishes

**Rosemary** — fish, poultry, meat, bread, sauces, soups

**Sage** — stuffing, tomato dishes, cheese dishes

**Tarragon** — salad dressing, egg dishes

**Thyme** — chowders, bread, poultry, soups, stock, stews, stuffing, butter, cheese, mustard, vinegar

**Turmeric** — stir-frys, soups, stews, smoothies, marinades, Asian dishes

Herbs and spices are rarely used alone. When mixed together, the effect is synergistic, symphonic, magnificent, delightful, and even transformational. When incorporating high quality herbs and spices with fresh whole foods, an ordinary meal can become memorable. A good chef will follow a good recipe and make a beautiful meal. A spice-savvy chef, will take a good recipe and modify it to make it even better by tasting his or her product as he or she prepares it and adding ingredients and flavors to take the dish to another level. Recipes provided in this book are starting points for a home cook to work with. Below is a basic list of suggested herb and spice combinations, that are presented to the home chef to experiment with in the kitchen, to adjust to his/her taste and tolerance level:

**Basil** — goes with chives, chili, garlic, oregano

**Bay leaf** — goes with parsley, thyme, garlic, oregano, marjoram, turmeric

**Chili** — goes with coriander, garlic, ginger, lemongrass, mint, oregano, turmeric

**Chives** — go with basil, garlic, tarragon

**Dill** — goes with chives, garlic, parsley, tarragon

**Garlic** — goes with basil, rosemary, sage, fennel, chili, coriander, turmeric

**Sage** — goes with rosemary, garlic, marjoram

**Thyme** — goes with bay, parsley, garlic, rosemary

**Oregano** — goes with basil, parsley, chives, thyme, bay, chili

## Herbs and Spices Differentiated

Culinary herbs are *herbaceous* (leafy) plants that add flavor and color to all types of meals. They have been used for centuries to preserve food due to the presence of antioxidant phytochemicals. The flavors are provided by the essential oils and *oleoresins* (natural plant substances) and the pungency or strength of the flavors is due to the *alkaloid* (organic compound) content. The antioxidant content of the herb can vary from plant to plant based upon where the herb was grown, the maturity of the plant when harvested, the plant variety and the part of the herb used. Herbs grown using natural agriculture mature slowly and as such have a superior taste, nutrient composition and influence on one's metabolism. Home grown herbs and spices are not irradiated, which is required of all commercially grown and distributed herbal products.

The parts of the plants used include the seeds, flowers, leaves and roots. In this book, herbs are most often the name we will use for the leaves of an aromatic plant. The roots, seeds and stems are what we will call spices. For example, cilantro is an herb, and coriander, the seed of the cilantro plant, is a spice. If you find that low-fat or low-salt foods taste bland, you can use herbs to enhance the flavor of virtually any dish, including desserts. Generally, herbs are delicately flavored, so add them to your cooking in the last few minutes. It helps to taste test. Too few herbs will contribute nothing to your dish, while too many will overpower the other subtle tastes.

## Herbal Cultivation

Originally, herbs grew wild in the woods, by streams and paths, and were sought out by animals for food and healing. Today, most herbs are not wild-crafted, but rather are grown commercially and sold fresh at farmers' or roadside markets. Dried culinary and medicinal herbs fetch a good price at natural health food stores or herbal apothecaries. Herbs do not require rich soil, abundant water or sunlight. The culinary herbs we will be featuring grow beautifully with the natural landscapes, where annuals and perennial plants can grow at their own pace without fertilizer or additional soil amendments.

Using herbs and spices at every meal as teas and seasonings provide wonderful booster foods to turn ordinary dishes into S.O.U.L. (seasonal, organic, unprocessed and local) satisfying meals that send a positive message to our genes and cells to *celebrate life* and perform optimally and efficiently.

## *How to Use This Book*

We invite you to first browse *Spice for Life* to get a sense of the breadth and depth of this transformative resource. Take note of the parts that are most interesting to you, the plant uses, health benefits, medical uses, recipes, remedies or cultivation techniques. Consider if you are most in need of finding some new recipes to feed your family, or remedies that will help you or your loved ones recover from ailments, injuries, nagging conditions, and even life-threatening diseases. Then, pick the plants you want to get acquainted with. See if you can grow them on your porch or in your backyard. Purchase the fresh form when possible, or the dried form, when fresh is not an option. Get to know the flavor of the herb or spice. In most cases, there are layers of flavor.

The first taste may be bitter, sour, savory, mildly sweet, salty or astringent (somewhat metallic). The flavor of the plant will enable you to appreciate its potency and compatibility with other foods, herbs and spices. If you have the inclination, you can make your own fresh tincture, by putting the herb or spice into apple cider vinegar, red wine, or into brandy, and let it soak for two weeks and then strain and use. Directions will be provided in each chapter.

Notice how and where the plant affects you. Is it calming or stimulating? Is it heating or cooling? Does it make you hungry, or is it satiating? Does it cool your inflammation or ease your pain? If so, how long does the effect last? What do you like or not like about adding a new spice to your life? Can you sense how much to use?

Our purpose is to reconnect you with the forces of nature that cannot be manufactured in a lab, or be provided in isolation. Herbs and spices are not drugs. You can't take two and call your doctor in the morning if your symptoms persist.

We encourage you to find ways to add herbs and spices to as many beverages and foods as you can, even those that are pre-packaged, as few of us will make all our food from scratch. Learning how to make a spice blend, salad dressing, sauce, or tonic beverage will not only empower you, but also be a source of curious conversation and benefit to your friends, family and associates. Even the most cynical skeptics will notice that you are looking and feeling better when you add healing herbs and spices to your food. They will at some point, ask what are you doing, how did you make that delicious soup, stew or chopped herbal salad? As time goes on, with daily use of quality herbs and spices, your desire to satisfy your cravings, or manage your stress with sugar, caffeine, alcohol or recreational drugs and negative behaviors will likely recede as you become less reactive and more resourceful.

A cup of tea is always a great remedy, when you need time to reflect, reset and chill out. Prepare a cup of herbal or green tea from one of the recipes in this book, as you set out to dig into the ancient wisdom and modern research found in *Spice for Life*. Enjoy the nutrition and culinary arts education found in the chapters to come. Allow yourself to progress at your own rate.

May the practical information and love of life and health found in *Spice for Life* guide your way forward to live longer, and better, with more joy, happiness and ability to serve others and the greater good as you pass on what you learn from experience to others just getting on the spice road to well-being.

# Eating for Health

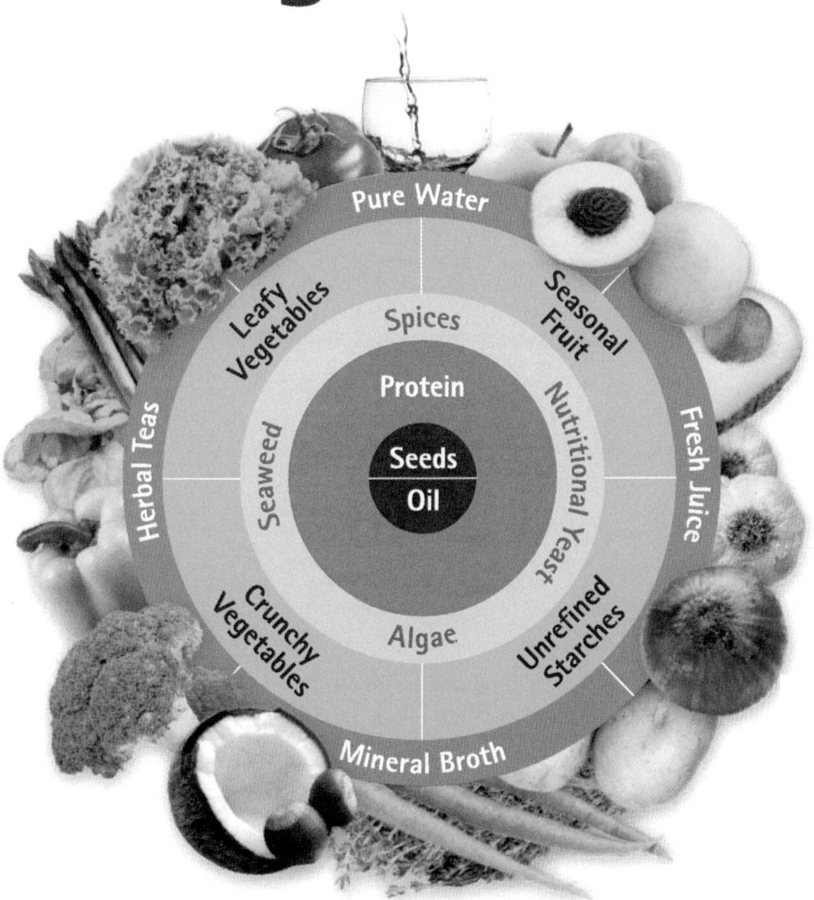


**Eating for Health Serving Chart**

| Food Group | Seeds/Oils | Protein | Leafy Vegetables | Crunchy Vegetables | Unrefined Starches | Seasonal Fruit | Booster Foods |
|---|---|---|---|---|---|---|---|
| Daily Servings | 2-3 | 2-4 | 2-3 | 2-3 | 2-4 | 2-4 | 2-4 |
| Serving Size | 1 Tbs oil 2 Tbs seeds | 3 oz animal 6 oz vegetable | 1 cup | ½ cup | ½ cup whole grain, 1 medium root vegetable | ½ cup or 1 medium piece | 1 tsp to 1 Tbs |
| Examples | flax, sunflower, sesame, almonds | poultry, fish, eggs, milk, beans | salad mix, spinach, kale | broccoli, string beans, onions, celery | grains, bread, yams, winter squash, corn, millet, rice | berries, apple, grape, citrus | nutritional yeast, algae, spices, seaweed |

© Bauman College Holistic Nutrition and Culinary Arts | baumancollege.org

**Created by Dr. Ed Bauman**

CHAPTER ONE

# *Turmeric*

*(Curcuma longa)*

*Harvested turmeric at the market in India.*

**Turmeric** with its most active constituent, *curcumin,* has been the top selling natural health product for the past three years. Our aim is to awaken the modern world to the benefit of using turmeric root and powder as an everyday spice. Asian populations who eat turmeric alone or in a blended *masala* or what we call curry, on a frequent basis, live long and well, free of cancer, heart disease and arthritis. All parts of the turmeric plant have healing properties, not only curcumin. Its taste is bitter and astringent (pungent), so it is a new flavor for a first world palate. This unique taste and effect from its array of carotenoids and bioflavonoids, is what makes turmeric potent. It is better absorbed when mixed with black pepper and consumed with a quality fat such as coconut or whole milk.

Turmeric has been a staple in the traditional cuisine and medicine of Ayurveda, Chinese Medicine and in Perso-Arabic systems, to alleviate inflammation, protect the liver, and help the body prevent and slow disease progression in cancer and nearly every illness. Recipes and remedies are provided to guide you to use turmeric often and safely for food and self-healing.

While traveling in India recently, my wife injured her toe (diagnosed colloquially as *shoe bite*) which became infected. It was a frightening situation which was not ameliorated quickly with antibiotics and topical cortisone cream. I suggested, and our Indian "Auntie" Pramila mixed up a poultice of turmeric powder and mustard seeds for topical application. With this breading like plaster, Chris' toe looked like a piece of fried chicken. By the next day the pain and swelling were down. Within three days, voila, the problem was resolved. Reach for turmeric root and powder as a number one booster food spice and for first aid remedy.

*Auntie Pramila Murthy and her masala dabba dish.*

*Fresh turmeric root and powder*

## Background and Uses

Turmeric (*Curcuma longa*), is a spice native to South Asia. It migrated to the Far East, the Mideast and the West via the silk route when the spice trade thrived nearly 5,000 years ago. Turmeric is a pungent spice that forms the basis for many curry powders. It is also used as a natural food colorant. Traditionally, turmeric has been used to heal bruises, sprains, leech bites, inflamed joints, severe chest congestion and common colds. While growing up in India, I (SM) would often drink "Milagu paal" (literally pepper milk in Tamil, a Southern Indian language), that my grandmother would serve as a palliative for a sore throat or chest congestion, and with a dash of her love that would ensure a good night's rest. I have seen my mother liberally use "haldi" (the term in Hindi or "manjal" in Tamil), in all types of curries, in her beauty regimen, for medicinal purposes and in religious ceremonies as well. Turmeric is abundantly available in India at turmeric plantations, herbal medicine preparations and in the spice bazaars.

Turmeric is a key ingredient in any "masala dabba," a round stainless steel container with inserts that contains key spices tailored to the needs of an Indian kitchen (See page 9 and 19). I (SM) have been indelibly influenced by the spices of both Northern and Southern India that flavored the food I ate growing up and my mother always used a "masala dabba." (See page 9.) My current "dabba" has turmeric at the center, surrounded by red chili, ginger, salt, coriander, cumin, mustard seeds, plus a channa dal seasoning blend.

## Plant Specifics

Turmeric is an herbaceous perennial plant belonging to the ginger family. It is different from most herbs in that you are not going to be harvesting the leaves, but the roots instead. The plant grows as an underground tuber or rhizome, much like ginger does. It can take 8-10 months for a new crop of roots to develop, and it's not a plant that you can harvest in small pieces throughout the season.

As many as 133 species of *Curcuma l.* have been identified worldwide. Most of them have common local names and are used for various medicinal formulations. The turmeric plant grows in temperatures ranging between 68-86˚F (20-30°C) and requires a considerable amount of annual rainfall to thrive. Individual plants grow to a height of 1m (3 feet), and have long, oblong leaves. Plants are gathered annually for their rhizomes, and are reseeded from some of those rhizomes in the following season. The rhizome, from which the turmeric is derived, is tuberous with a rough and segmented skin. The rhizomes mature beneath the foliage in the ground. They are yellowish brown with a deep orange interior. The main rhizome is pointed or tapered at the distal end and measures 1-3 inches (2.5-7 cm) in length and 1 inch (2.5 cm) in diameter, with smaller tubers branching off. When the turmeric rhizome is dried, it can be ground to a yellow powder with a bitter, slightly acrid, yet sweet taste.

## Active Constituents

The rhizome or the root part of turmeric is the part used medicinally. More than 100 components have been isolated from turmeric. The main component of the root is a volatile oil, containing *turmerone,* and there are other coloring agents called *curcuminoids* in turmeric. Curcuminoids consist of curcumin demethoxycurcumin, 5′-methoxycurcumin, and dihydrocurcumin, which are found to be natural antioxidants (Ruby, et al., 1995; Selvam, et al., 1995). The yellow-pigmented curcuminoids represent 2%-5% of the root, typically 85% as curcumin, 10% as demethoxycurcumin and 5% as disdemethodoxyycurcumin. Curcumin is the most studied component.

## Traditional Medicine

In Ayurvedic medicine, turmeric is thought to have many medicinal properties including strengthening the overall energy of the body, relieving gas, dispelling worms, improving digestion, regulating menstruation, dissolving gallstones, and relieving arthritis. Many South Asian countries use it as an antiseptic for cuts, burns, and bruises, and as an anti-bacterial agent, for respiratory conditions (e.g., asthma, bronchial hyper-activity, and allergies), as well as for liver disorders, anorexia, rheumatism, diabetic wounds, runny nose, cough, and sinusitis (Araujo, 2001). In traditional Chinese medicine, it is used to treat diseases associated with abdominal pain (Aggarwal, et al., 2004).

From ancient times, as prescribed by Ayurveda, turmeric has been used to treat sprains and swelling (Araujo, 2001). In both Ayurvedic and traditional Chinese medicine, turmeric is considered a bitter digestive and a carminative. *Unani* (is the term for Perso-Arabic traditional medicine as practiced in Mughal India and in Muslim culture in South Asia and modern day Central Asia) practitioners also use turmeric to expel phlegm or kapha, as well as to open blood vessels in order to improve blood circulation. It can be incorporated into foods, including rice and bean dishes, to improve digestion and reduce gas and bloating. It is a *cholagogue*, stimulating bile production in the liver and encouraging excretion of bile via the gallbladder, which improves the body's ability to digest fats. Sometimes, turmeric mixed with milk or water is taken to treat intestinal disorders as well as colds and sore throats.

## Uses in Modern Medicine

Scientific research over the past fifty years, has demonstrated that a key ingredient in turmeric, *curcumin* (diferuloylmethane), can modulate cell signaling pathways. Extensive clinical trials have been conducted addressing pharmacokinetics, safety and efficacy against several diseases in humans. Certain promising effects have been observed in patients with various pro-inflammatory diseases such as: arthritis, cancer (brain, breast, colon, prostate, colorectal, pancreatic, melanoma) cardiovascular disease, diabetes, Crohn's disease, ulcerative colitis, irritable bowel syndrome, peptic ulcer, gastric ulcer, gastric inflammation, psoriasis, acute coronary syndrome, atherosclerosis, lupus, nephritis, renal conditions, vitiligo, AIDs, chronic arsenic exposure, alcohol intoxication and hepatic conditions (Gupta, et al., 2013).

In dose escalating studies, turmeric has been shown to be safe at levels as high as 12 grams a day for over 3 months. Various formulations have been studied including nanoparticles, liposomal encapsulation, emulsions, capsules, tablets and powder. Some of these delivery mechanisms have managed to improve its bioavailability, metabolism and pharmacokinetics (Gupta, et al., 2013).

Although curcumin has shown efficacy against numerous human ailments, poor bioavailability due to poor absorption, rapid metabolism, and rapid systemic elimination have been shown to limit its therapeutic efficacy (Anand, et al., 2007). As a result, numerous efforts have been made to improve curcumin's bioavailability by altering these features. The use of adjuvants that can block the metabolic pathway of curcumin is the most common strategy for increasing the bioavailability of curcumin. The effect of combining *piperine* (black pepper), a known inhibitor of hepatic and intestinal glucuronidation, was evaluated on the bioavailability of curcumin in healthy human volunteers (Shoba, et al., 2006). In humans receiving a dose of 2g of curcumin alone, serum levels of curcumin were either undetectable or very low. Concomitant administration of 20 mg of piperine with curcumin, however, produced much higher concentrations within 30 minutes to 1 hour after drug treatment; piperine increased the bioavailability of curcumin by 2,000%. The results imply that by adding just 1% of piperine to turmeric could enable better absorption and metabolism.

Most of curcumin's clinical studies have been focused mainly on people with health problems. A recent study, however, evaluated the health-promoting efficacy of lipidated curcumin in healthy middle-aged participants (40-60 years old). In this study, the participants were given either lipidated curcumin (80 mg/day) or placebo for 4 weeks. Curcumin, but not placebo, decreased in plasma levels of triglycerides and *beta amyloid* (plaque). Further, curcumin administration in these participants increased free radical scavenging capabilities. These results demonstrated the health-promoting effects of lipidated curcumin in healthy middle-aged people (Disilvestro, et al., 2012). Adding ghee or extra-virgin coconut oil to turmeric can better its absorption.

## *Health Benefits of Turmeric*

- Potential benefits from regular use are numerous. They include improved circulation, the prevention of blood clots, and alleviation of menstrual and menopausal complaints (Marcus, et al., 2000).
- It can stimulate the flow of bile, promoting the digestion of fats, and expedite the liver's ability to detoxify fat soluble metabolic and environmental toxins, such as pesticides, herbicides, medications, and synthetic hormones given to commercial animals to increase their size and yield of milk and meat.
- Turmeric has hepato-protective activity and can help prevent viral- or chemical-induced liver damage, as well as enhancing hepatic glutathione, a powerful cell protector and phase 2 liver detoxification enzyme precursor.
- Turmeric is a powerful anti-inflammatory, immune-regulator and mild analgesic used in the amelioration of osteoarthritis, rheumatoid arthritis, and bursitis. It is also effective in healing inflammatory conditions of the gastrointestinal tract such as ulcerative colitis, Crohn's disease, celiac disease, gastritis and gastric ulcers.
- Turmeric gradually lowers blood pressure, reduces LDL cholesterol levels and oxidative damage to the liver, blood vessels (atherosclerosis) and eyes.
- Curcumin is used in the treatment of viral infections such as HIV, Zika and Epstein Barr (Bernhardt, 2016).
- Since the discovery of turmeric's antioxidant phenolic compounds, and the protection these compounds provide against free radicals, this spice is now viewed as much more than just an ingredient in curry or a yellow dye. Turmeric's potential use in cancer prevention and recovery is now the subject of intense laboratory and clinical research. Curcumin extracted from turmeric has been found to down-regulate over 70 cell signaling pathways and oncogenes that promote cancer growth.

## *Cancer: Select Clinical Data*

Below is a selection of trials demonstrating the power of curcumin to slow cancer progression.

| DISEASE | DURATION | BENEFIT | DOSAGE |
|---|---|---|---|
| **Breast Cancer** | **20 clinical trials** | • Data suggest significant chemopreventive and anticancer potential for curcumin (Alshuler, 2017). | • 500-8,000 mg of curcumin per day.<br>• Standardized extracts in lower amounts between 250-2,000 mg. |
| | **6 days** | • This study demonstrated that 20-80 μM CUR significantly down-regulates both p53 and ER$\alpha$ protein levels with a concomitant decrease in T-47D cell viability.<br>• CUR alone caused a 10-fold decrease compared with the treatment with estrogen, which suggests its antiproliferative effects et al., 2017). | • T-47D cells were treated with 5-80 μM CUR for a duration of 24 hours.<br>• and control group |
| | | • Curcumin killed breast cancer cells by arresting their development in various phases of cell cycle and growth and inducing cell death (Ali, et al., 2017). | • DK1 a curcumin derivatives cytotoxicity was tested on breast cancer cell MCF-7 and normal cell MCF-10A. |
| | | • Curcumin nanoparticles were found to be more effective than curcumin in exerting anti-proliferative effect against breast cancer cells.<br>• It also prevented metastasis of breast cancer cells (Khosropanah, et al., 2016). | • To examine the in vitro cytotoxic activity of cell death of curcumin and nanocurcumin on human breast adenocarcinoma cell line (MDA-MB231).<br>• Cytotoxicity and viability of curcumin and nanocurcumin were assessed by 3-(4,5-dimethylthiazol-2-yl)-2,5-diphenyltetrazolium bromide (MTT) and dye exclusion assay. |
| | | • Research by Saab et.al highlights that curcumin may be beneficial for treating non-malignant or benign breast tumors as well.<br>• A study published in Anticancer Research 2005, demonstrates that curcumin regulates as many as 30 genes and acts on multiple biochemical pathways in order to destroy breast cancer cells (Saab, et al., 2011). | • In mammalian, nonmalignant HMEC 184A1 and cancerous MCF-7 cells during curcumin treatment was studied using multiphoton, fluorescence, and *atomic force* (AFM) microscopies. |
| **Breast Cancer** | **3 weeks** | • Researchers have identified dosing for advanced metastatic breast cancer at 6000 mg and concomitant use with chemotherapy (Bayet, et al., 2010). | • 6000 mg per day for 7 consecutive days every 3 weeks along with standard docetaxel treatment. |
| | | • Topical treatment helped with external breast cancer lesions. 90% of individuals experienced a reduction in smell. Itching reduced in almost all cases. 70% of individuals experienced drying up of lesions. 10% of patients experienced reduction in lesion size and pain (Kuttan, et al., 1987). | • An ethanol extract of turmeric as well as an ointment of curcumin (its active ingredient) were found to produce remarkable symptomatic relief in patients with external cancerous lesions. |
| | | • A study published in the International Journal of Oncology, revealed that curcumin increases the apoptotic (apoptosis means "cell death") effect of paclitaxel (chemotherapeutic drug) in breast cancer and its concomitant use may reduce the toxicity of the therapy (Quispe-Soto, 2016). | • Curcumin and paclitaxel were evaluated with two human breast cancer cell lines as the luminal MCF-7 and the basal-like MDA-MB-231 that are either positive or negative for hormonal receptors estrogen receptor, progesterone receptor and HER2, respectively. |

## *Cancer: Select Clinical Data (continued)*

| DISEASE | DURATION | BENEFIT | DOSAGE |
|---|---|---|---|
| **Breast Cancer** | | • Researchers at the University of Rochester Medical Center have proven that daily supplementation of turmeric significantly reduces the rate of radiation dermatitis in patients suffering from breast cancer and receiving radiotherapy (Ryan, et al., 2013) | • 2g curcumin three times a day (total 6g) and radiotherapy |
| **Colorectal Cancer** | | • The body weight of curcumin patients increased by approximately 4% versus weight loss of 6% in the placebo group (He, et al., 2011). | • 360 mg curcumin 3 times per day followed by radiotherapy, chemotherapy, chemoradiotherapy<br>• Or no additional therapy |
| **Lung Cancer** | **1 month** | • Dietary turmeric can act as an effective anti-mutagen in smokers and can reduce the risk of lung cancer and cancer lesions (Polasa, et al., 1992). | • 1.5g of turmeric for 30 days<br>• Or control group |
| **Multiple Myeloma** | | • Both 4g and 8g daily doses reduced the serum free light chain ratio (35% and 36%, respectively) and reduced total serum protein (P=0.04) in the urine in both MGUS and SMM patients Curcumin also decreased markers of bone turnover (urinary DPYD) and excretion of crosslinked N-telopeptides by more than 25% (Golombick, et al., 2012). | • A double-blind placebo-controlled cross-over of 19 patients with MGUS and 17 patients with smoldering MM examined the effects of daily curcumin. |
| **Pancreatic Cancer** | **12 months** | • There was improvement of chemotherapy related symptoms after starting curcumin. The median survival after initiation of curcumin was 161 days. One-year survival rate was 19%. Median survival after gemcitabine is 70 days. (Kanai, et al., 2011). | • 8g curcumin with gemcitabine (Gemzar) |
| **Prostate Cancer** | **6 months** | • Isoflavones and curcumin could modulate serum PSA levels. The authors of this study concluded that curcumin presumably synergizes with isoflavones to suppress PSA production (Ide, et al., 2010). | • 100 mg of curcumin and 40 mg of isoflavones and placebo |

## *Other Inflammatory Diseases: Select Clinical Data*

Curcumin has exhibited powerful benefit to effectively manage a variety of inflammatory conditions.

| DISEASE | DURATION | BENEFIT | DOSAGE |
|---|---|---|---|
| **Arthritis** | 8 months | • Improved joint pain, stiffness, physical function, social and emotional function (Belacore, et al., 2010). | • Curcuminoid and phosphotidylcholine 1000 mg curcuma extract 200 curcuma extract daily<br>• Standard conventional treatment |
| **Allergic Rhinitis (AR)** | 2 months | • Curcumin alleviated nasal symptoms (sneezing and rhinorrhea) and nasal congestion through reduction of nasal airflow resistance.<br>• This pilot study provides the first evidence of the capability of curcumin of improving nasal airflow and modulating immune response in patients with AR (Wu, et al., 2016). | • 241 patients with AR received either placebo or oral curcumin.<br>• The therapeutic effects of curcumin were evaluated by nasal symptoms and nasal airflow resistance. |
| **Asthma** | 5 weeks | • Findings suggest that curcumin administered through nasal route might prove therapeutically efficient in inhibiting allergic airway inflammation and maintaining structural integrity in the mouse model of allergic asthma. This may lead to the development of curcumin aerosol in the near future (Subhashini, et al., 2016) | • Mouse study; short exposure to ovalbumin (4 days)<br>• Repeated exposures for longer (twice per week until 5 weeks) represents chronic asthma<br>• Disodium cromoglycate (DSCG, 50mg/kg, i.p.) and dexamethasone (1mg/kg, i.p.) were used as standard drugs in acute and chronic model of asthma respectively |
| **Cardio-vascular Disease** | 8 weeks | • Adding curcumin to regular exercise provides enhanced CV fitness in postmenopausal women (Sugawara, et al., 2012). | • 150 mg curcumin with exercise training<br>• and placebo with exercise training |
| **Diabetes** | 8 weeks | • Significant increase in endothelial function in both the atorvastatin and curcumin groups. Additionally, all biomarkers decreased in the treatment group and no improvement in the placebo (Usharani, et al., 2008). | • 300 mg curcumin twice daily<br>• Atorvastatin 10 mg daily<br>• Or placebo |
| **Irritable Bowel Syn-drome** | 8 weeks | • Prevalence of IBS decreased by 53% in the one tablet group and 60% in the two-tablet group. Additional abdominal pain and discomfort decreased (Bundy, et al., 2004). | • One of 72 mg or two tablets of 72 mg each, standardized turmeric extract taken daily for 8 weeks |
| **Gastric Ulcer** | Phase II | • Ulcers completely healed in 48% after 4 weeks. and 76% after 12 weeks. (Prucksunand, et al., 2001). | • 600 mg with powdered turmeric 5 times/day<br>• Or placebo |

## Summary of Clinical Findings

The underlying effects of turmeric are: anti-inflammatory, anti-microbial, antioxidant, and wound healing. The clinical trial data suggest that turmeric either alone or in combination with conventional modalities reduces rates of morbidity or mortality from several disease states. The use of turmeric along with the conventional modalities produces better health outcomes and reduces the adverse events profile.

Using turmeric as a culinary spice and as a medicinal agent, may change the course of several chronic diseases such as arthritis, allergic rhinitis, asthma, cancer (breast, pancreatic, prostate, colorectal, lung, multiple myeloma) cardiovascular disease, diabetes, digestive disorders such as irritable bowel syndrome and gastric ulcer to name a few disease states. While it is not entirely clear as to how turmeric works, clinical trial data for cancer show its influence in inhibiting networks of cancer cell growth. Curcumin is a natural polyphenol molecule derived from the *Curcuma longa* plant which exhibits anti-cancer, chemo-preventive, chemo- and radio-sensitization properties. Curcumin increases the sensitivity of chemotherapeutic drugs and protects from toxicity of cancer therapy.

## Dosage Range

Doses of 500-8,000 mg of turmeric per day have been used in human studies. Standardized extracts are typically used in lower amounts, in the 250-2,000 mg range (Alshuler, 2017).

## Contraindications

Having been granted *Generally Recognized as Safe* (GRAS) status in the United States by the *Food and Drug Administration* (FDA), turmeric is well tolerated by most people. Turmeric usage should be avoided during pregnancy unless otherwise directed by a qualified expert. Therapeutic quantities should not be taken by people with bile duct obstructions or gallstones (Winston, 2014).

## Toxicity

No significant toxicity has been reported following short- or long-term administration of turmeric extracts at standard doses.

## Supplementation

Fresh turmeric root and dried powder are healthy to take daily. Please ask your health care provider if turmeric supplement is appropriate for you. For supplementation of curcumin, adding 1% *piperine* (black pepper) in the formulation can increase bioavailability by 2000%. Additionally, having some good quality fat such as ghee or butter can make the supplement more bioavailable.

Turmeric supplements have not been well studied in children. While there is no one single recommended dose for a child or adolescent, they can benefit from a reduced turmeric dose that can be calculated for each individual weight by dividing their weight with the average weight (in their gender) to determine the proportion of the adult dose that would be applicable. For example, if a boy or girl weighs 75 pounds (30 kgs), dividing that by the average gender weight in the U.S. would reduce the adult dose down to 38% for a boy and 45% for a girl. Apply this methodology to calculate the reduced turmeric dosage for your child or adolescent. The following doses are recommended as a guide for adults, children and adolescents.

## Kitchen Medicine

Turmeric can be used as either fresh or dried and ground in curries, stir-fries, rice pilafs, grains such as millet and quinoa, and in tofu, smoothies, soups and drinks before bedtime. It is a great flavoring agent that can blend well with other spices from diverse geographic regions as its use has expanded beyond South Asia to all parts of the globe and incorporated into diverse local cuisines. Turmeric has been used as a natural additive in beauty products. Recipes are provided for experimentation as it is easy to incorporate in home cooking, by adding to vegetables, grains, beans, legumes, yogurt, meats, fish, and marinades.

## *Turmeric (Curcumin) Supplementation*

Turmeric and curcumin, its most widely studied active constituent, can be taken as needed, as a dietary supplement. Recommended forms and dose ranges are indicated below.

| TYPE OF SUPPLEMENT | ADULT | CHILD/ADOLESCENT MALE | CHILD/ADOLESCENT FEMALE |
|---|---|---|---|
| **U.S. Average Weight (CDC)** | Male:196 pounds (89 kg)<br>Female:168 pounds (77kg | How to calculate the proportional weight for boys?<br>If boy's weight is 75 pounds (30 kgs), proportional dose calculation for curcumin is: (75/196) = 38%. The below table illustrates dose levels for 38%. | How to calculate the proportional weight for girls?<br>If a girl's weight is 75 pounds (30 kgs), the proportional dose calculation for curcumin is: (75/168) = 45%. The below table illustrates dose levels for 45%. |
| **Cut root** | 1.5-3g per day | .6-1.1g | .7-1.3g |
| **Dried powdered root** | 1-3g per day | .3-1.1g | .4-1.3g |
| **Standardized powder (curcumin)** | 400-600 mg, 3 times per day | 153-230 mg | 178-267 mg |
| **Fluid extract** | (1:1) 30-90 drops a day | 11.5-34 drops per day | 13-40 drops per day |
| **Tincture** | (1:2): 15-30 drops, 4 times per day | 6-11 drops twice a day | 7-13 twice a day |

*Dr. Ed in The Spice Shop, Kochi, India.*

# Turmeric Spice Blends

## Madras Curry Powder

*In traditional Indian cuisine the concept of curry powder does not exist. It was a term made popular by the colonial empire and anglicized to suit the Anglo Indian palate. It became popular in the British Raj where a mix of spices was used. Later curry became very popular in Britain and in other parts of the western world. What makes the madras curry powder different is the inclusion of mustard seeds and curry leaves. Here is a great recipe for curry powder.*

YIELD: 1 CUP POWDER (Use ½ teaspoon per serving or as suggested in recipes.)

**INGREDIENTS**

2 tablespoons coriander seeds
1 tablespoon cumin seeds
1 teaspoon fenugreek seeds
4 dried red chilies
½ teaspoon fennel seeds
1 teaspoon mustard seeds
1 teaspoon ground black pepper
1 bay leaf
Seeds from 4 cardamom pods
4 whole cloves
1-inch (2.5 cm) cinnamon stick
2 teaspoons dried curry leaves
½ teaspoon sea salt
½ teaspoons ground turmeric

**METHOD**

1. Dry roast all the ingredients, except salt and turmeric, in a saucepan on a low heat until golden and fragrant.
2. Remove from heat and allow to cool.
3. When cooled, add turmeric and salt and process in a spice grinder to desired coarseness.
4. Stays fresh for 6 months if you store in a sealed container.
5. Use for curries.

**SOURCE:** Pramila Murthy

## Sambhar Powder

*Sambhar is delicious with vegetables and rice. Please explore with any vegetables and dal combinations from Brussels sprouts to okra, spinach, Swiss chard, potatoes, onions, green beans and carrots. You can cut this recipe in half, depending on your need for the Sambhar curry spice.*

YIELD: 1-1½ CUP

**INGREDIENTS**

1 cup dried red chilies
¾ cup coriander seeds
½ teaspoon fenugreek seeds
1 teaspoon cumin seeds
½ teaspoon ground pepper, optional
½ teaspoon asafetida
¼ cup red gram (pigeon peas)

**METHOD**

1. Roast all ingredients to a light golden brown until fragrant.
2. Cool and grind into a smooth powder.
3. Store in a glass jar at room temperature.
4. Use it to make a *South Indian Sambhar* (see page 21).

**SOURCE:** Pramila Murthy

## *Tandoori Masala*

*Tandoori chicken is a dish Westerners think of when Indian food is mentioned. The smoky flavor of the tandoori meat or fish comes from the clay oven in which it is cooked, the slightly sour flavor from the spicing and yogurt marmalade. You can use this spice mixture for food cooked in the oven or over a grill.*

YIELD: ⅓ CUP POWDER (Use as indicated in tandoori recipes.)

### INGREDIENTS

2 teaspoons cumin seeds
2 teaspoons coriander seeds
1 teaspoon fennel seeds
¾-inch (2 cm) cinnamon stick
13-15 green cardamom pods
3 black cardamom pods
5-6 whole cloves
1 teaspoon black pepper
1 star anise
2 blades mace
2 pieces dried ginger
6-8 whole dried red chilies
1 teaspoon coarse salt

### METHOD

1. Place all the ingredients in a sauté pan and dry roast until fragrant. Do not allow to burn.
2. Cool spices and place in a blender or spice grinder. Process until finely ground and pour into a glass jar.
3. Mark the jar with the date it was made and store in your pantry.
4. Retains optimum flavor for six months.

**SOURCE:** Recipe modified from Rimli Dey https://youtu.be/lTiAzfTBdCQ

# Turmeric Beverages

## Golden Milk

*I (SM) grew up drinking this recipe with cow's milk, turmeric and black pepper. I have modified my grandmother's recipe to add cinnamon (both stick and powdered).*

SERVES 1

### INGREDIENTS

1 cup organic coconut milk
1 cinnamon stick
1 teaspoon ground turmeric
¼ teaspoon ground black pepper
10-12 strands of saffron
½ teaspoon cinnamon powder to sprinkle

### METHOD

1. Heat coconut milk in a pan with the cinnamon stick.
2. Add the turmeric, pepper and saffron strands.
3. Pour the warmed golden milk into a mug.
4. Sprinkle with cinnamon powder and enjoy as a bedtime drink.

NOTE: *You can also try the above recipe with goat or cow's milk if you are not lactose intolerant. We recommend organic cow's milk to avoid growth hormone-injected cow's milk.*

## Savory Cleansing Smoothie

*This is my "go to" recipe to rehydrate after a workout. The fresh turmeric adds a rich savory taste.*

SERVES 1

### INGREDIENTS

1 medium apple
½ cup berries
½ cup celery
½ cup leafy greens
1-inch (2.5 cm) fresh ginger
1-inch (2.5 cm) fresh turmeric
2 tablespoons flax seeds
1 scoop protein powder
6 oz. kefir
3-6 oz. water or green tea

### METHOD

1. Wash the apple, berries, celery and greens and roughly chop.
2. Peel the skin of the fresh ginger and turmeric and cut into smaller pieces.
3. In a blender, place a few ice cubes (optional) at the bottom, add all the ingredients and blend until smooth.

# Turmeric Entrees

## Brussels Sprouts Sambhar

*A South Indian inspired creation, Sambhar is a staple for the region. You can substitute almost any vegetable to suit your tastes.*

SERVES 4

### INGREDIENTS

1 cup toor dal (split pigeon peas)
1 tablespoon ground turmeric
1 tablespoon tamarind, fresh or concentrate
4 cups Brussels sprouts, sliced in half
2 tablespoons ghee or extra-virgin coconut oil
1 teaspoon mustard seeds
1-2 tablespoons shredded coconut, grated fresh or dried (unsweetened)
1-2 green chilies*
A handful curry leaves
1 pinch asafetida (optional)
1-2 tablespoons sambhar powder, depending on heat tolerance
Sea salt to taste

### METHOD

1. Soak the toor dal (peas) for 3-4 hours. Rinse with fresh filtered water. Boil in 3-4 cups of water with the turmeric powder until soft. Add water, if it becomes too dry. Drain any excess water and set aside.
2. Soak the fresh tamarind in hot water for 10 minutes. If fresh is in season, otherwise use concentrate.
3. In a saucepan, steam the Brussels sprouts until bright green.
4. In a large sauté pan, gently heat the ghee or coconut oil until melted, add mustard seeds, chilies, curry leaves and asafetida. Stir to combine and heat until the spices release their scent (a few minutes).
5. Stir in the steamed vegetables and then add the dal.
6. Add the sambar powder and the soaked and drained fresh tamarind, or concentrate, and salt. Cook for 2-3 minutes to combine flavors.
7. Remove curry leaves. Sprinkle shredded coconut on top before serving.
8. Serve with quinoa, brown rice or millet and a side of green beans.

**If you can't find Indian chilies in your local market, you can use ½ Anaheim or 1-2 Thai chilies depending on your heat level tolerance.*

## *Turmeric Entrees (continued)*

# *Chicken Tikka Masala*

*Chicken Tikka is seasoned chicken pieces cooked in a tandoor oven over high heat.*

SERVES 4

### INGREDIENTS

1 teaspoon Kashmiri red chili powder
Salt to taste
Juice of ½ lemon
1 pound boneless chicken, cut into small pieces
4 tablespoons yogurt
1 tablespoon ginger garlic paste (equal parts garlic and ginger with salt)
2-3 tablespoons tandoori masala (see page 19)
1 teaspoon ground turmeric
1 teaspoon kasuri methi (dried fenugreek powder)
1 teaspoon ground black pepper
2 tablespoons butter
1 onion, thinly sliced
2 tablespoons mint, minced

### METHOD

1. Place Kashmiri red chili powder, salt and lemon juice in a large bowl. Add chicken, stir to coat pieces, cover and set aside for 30 minutes.
2. In a second bowl mix the yogurt, ginger garlic paste, tandoori masala mix, turmeric, kasuri methi, and black pepper. Add the chicken, cover and set aside again for 30 minutes.
3. You have two options for cooking. First, on the stove, using a griddle pan. Brush the grill with butter. Cook until browned. Flip and cook the reverse side.
4. The second method is in the oven if you don't have a griddle.
5. Preheat oven to 450°F (232°C). Arrange on a parchment lined baking sheet.
6. Bake the chicken for about 10 minutes, on one side. Flip and bake another 10-15 minutes. Broil the last 2 minutes for a little more color, being careful not to burn.
7. Serve the cooked pieces on a platter. Garnish with onions and fresh mint. Serve with mint chutney.

**SOURCE:** Recipe modified from Sanjeev Kapur Khazana: https://youtu.be/uxJIXHH-Wys

# *Delicious Daily Dal (Moong Dal)*

*A North Indian inspiration will go well with cauliflower curry and quinoa. You can substitute almost any dark leafy greens you can find.*

SERVES 4

### INGREDIENTS

1 cup moong dal (yellow lentils)
Filtered water for soaking and cooking
1 tablespoon turmeric powder
3 cups spinach (or Swiss chard or kale), chopped
2 tablespoons extra-virgin coconut oil
1 teaspoon cumin seeds
1 teaspoon cayenne pepper
I pinch asafetida
Sea salt to taste

### METHOD

1. Soak the dal (lentils) for 3 hours in a bowl of filtered water. Then cook with filtered water and turmeric. This is a relatively soft dal and cooks fast.
2. Steam or sauté the spinach or greens of your choice.
3. In a large sauté pan, heat the coconut oil on low and add the cumin seeds first, then the dal and the cooked greens.
4. Add the cayenne pepper, asafetida and salt last.
5. Taste and adjust seasonings.

## Curried Cauliflower (Gobhi)

*This is my (SM) favorite easy to make cauliflower recipe that is also flavorful and inspired by North Indian cuisine.*

SERVES 4

### INGREDIENTS

1 tablespoon ground turmeric
1 tablespoon ground cumin
1 tablespoon ground coriander
1 teaspoon cayenne pepper
1 tablespoon extra-virgin olive oil
1 teaspoon cumin seeds
2 small green chilies*, thinly sliced
1 tablespoon fresh ginger, cut into thin strips
1 medium head cauliflower, cut into florets
2 tablespoons fresh cilantro, chopped and divided
Sea salt to taste

### METHOD

1. Combine turmeric, cumin, coriander and cayenne in a small bowl and set aside.
2. In a large pot or sauté pan, heat the olive oil on low for about a minute and then add the cumin seeds. Heat until the seeds start making popping sounds.
3. Add the sliced green chilies and fresh ginger strips. Cover the pan to allow them to soften for a minute or two.
4. Stir in the cauliflower florets.
5. After a minute add half the dried spices in the bowl, and some fresh cilantro leaves, saving the rest for garnish.
6. Stir and cover, continue cooking on low. After a few minutes stir in the remaining dried spices from your bowl.
7. Cover and cook on low heat for 5-10 minutes more or until cauliflower is tender.
8. Add sea salt to taste.
9. To serve, garnish with remaining fresh cilantro.

NOTE: *To make this dish a meal, add cubed red skinned potatoes and peas to complement the spices and flavors.*
**If you can't find Indian chilies in your local market, you can use Anaheim or Thai chilies depending on your heat level tolerance.*

## *Turmeric Entrees (continued)*

# *Fenugreek Pilaf (Methi Garlic Pulav)*

*Fenugreek leaves, when combined with garlic and basmati rice, exude a rich aroma. If not available, you can substitute kale, spinach or Swiss chard.*

SERVES 4

**INGREDIENTS**

- 2 cups basmati brown rice
- 1 tablespoon ghee
- 2 tablespoons extra-virgin olive oil
- ½ teaspoon asafetida
- ½ teaspoon cumin seeds
- 12 cloves garlic, crushed or chopped fine
- 1-inch (2.5 cm) ginger, minced or grated
- 3 green chilies*, thinly sliced
- 2 large bundles methi or fenugreek leaves, rinsed well and roughly chopped
- 3-4 medium tomatoes, diced medium
- ½ teaspoon ground turmeric
- 1½ teaspoon chili powder
- Sea salt to taste
- 1 cup peas, thawed if frozen

**METHOD**

1. Wash the basmati brown rice and soak for 3-4 hours.
2. In a heavy pot, over low heat, melt the ghee and extra-virgin olive oil. Add the asafetida, cumin, garlic, ginger and chilies. When the garlic starts to take on color, add the methi leaves and allow to soften for a couple of minutes. Add the tomatoes and continue to sauté until they break down.
3. Add the ground turmeric and chili powder and stir for a minute or two.
4. Add the basmati brown rice and sauté for a few more minutes. Then add the salt and four cups of boiling water.
5. Raise the heat and bring to a boil. Then cover and reduce heat to low for approximately 40-45 minutes until the rice is soft. Stir in the peas in the last five minutes.

NOTE: *This can be served with raita (yogurt sauce) Accompaniments can be the dal for protein and vegetables for fiber.*

**If you can't find Indian chilies in your local market, you can use 1 Anaheim or 3 Thai chilies depending on your heat level tolerance.*

**SOURCE:** Modified from Moorthy, V., *The Vegetarian Menu Book, A Comprehensive Guide to Authentic Indian Vegetarian Cuisine*. UBS (1993);

# *Green Bean Supreme*

*Green bean curry with rice or quinoa makes a deliciously satisfying meal.*

SERVES 2

**INGREDIENTS**

- 2 tablespoons extra-virgin coconut oil
- 1 teaspoon mustard seeds
- 1-2 green chilies, thinly sliced
- A handful of curry leaves
- 1 teaspoon turmeric powder
- 1 pinch asafetida (optional)
- 2 cups green beans, minced fine
- 1-2 tablespoons fresh grated coconut or dried unsweetened
- Sea salt to taste

**METHOD**

1. In a sauté pan, heat the coconut oil, add the mustard seeds, chilies, curry leaves, turmeric and asafetida if using. Stir to combine and heat until the spices release their scent (a few minutes).
2. Add the greens beans, stir and cover. Add the coconut and salt and cook for 5 minutes more.
3. Remove curry leaves. Taste and adjust seasonings.
4. Serve with quinoa, brown rice or millet and "Brussels Sprouts Sambhar" (see page 21).

## Savory Sauté

*This versatile, nicely spiced recipe can be made with you choice of protein and vegetables.*

SERVES 2

**INGREDIENTS**

8 oz. extra firm tofu or chicken
1 teaspoon cumin powder
1 teaspoon coriander powder
½ teaspoon garam masala
½ teaspoon ground turmeric
2 teaspoons sesame seeds
Juice of ½ a lemon
2 tablespoons extra-virgin olive oil, divided
1 teaspoon cumin seeds
½ cup onion, minced
2 teaspoon ginger, minced
2 cloves garlic, minced
1 cup spinach, roughly chopped
½ cup mushrooms, sliced
2 tablespoon cilantro, minced
Sea salt to taste
4-6 lettuce leaves

**METHOD**

1. Cube the tofu into ½-inch (1.27 cm) squares or slice chicken into strips.
2. Prepare a marinade with the cumin, coriander, garam masala, turmeric, sesame seeds, lemon juice and half the oil. Add chicken or tofu and set aside.
3. Heat the remaining oil over medium high heat in a sauté pan or wok and add the cumin seeds.
4. Once they start to pop, add the onions and sauté for a minute. Lower the heat to medium and add ginger and garlic, taking care not to burn the garlic.
5. When the onions are starting to soften, add the mushrooms and cook until golden. Stir in the spinach and cilantro until wilted. Add the tofu or chicken last.
6. Sauté for 2-3 minutes, or until chicken is cooked, then add remaining marinade and sea salt. Stir to combine. Taste and adjust seasonings.
7. To serve, take a lettuce wrap and add the tofu or chicken mixture and enjoy.

## Turmeric Vinaigrette

*Adding turmeric to a salad dressing or sauce offers a tangy flavor and bright orange color.*

SERVES 4

**INGREDIENTS**

¼ cup vinegar
1 tablespoon maple syrup
1-2 cloves garlic, minced
1 tablespoon green herbs
1 tablespoon chia seeds
½ teaspoon salt
1 teaspoon turmeric
½ cup extra-virgin olive oil

**METHOD**

1. Mix all the ingredients in a blender except the oil. Turn on the machine and slowly add the oil until dressing is emulsified.
2. Store in a glass container until ready to serve.

## How to Grow Turmeric

Healthy herbs, grown in healthy soil, provide concentrated macro- and micro-nutrients, volatile oils and bioflavonoids that support tissue growth and repair, improve circulation, enhance digestion, absorption and cellular detoxification. They are nature's antidote to pollution, stress, and malnutrition that lead to chronic inflammation, which over time leads to depletion of our nervous, endocrine, immune, respiratory and muscular skeletal systems.

Turmeric is easy to grow in your home garden or greenhouse, if the soil is loamy, and there is sufficient heat and water during the warm weather months. The roots form an underground network, which will spread into a garden plot or field if you allow it. The chopped leaves can be added to herbal tea (Bernhardt, 2008).

Similar to ginger, turmeric is grown from *rhizomes* (root cuttings). Turmeric does not propagate seeds. All you need is one turmeric root which you can find at your local healthy food market.

To grow turmeric indoors, just follow these simple steps:

- Break a larger rhizome into a small rhizome piece that has two or three buds.
- Fill your pots with rich organic soil, which is slightly moist, but well drained.
- Place the rhizome pieces about 2 inches (5 cm) below the surface of the soil, with the buds facing up.
- Water the container.
- Turmeric will benefit from bi-monthly feedings of a good organic fertilizer or compost tea.

### How to Water Turmeric

Turmeric likes water. Keep the soil moist, particularly in hot, dry climates. Try watering it once every 2 days or misting with a spray bottle. If you live in cooler climates, water less frequently. The key here is to keep the soil from ever getting soggy.

### How to Harvest Turmeric

- Turmeric takes 8-10 months for the edible rhizomes to mature. While the leaves and stems are edible, most people harvest turmeric only for its roots. Most herbs can be harvested throughout the growing season, but turmeric root is best if harvested all at once when mature.
- When the rhizomes are large enough, dig up all rhizomes from the pot. They are best if all harvested at once.

### How to Grow Turmeric (continued)

- Dig up the rhizomes and save a few pieces to plant for the following season. Make sure to change the soil, though, because the original plant probably depleted it of all its nutrients.
- Turmeric roots should be kept in a cool, dry place until use.

**How to Make Turmeric Powder**

When you are ready to use them, follow these directions:

1. Boil the roots for 45 minutes. Peel the roots, wearing gloves to prevent dyeing your hands bright yellow.
2. Dry the turmeric for approximately one week, or dehydrate in an oven at 200°F (93°C) for 2 hours.
3. Grind the peeled rhizomes into the lovely spice that is used in so many recipes.

**SOURCE:** dailyhealthpost

## Sunburn Support and Exfoliant

*This recipe is from my mother's armamentarium of using turmeric if you have had a sunburn.*

SERVES 1

**INGREDIENTS**

¼ cup extra-virgin coconut oil
1 teaspoon ground turmeric
¼ cup wheat flour
Water to mix

**METHOD**

1. Apply coconut oil liberally on your body.
2. Mix turmeric with flour and water.
3. Apply on the oiled surface.
4. Let sit for 2-3 minutes.
5. Remove using an exfoliating motion. Take a tepid to cool shower.

**SOURCE:** Pramila Murthy

CHAPTER TWO

# Basil

## (Ocimum basilicum/ sanctum/tenuiflorum)

**Basil** is at the top of the green herbal pantheon. It is beautiful, aromatic, and divinely refreshing. Laboratory science cannot do justice to the energy and effect varieties of basil have on the body, mind, heart and spirit of human beings, toiling away in a largely plant-deficient world.

Growing fresh basil, be it Tulsi holy basil or sweet basil, is a blessing and a healing balm. Research on Tulsi holy basil demonstrates its many psychological and physiological benefits. All varieties of basil are soothing, healing and restorative to the blood and brain due to its rich chlorophyll and mineral content.

Hinduism and Ayurveda celebrate Tulsi as a plant to be worshipped, ingested, and made into tea. Sweet basil has been revered throughout time, culture and history, in Europe and the Mediterranean countries. Both sweet basil and Tulsi holy basil have unique benefits they offer by way of their fragrant essential oils.

Basil is great to include in our day-to-day cooking, whether fresh or dried. I suggest growing basil as a kitchen spice in a pot as it is quickly eaten by all varieties of outdoor animals when grown in an unprotected garden. Basil loves the sun and generates a sunny mood when noticed by the eye, inhaled by the nose or tasted on the tongue. I use fresh basil as a garnish to top a soup, salad or main dish. I also use it to add fresh flavor to breakfast smoothies and fruit salads.

*Dr. Ed at Akha Cooking School, Chaing Mai, Thailand.*

*Thai Basil*

*Tulsi Holy Basil*

## Background and Uses

Belonging to the genus *Ocimum*, sweet basil is a diverse aromatic herbaceous plant. Over 150 types of basil are grown for their aromatic leaves and volatile oils. One commonly grown variety, sweet basil (*Ocimum basilicum Linn*) is an annual plant grown for its rich green plants and intense flavor. Belonging to the family of mint (Lamiacea), sweet basil is used fresh or dried in preparing soups, salads, pesto, sauces and stir-fry dishes of Mediterranean and world cuisine. I (SM) love the flavor of fresh sweet basil. I grow it in my backyard each year. I enjoy using it fresh in salads, pesto and to flavor olive oil. Other types of basil commonly used in soups, salads and stir-frys are lemon basil (*Ocimum citriodorum*), Thai basil (*Ocimum basilicum variant thyrsiflora*), and Tulsi holy basil (*Ocimum tenuiflorum*), a key ingredient in Thai, Vietnamese, Indonesian, Chinese and Laotian cuisine.

The origins of basil are attributed to India and Indonesia dating back 5,000 years. It was likely introduced in Europe by Greeks and Romans, coming from commercial routes originating in the Middle East. Genus *Ocimum* (sweet basil) is now cultivated in many Asian, Western and Mediterranean countries. The main exporters for the European market are France, Italy, Morocco and Egypt. There is also significant basil production in California.

A remarkable cultivar of this family is Tulsi holy basil (*Ocimum Sanctum Linn* or *Ocimum Tenuiflorum*), native to South Asia. Growing up in India I (SM) experienced this plant in my Grandmother, Jayakka's backyard where a special box-like structure was built to house her precious tulsi. She cared for the perennial tulsi plant and container at her Bangalore home, in tropical southern India. For years, she prayed to the Goddess Tulsi and performed daily *puja* (prayer) ceremonies. Tulsi was not used in her cooking, nor in that of her neighbors. It was first and foremost a ceremonial plant. Secondly, it was used for medicine. If someone experienced a sore throat or early onset of a cold, tulsi leaves were prepared to make a "Kashayam." For this preparation, tulsi leaves alone or in combination with other herbs, were boiled, reduced by heating for 20 minutes or more, and ingested warm with a touch of honey. Within hours or days, sore throat and cold symptoms diminished or disappeared altogether.

Tulsi has been used in Ayurvedic therapy for numerous health conditions as a medicinal tea or extract, alone, or with other ingredients. Scientific findings have been widely reported on its salutatory benefits as an adaptogen (stress mediator) that is immunomodulatory, anti-inflammatory, anti-carcinogenic, hepato-protective, cardio-protective, neuro-protective, anti-microbial, and anti-diabetic.

## Plant Specifics

Basil is cultivated worldwide as an annual or perennial plant. There are several varieties, differing in the size, shape, odor and color of the leaves. Many varieties have different compositions and flavoring characteristics. Basil is strongly affected by environmental factors like temperature, geographic location, soil and amount of rainfall. Its thin branching root produces bushy stems growing from 1-2 feet high and bearing leaves of a purple hue, and two-lipped flowers, varying in color from white to red, sometimes with a purple tinge. All parts are utilized including leaves; flowering tops, essential oil, and the entire herb (all aerial parts) are harvested. Best harvesting season is before flowering. Basil leaves should always be used fresh, as they lose much of their flavor within a few weeks after drying. Basil can be dried and ground into a powder to be used in herbal formulas.

## Active Constituents

**Sweet Basil** *(Ocimum Basilicum Linn):* Sweet basil contains a volatile oil about 1%, which consists principally of linalool and methyl chavicol, along with small quantities of methyl cinnamate, cineole, and other terpenes. The essential oil (less than 1%) is of complex and variable composition. Within the species, several different chemical alkaloids exist, whose potency depends upon climate, soil and time of harvest that influence not only the amount of leaf produced by a plant, but also the composition and potency of its essential oil.

**Tulsi Holy Basil** *(Ocimum Sanctum Linn or Ocimum Tenuiflorum):* The primary phytochemical constituents of tulsi are oleanolic acid, ursolic acid, rosmarinic acid, eugenol, carvacrol, linalool, β-caryophyllene (about 8%). (Rai, et al., 1997) Tulsi holy basil leaf active essential oils consist of eugenol (~70%) β-elemene (~11.0%), β-caryophyllene (~8%) and germacrene (~2%), with the balance being made up of various trace compounds, mostly terpenes (Sen, et al.,1992).

## Tulsi Uses in Traditional Medicine

In Ayurveda, Tulsi holy basil is referred to as "The Incomparable One," "The Queen of Herbs" and revered as "The Elixir of Life." Daily consumption of Tulsi holy basil is renowned to be health enhancing and disease preventive. In traditional natural medicine, it is recommended to manage bronchitis, bronchial asthma, chronic fever, malaria, dysentery, arthritis, skin diseases, and painful eye diseases. Eugenol, the active constituent present in Tulsi holy basil, is largely responsible for its therapeutic effects.

## Tulsi Uses in Western Medicine

The medicinal properties of Tulsi holy basil are being studied in hundreds of scientific studies. In vitro, and animal experiments and human trials have documented its value as being anti-diabetic, anti-arthritic, hepato-protective (protects against liver damage), anti-cancer, chemo-preventive, radio-protective, cardio-protective, anti-hypertensive (lowers high blood pressure), anticoagulant activities (blood thinner) anti-hypercholesterolemia (prevents excess cholesterol in blood), antidepressant, anti-stress, anti-thyroid, infertility, anti-diarrheal, anti-ulcer, anti-asthmatic, anti-pyretic (fever reducing), anti-spasmodic (reduces muscle spasms), anti-emetic (reduces vomiting and nausea), anthelmintic (expels worms and parasites), anti-bacterial, anti-viral, antitussive (cough suppressant), anti-malarial, antioxidant, anti-cataract, anti-allergic and memory enhancer (Cohen, 2014).

## Health Benefits of Tulsi Holy Basil

**Tulsi Holy Basil** *(Ocimum sanctum Linn)*

- Promotes well-being and improves resilience, by modulating the body's response to stress and promoting a recuperative homeostasis after a disturbing stimulus.
- Helps the body correct blood sugar irregularities associated with the metabolic syndrome and mitigates its consequences.
- Studies have shown that Tulsi holy basil can reduce blood glucose, correct abnormal lipid profiles, and protect the liver and kidneys from the metabolic damage caused by high glucose levels.
- In human clinical trials, Tulsi holy basil has been shown to decrease glucose levels, improve blood pressure and lipid profiles and reduce many symptoms experienced by patients with type-2 diabetes (Cohen, 2014).
- Has been reported to prevent cancers caused by toxic compounds by reducing DNA damage and inducing apoptosis in pre-cancerous and cancerous cells, thereby reducing the growth of experimental tumors and enhancing survival (Cohen, 2014).
- Has been cited in various studies to stabilize gene expression altered both by cancer and radiation therapy (Jockers, 2017; Gunes, 2016).
- Has demonstrated antibacterial, antiviral and antifungal activity that includes activity against many pathogens responsible for infections (Cohen, 2014).

## *Clinical Trial Data for Tulsi Holy Basil (Ocimum Sanctum Linn)*

Holy Basil is a classic Ayurvedic remedy. Below are data on recent clinical applications.

| THERAPEUTIC AREA | STUDY | BENEFIT | DESCRIPTION |
|---|---|---|---|
| **Generalized Anxiety Disorder** | **Human trial 2 months** | • The study showed that, *Ocimum Sanctum* (OS) significantly lowered anxiety, stress and depression.<br>• The study concluded that OS may be useful in the treatment of lowering stress and anxiety from Generalized Anxiety Disorder (Bhattacharya, et al., 2008). | • Study sample = 35 (21 male and 14 females; average age 38.4 years)<br>• Two groups Male and Female: Given plant extracts of OS in a fixed oral dose regime 500 mg 2 times/day |
| **Diabetes type-2** | **Human trial 30 days** | • The experimental group receiving *Ocimum Sanctum* (OS) exhibited a reduction in fasting blood glucose levels.<br>• Additionally, there was a significant reduction in the levels of total cholesterol, LDL-cholesterol, VLDL-cholesterol and triglycerides after supplementation with OS powder. Meanwhile, the control group had higher levels of glucose (Rai, et al., 1997). | • All diabetics, total sample size = 27 (M = 17 & Female = 10) type-2 diabetes<br>• All patients to take 1g of OS powder, first thing in the morning |
| **Immunomodulatory** | **Human trial 4 weeks** | • There was a statistically significant increase of IFN-y, T-helper cells and NK-cells in the intervention group that took *Ocimum Sanctum* (OS) leaves in contrast to the placebo group. They are supportive of a healthy immune system (Mondal et al., 2011) | • Double blind, randomized control trial on 24 healthy volunteers<br>• Daily intake of 300 mg ethanolic extract of OS leaves on an empty stomach or placebo |
| **Stress** | **Human trial 6 weeks** | • The study demonstrated that lower levels of stress were observed in the control group taking *Ocimum Tenuiflorum* (OT). There was also significantly less forgetfulness and sexual dysfunction observed in the control group. The extract was well tolerated for the six weeks (Saxena, et al., 2012). | • Extract of OT<br>• An adult study, Sample sizes: placebo = 79<br>• OT extract = 71; were given 1,200 mg of extract daily for 6 weeks |
| **Gastric Ulcer** | **Rat study 5 days** | • Optimal effective dose 100 mg/kg of *Ocimum Sanctum* (OS) extract showed significant ulcer protection and significantly healed ulcers (Goel, et al., 2005). | • The standardized methanolic extract of leaves of OS eugenol content 5% given in doses of 50-200 mg/kg, orally, twice daily for 5 days. |
| **Anti-inflammatory** | **Rabbit Study** | • Anti-inflammatory effects were observed in all compounds tested.<br>• The study suggests *Ocimum Sanctum* (OS) extracts had the same benefit as ibuprofen, naproxen and aspirin and could potentially be used for inflammation and pain (Kelm, et al., 2000). | • Extraction of 6 compounds from OS |

## *Cancer Clinical Trial Data for Tulsi Holy Basil (Ocimum Sanctum Linn) – (continued)*

| THERAPEUTIC AREA | STUDY | BENEFIT | DESCRIPTION |
|---|---|---|---|
| **Prostate Cancer** | Prostate Cancer Cell Study<br>24-48 hours | • This study focuses on apoptosis-inducing ability of *Ocimum Sanctum* (OS) extract on prostate cancer cells.<br>• Findings suggest that, ethanolic extract of OS can effectively induce apoptosis, leading to cell death in prostate cancer cells (Dhandayuthapani, et al., 2015). | • Prostate cancer cells were treated with different concentrations of 70% ethanolic extract of OS and then the cytotoxicity was determined after 24 and 48 hours. |
| **Breast Cancer** | Breast Cancer Cell Study | • The study found that *Ocimum Sanctum* (OS) inhibited proliferation of breast cancer cells.<br>• The study findings indicate that OS has the ability to cause apoptosis and reduce proliferation of breast cancer cells, suggesting its potential for use as an anti-cancer agent (Manaharan, et al., 2016). | • Essential oil OS was extracted using hydro-distillation of the leaves.<br>• Cell proliferation was measured at different concentrations |
| **Oral Cancer** | Oral Cancer Cell Study | • The antiproliferative activity of *Ocimum Tenuiflorum* (OT) on oral cancer cell line was evaluated.<br>• The aqueous extract of OT of Krishna and Rama Tulsi exhibited significant anti-proliferative properties, causing apoptosis in oral cancer cell line, suggesting the potential for use as an anti-cancer agent (Shivpuje, et al., 2015). | • Aqueous and dry extract of OT with both Krishna Tulsi and Rama Tulsi leaves were prepared. |
| **Pancreatic Cancer** | Pancreatic Cancer Cell Study | • *Ocimum Sanctum* (OS) leaf extract inhibit the proliferation, migration, invasion, and induce apoptosis of pancreatic cancer cells.<br>• Overall, the study suggests that leaves of *Ocimum Sanctum* (OS) could be a potential source of novel anti-cancer compounds in the future (Shimizu, et al., 2013). | • OS leaf extract |
| **Lung Cancer** | Lung Cancer Cell Study | • Overall, the results demonstrate that *Ocimum Sanctum* (OS) ethanol extract induces apoptosis in lung cancer cells suggesting that it can be applied to lung carcinoma as a chemopreventive candidate (Magesh, et al., 2009). | • OS ethanol extract |
| **Skin Cancer** | Mice Study | • The study concluded that leaf extract of *Ocimum Sanctum* (OS) provides protection against proliferation of skin cancer cells (Rastogi, et al., 2007). | • Alcoholic extract of the leaves of OS |

## Summary of Clinical Findings

**Tulsi holy basil** *(Ocimum Sanctum Linn):* Numerous clinical trials indicate the stress lowering property of Tulsi holy basil, and its value in managing anxiety disorder and depression. Tulsi has been safely and reliably used to lower serum glucose levels, serum triglycerides, and are found to be cardio-protective. Tulsi's anti-inflammatory effect enables it to be efficacious in healing ulcers and useful as a mild analgesic.

In select cell studies of prostate, breast, pancreatic, oral, lung, and skin cancer, tulsi has demonstrated benefit-inducing apoptosis to contain the proliferation of cancer cells. Tulsi has been shown to minimize the side effects of radiation therapy and stabilize healthy cell gene expression. Too few oncologists and persons suffering with cancer know of the significant benefit tulsi can provide them to slow cancer progression and protect healthy cells from aggressive treatment side effects. Clearly, more human trials are required to explore the optimal dose, duration and synergistic use of tulsi with other plants such as turmeric, ashwagandha, and others with organ and endocrine specificity.

## Health Benefits

**Sweet Basil** *(Ocimum Basilicum Linn):* Historically, touted by the Greeks, Romans and Egyptians as an herb worthy of kings, sweet basil has been used in cooking sumptuous foods. Its volatile oils, used in ancient religious ceremonies and embalming, were considered a symbol of fertility. While sweet basil has not been studied extensively by modern medicine, it has been found to be beneficial for preventing and managing common ailments due to its antioxidant properties.

- Has shown potential for use in acne control.
- Has been used as an essential oil inhalant to reduce the stress from mental exhaustion and burnout.
- Can serve as an insect repellent for prevention of malaria and dengue.
- Has potential for heart health, in the treatment of hyperlipidemia.

## Summary of Clinical Findings

Far too little research has been done investigating the preventive and healing benefits of sweet basil. Its strong aromatic oil has been found to be beneficial in acne prevention, useful as an insect repellent, in lowering of mental stress, and in the treatment of heart health and circulation.

## Dosage Range: Sweet Basil

There is no supplemental dose range for Sweet Basil in the scientific literature.

## Dosage Range: Tulsi Holy Basil

Doses of 300-2,500 mg of Tulsi holy basil *(Ocimum Sanctum Linn)* per day have been used in human studies. Standardized extracts are typically used in lower amounts, in the 250-2,000 mg range (Yates, 2017).

## Contraindications

Having been granted *Generally Recognized as Safe* (GRAS) status in the United States by the *Food and Drug Administration* (FDA), Tulsi holy basil (*Ocimum Sanctum Linn*) is well tolerated by most people.

Patients with known allergy hypersensitivity to *Ocimum sanctum Linn*, its constituents or to members of the Lamiaceae family, should avoid using this botanical agent. The plants included in the Lamiaceae are mints and balms.

Based on animal studies, use Tulsi cautiously for:

- Patients with hypoglycemia.
- Patients with bleeding disorders or those taking anti-coagulant or antiplatelet drugs.
- Patients who want to conceive a child due to possible anti-spermatogenic or anti-fertility effects at higher dosages.
- Pregnant and breast-feeding women, as Tulsi holy basil may stimulate uterine contractions, based on traditional use (Yates, 2017).

## *Clinical Trial Data for Sweet Basil (Ocimum Basilicum Linn)*

Below are data on the benefit of sweet basil for managing common conditions.

| THERAPEUTIC AREA | STUDY | BENEFIT | DESCRIPTION |
|---|---|---|---|
| **Acne** | **Human Trial 8 weeks** | • Experimental study of three gel formulations on 28 volunteer patients, separated into 4 groups of 7 patients. All groups reported an improvement of the acne condition (Matiz, et al., 2012). | • Orange *(Citrus Sinensis)* and sweet basil (Ocimum Basilicum ) essential oils were tested.<br>• Treatments were applied daily for 8 weeks. |
| **Mental Exhaustion and Burnout** | **Human Trial 3 weeks** | • The aromatherapy group taking *Ocimum Basilicum* (OB) had a much greater reduction.<br>• The results suggest that inhaling essential oils may reduce the perceived level of mental fatigue and burnout. (Matiz, et al., 2012) | • Study was a randomized, controlled, double-blind pilot study. Data was collected for 3 weeks.<br>• Participants used an OB personal inhaler at home or at work. |
| **Insect Repellant** | **Lab Study Mosquitoes** | • This study tested against three mosquito species, *Aedes aegypti, Anopheles minimus* and *Culex quinquefasciatus,* under laboratory conditions.<br>• Both substances were effective as repellents and feeding deterrents against all three mosquito types (Phasomkusolsil, et al., 2010). | • Insect bite protection and length of protection with repellents was tested.<br>• Phlai *(Zingiber cassumunar)* and Sweet basil *(Ocimum Basilicum)* whose oils were included. |
| **Atherosclerosis** | **Rat Study 7-24 hours** | • This study evaluated the lipid lowering effect of aqueous *Ocimum Basilicum* (OB) extract.<br>• The results indicated that *Ocimum Basilicum* (OB) may contain hypolipidemic and antioxidant substances and its use as a therapeutic tool in hyperlipidaemic subjects may be of benefit. (Amrani, et al., 2006) | • The animals were given 200 mg/kg of the OB extract. |

## Toxicity

No significant toxicity has been reported following short- or long-term administration of Tulsi holy basil at standard doses.

## Supplementation

Tulsi holy basil *(Ocimum Sanctum Linn)* has very low toxicity, providing general beneficial effects without adverse events. The Tulsi holy basil leaves offer a rich source of essential oil, containing eugenol, nerol, camphor and a variety of terpenes and flavonoids. The oil is a strong antiseptic against many kinds of disease causing organisms. Tulsi holy basil comes in the following forms: fresh, dried leaf, capsules, extract and tincture. The dosing is best determined by your health practitioner based on your height, weight, age, and health status.

## Holy Basil (Ocimum Sanctum Linn) Supplement Recommendation

Holy basil supplement forms and dose ranges are indicated below.

| THERAPEUTIC AREA | STUDY | BENEFIT |
|---|---|---|
| **For Prevention** | 300 mg-2,000 mg once daily | Extract |
| **For Therapy** | 600-1,800 mg daily in divided dosages | Extract |
| **For Diabetes** | 2,500 mg or 1 teaspoon of dried herb brewed daily in 1 cup of water, 2-4 times per day | Dried leaf |

**SOURCE:** (Yates, 2017)

## Summary

**Tulsi Holy Basil** *(Ocimum Sanctum Linn):* Modern scientific studies have demonstrated that Tulsi holy basil is effective in treating a range of stressful conditions. Within Ayurveda, it is more commonly recommended as a preventive measure to enhance the ability to adapt to both psychological and physical stress and therefore prevent the development of stress-related diseases. Both of these findings are significant. Clinical trial data are indicative of the broad power and diverse health benefits of Tulsi holy basil. Tulsi is not widely used in western clinical medicine despite the data we have presented. Tulsi is affordable, accessible and very palatable as a tea or extract. We recommend daily consumption of Tulsi holy basil tea as a foundational diet and lifestyle practice.

**Sweet Basil** *(Ocimum Basilicum Linn):* Sweet basil has been a staple spice in Mediterranean and global healthy cuisine. It, too, is affordable, accessible and safe to use on a daily basis. Modern day trials are limited, but promising. We recommend using it in your everyday cooking, preferably fresh and uncooked or lightly heated.

## Kitchen Medicine

We have showcased several cultivars of basil. Feel free to experiment with different varieties either fresh or dried basil in any dish, using sweet or spicy herbs and spices. You can also include sprigs of fragrant basil in fresh floral arrangements.

**Tulsi Holy Basil:** Regular consumption of Tulsi holy basil is nourishing to the body, mind and spirit, while fostering a sense of relaxation and well-being. It has a calming effect that leads to clarity of thought, along with a more relaxed and calm disposition. The cognitive and memory-enhancing properties of Tulsi holy basil differ from caffeine beverages such as coffee and tea, which stimulates the nervous system and may cause physical and mental agitation, plus blood sugar decline several hours after ingestion. Tulsi holy basil does not produce the same physical dependence as caffeine and can be safely consumed on a regular basis. Powdered Tulsi is stronger than dried Tulsi.

**Sweet Basil:** Combines nicely with virtually all herbs, especially rosemary, thyme, oregano and marjoram. Experimentation is the best way to determine how much seasoning tastes best to you and for your meal mates. Sweet basil combines with virtually all spices especially with thyme and marjoram and with pungent and sweet spices. A good rule of thumb for using dried basil is 1 teaspoon to 1 tablespoon for a dish that serves 4 people.

# Basil Remedies

## Tulsi and Ginger Tea

*I (SM) drink this combination at least once daily. It is calming and caffeine free.*

SERVES 1

**INGREDIENTS**

1 cup of water
¼ teaspoon dried ginger or 1 tablespoon fresh ginger
½-1 teaspoon dried or 2 tablespoons fresh Tulsi holy basil leaves
½-1 teaspoon freshly squeezed lemon to taste (optional)
½-1 teaspoon honey (optional)

**METHOD**

1. In a cup of water, boil the ginger root or powder for 5 minutes.
2. Add the dried or fresh tulsi leaves and steep 3-5 minutes.
3. Strain the solids and drink hot.
4. Add lemon and honey if you wish or store in the refrigerator for a cool drink in the summer.

NOTE: *Finer powdered Tulsi will yield a stronger brew than coarse dried tulsi.*

## Tulsi Kashayam (For Cough and Cold)

*Kashayam is an Ayurvedic home remedy for the common cough and cold. Sip on the warm beverage twice a day for relief from symptoms.*

SERVES 1

**INGREDIENTS**

2 tablespoons dried or ⅓ cup fresh Tulsi holy basil leaves
¼ teaspoon ajwain (if available, also called carom seeds)
1 teaspoon honey
200 ml water

**METHOD**

1. Toast the ajwain and dried Tulsi, if using (but not the fresh)
2. Heat the water and add the dried Tulsi and ajwain mixture. If using fresh, remove leaves and discard stems.
3. Bring the mixture to a boil. Allow to slightly cool.
4. Strain the solids, add the honey and drink hot.
5. Can be stored up to 3 days.

## Tulsi (For Cough and Sore Throat)

*I (SM) have used fresh tulsi leaves as indicated below to alleviate a cough and sore throat. It has reduced the severity and duration of both.*

SERVES 1

**INGREDIENTS**

6-12 fresh Tulsi holy basil leaves

**METHOD**

1. Fold the leaves into a ball and chew on them.

## Basil Remedies (continued)

### Tulsi Kashayam (For Cough, Cold, and Flu)

*This more complex variation is also good for indigestion and the flu.*

SERVES 1

**INGREDIENTS**

2 tablespoons dried or ⅓ cup fresh Tulsi holy basil leaves
1 tablespoon black peppercorns
1 tablespoon cumin
1 tablespoon coriander seeds
1 tablespoon fresh ginger
I tablespoon fresh mint leaves
2 cups (500 ml) water
1 freshly squeezed lemon to taste
1 teaspoon honey

**METHOD**

1. Dry roast all the dried spices in a pan until fragrant. Set aside to cool slightly.
2. Bring water to boil, add all the fresh and dried ingredients and boil until the decoction is reduced to half.
3. Strain the solids and drink hot.
4. Add lemon and honey if you wish or store in the refrigerator for a cool drink in the summer.

## Basil Beverages

### Basil Ginger Smoothie

*This is my favorite recovery drink after a workout. Adding fresh turmeric provides a savory taste and healing benefit.*

SERVES 1

**INGREDIENTS**

1 medium apple
½ cup celery
½ cup leafy greens
½ cup berries
1 tablespoon dried Tulsi powder or 2 tablespoons fresh Tulsi leaves
1-inch (2.5 cm) fresh ginger, peeled
1-inch (2.5 cm) fresh turmeric, peeled
2 tablespoons fresh sweet basil leaves or ½ tablespoon dried sweet basil
2 tablespoons flax seeds
1 tablespoon whey protein powder
6 oz. kefir
3-6 oz. water or green tea

**METHOD**

1. Chop the apple, celery, greens, ginger, turmeric and sweet basil.
2. In a blender, place a few ice cubes (optional) at the bottom, add all the ingredients and blend until smooth.

# Basil Sauce, Dressing and Salad

## Italy Meets India Pesto

*Basil pesto is a staple of fine Italian cuisine. We have added a seed mixture to enhance its nutritional value.*

SERVES 4

**INGREDIENTS**

1/4 cup hemp seeds
1/8 cup raw sunflower seeds
1/8 cup pumpkin seeds
1/4 cup pine nuts
2 cups packed fresh sweet basil leaves
1 tablespoon Tulsi holy basil dried powder
2 cloves garlic
1 tablespoon fresh turmeric root, grated
2/3 cup extra-virgin olive oil
Sea salt and freshly ground black pepper to taste
1/2 cup fresh Pecorino Romano cheese, grated

**METHOD**

1. Pulse the seeds, nuts, fresh sweet basil leaves, dried tulsi powder, garlic, turmeric root, cheese, salt and black pepper in a food processor until combined.
2. With the motor running, slowly add the olive oil through the feed tube at the top.
3. Stop and scrape down sides. Blend until a smooth consistency is reached.
4. Serve with rice crackers, buckwheat bread or toss with some quinoa pasta.

## Basil Yogurt Dressing

*Using sweet or holy basil with turmeric gives your salad dressing a great taste and potent health benefit.*

SERVES 4

**INGREDIENTS**

1/8 cup rice vinegar
1 tablespoon maple syrup
1-2 cloves garlic, minced
1 tablespoon green herbs (dried or fresh)
1 tablespoon chia seeds
1/4-1/2 teaspoon salt
1 tablespoon dried Tulsi holy basil
2 teaspoons fresh turmeric, peeled and chopped
1 tablespoon fresh sweet basil
1 tablespoon yogurt
1/2 cup extra-virgin olive oil

**METHOD**

1. Mix all the ingredients in a blender except the oil. Turn on the machine and slowly add the oil until dressing is emulsified.
2. Store in a glass container until ready to serve.

## Basil Sauce, Dressing and Salad (continued)

### Captivating Caprese Salad

*Fresh, whole milk mozzarella cheese, with tasty spices and sun ripened tomatoes make this a delectable dish.*

SERVES 2

**INGREDIENTS**

2 medium tomatoes, sliced
8 oz. fresh mozzarella balls, sliced
12 fresh or 1 tablespoon dried sweet basil leaves
1 tablespoon extra-virgin olive oil
1 tablespoon balsamic vinegar
¼ teaspoon salt
¼ teaspoon fresh ground pepper

**METHOD**

1. Arrange the sliced tomatoes and mozzarella on a plate.
2. Gently massage the basil to release flavors and garnish the salad.
3. Drizzle with olive oil and balsamic vinegar.
4. Add salt and fresh ground pepper to taste.

## Basil Entrees

### St. Paddy's Day Eggs

*Fresh basil, alone or with other spices, enhances the flavor and digestibility of a well-made omelet.*

SERVES 1

**INGREDIENTS**

2 tablespoons extra-virgin olive oil, divided
¼ cup onions, minced fine
½ cup spinach, chopped medium
2 tablespoons cilantro, minced fine
2 tablespoons fresh or 2 teaspoons dried sweet basil leaves
2 large eggs
Sea salt and pepper to taste

**METHOD**

1. Heat half the oil, add the onions and sauté for a few minutes.
2. Fold in spinach and cook just until wilted. Stir in basil and cilantro, turn off heat and set aside.
3. Whisk the eggs with 1 tablespoon water, salt and pepper.
4. In a small sauté pan, heat remaining oil and coat the pan before pouring in the egg mixture.
5. When the eggs start to set, lay the sautéed vegetables and herbs down the middle of the pan.
6. Flip in the sides or fold in half. Cook until completely set and gently slide onto a plate.

### Best Broth Ever

*Homemade vegetable, spice broth is easy to make and wonderful to use as a basis for soup, sauces and grain dishes.*

SERVES 8 CUPS

**INGREDIENTS**

6 cups of water
2-inches (5 cm) turmeric root
1 tablespoon dried Tulsi
1½ cups dried shitake or oyster mushrooms
½ yellow onion, peeled and sliced in chunks
A handful of pineapple sage
2 tablespoons flax seeds

**METHOD**

1. Put all the ingredients into a medium saucepan. Heat to a low simmer.
2. After 30 minutes, or longer if you have time, strain out the solids, and use the liquid for the brown rice recipe on page 41.

## *Herb Vegetable Pilaf*

*A pilaf is a spiced grain dish. Cooking it in homemade broth and adding savory spices creates a tasty staple dish.*

SERVES 6

**INGREDIENTS**

2 cups basmati brown rice, cooked
4 cups filtered water or broth (see page 40)
2 tablespoons extra-virgin olive oil or ghee
2 bay leaves
1 tablespoon cumin seeds
1 cup onion, minced
2 tablespoons fresh ginger, minced
2 cloves garlic, minced
½ teaspoon ground turmeric
2 teaspoons ground cumin
2 teaspoons ground coriander
½ teaspoon garam masala (optional)
1 pinch saffron
1 cup leafy greens
½ cup carrots
½ cup green beans
½ cup fresh or frozen English green peas
2 tablespoons cilantro, minced
8 fresh leaves sweet basil
½ teaspoon sea salt

**METHOD**

1. Soak the rice overnight. Strain the rice and rinse well until the water runs clear. Add rice to a medium saucepan with cold filtered water (or broth). Bring to a boil. Turn the heat to low and cover with a tight fitting lid. Cook without lifting the lid for about 50 minutes. Turn off the heat and set aside.
2. Heat the oil in a large pot or skillet over medium heat. Add the bay leaf and cumin seeds. When spices start to crackle, add onions and sauté for a minute.
3. Add ginger and cook until onions are golden. Add garlic and heat for 30 seconds.
4. Next add turmeric, cumin, coriander and saffron and stir until fragrant.
5. Add the greens, carrots and beans. Lightly sauté for 5-7 minutes.
6. Turn the heat down to low and add peas, cilantro and basil. Cook until peas are vibrant and slightly soft (1-2 minutes).
7. Fold in the pre-cooked brown rice to the mixture.
8. Add sea salt. Taste and adjust seasonings. Serve warm.

## *Tuscan Bean, Herb and Cabbage Soup*

*This Italian inspired classic can be made with any seasonal roots and greens.*

SERVES 4-6

**INGREDIENTS**

1 cup dry cannellini or butter beans
2 tablespoons extra-virgin olive oil
1 medium onion, sliced
2 cloves garlic, minced
1½ cups cabbage, shredded
1 cup dandelion greens, chopped
2 medium carrots, thinly slice
2 medium turnips, thinly sliced
1½ quarts vegetable stock
6-8 fresh sweet basil leaves
2 tablespoons parsley, minced
Sea salt to taste
¼ tablespoon pepper

**METHOD**

1. Soak the beans for at least 7 hours or overnight. Cook in a pot or a pressure cooker. While it is preferred that you freshly cook the beans, you can use 1½ cans if you are in a hurry.
2. Heat the oil in a large stockpot. Sauté the onions for several minutes until translucent. Add garlic and reduce heat to prevent browning.
3. Add the carrots and turnips next, cover to soften for about 5 minutes.
4. Stir in the cabbage and dandelion greens to coat with oil.
5. Pour in the vegetable stock and bring to a boil. Turn down heat to a low simmer, cover the pan and let it cook for 15 minutes or until all the vegetables are tender.
6. Add the cooked beans, basil and parsley to combine.
7. Add salt and pepper to taste.

**SOURCE:** Adapted from the "Tuscan Bean and Cabbage Soup" in *Linda's Winter Kitchen*, by Linda McCartney.

## Basil Entrees (continued)

# Thai Holy Basil Chicken Stir Fry

*This dish is a staple of Thai cuisine. The aromatic Thai holy basil cools the warming spices in the dish.*

SERVES 1 (RECIPE CAN BE DOUBLED)

**INGREDIENTS**

- 1 tablespoon extra-virgin coconut oil
- 1 chicken breast, sliced into small pieces
- 1 small bird's eye chili, crushed to expose seeds (optional)
- ½ onion, thinly sliced
- 1 clove garlic, minced
- 1 tablespoon fish sauce
- 2 teaspoons Thai chili paste
- 2 teaspoons tamari sauce
- ½ red pepper, thinly sliced
- 10 Thai holy basil leaves

**METHOD**

1. Heat oil in a wok over medium-high heat. Add chicken and cook, stirring until golden.
2. Add chili, onion, garlic, fish sauce, chili paste and tamari sauce to the pan. Cook stirring constantly, until onions begin to soften, and liquids thicken slightly, 3-4 minutes.
3. Add red pepper and cook for another 2 minutes.
4. Stir in basil and remove from heat.

**SOURCE:** Recipe modified from https://inquiringchef.com/chicken-with-thai-holy-basil/

# Thai Holy Basil Vegetarian Stir Fry

*This is a vegetarian rendition of savory Thai Stir Fry using tofu rather than chicken.*

SERVES 2

**INGREDIENTS**

- 4 oz. extra firm tofu
- ½ cup tamari
- 2 teaspoons ginger, minced
- 2 cloves garlic, minced
- 1 tablespoon extra-virgin olive oil
- ½ cup onion, minced
- 3 Thai (or other) chili peppers*, seeded and minced
- 1 cup cabbage, chopped
- ½ cup mushrooms, chopped
- ½ cup green beans, cut in 1-inch (2.5 cm) pieces
- ½ cup broccoli, cut into florets
- 1 packed cup fresh Thai holy basil

**METHOD**

1. Cube the tofu into ½-inch (1.27 cm) squares. Prepare a marinade with tamari with ginger and garlic. Add the tofu, cover and set aside for 10 minutes.
2. Heat the oil in a pan; add the onions and sauté for a minute. Add the Thai chilies with all the vegetables. Stir-fry until they begin to soften and brighten in color.
3. Add the tofu with the marinade and toss to combine. Add basil leaves and stir until wilted.
4. Serve with brown rice.

**Thai chilies are very hot — you might want to avoid the seeds.*

# Basil Extract and Tincture

## Sweet Basil Extract

*There are different ways to extract the phytonutrients from basil, such as extraction by water, vinegar, oil, wine, brandy, vodka or grain alcohol. Below are recipes for water and vinegar extraction:*

### Water Based

INGREDIENTS

1 tablespoon fresh sweet basil or 1 teaspoon dried
1 cup hot water

METHOD

1. Crush the sweet basil ever so gently using a mortar and pestle.
2. Heat water until it just reaches a boil.
3. Add the hot water to the leaves and cover for 10 minutes or longer.
4. Strain the water and you have your basil-infused water. It will look like green tea.
5. Use right away or refrigerate up to 2 days.

### Vinegar Based

INGREDIENTS

1 tablespoon fresh sweet basil or 1 teaspoon dried
1 cup apple cider vinegar

METHOD

1. Crush the sweet basil ever so gently in a pestle and mortar.
2. Put basil in a jar and add vinegar.
3. Flip jar over, or shake well, every day for 14 days.
4. Begin using it in salads.

## Tulsi Holy Basil Tincture

*Tinctures extract beneficial alkaloids and natural flavones from herbs using alcohol. It's concentrated, so use in small doses.*

INGREDIENTS

Dried Tulsi holy basil
Vodka or Brandy 80-90 proof (non-GMO)

METHOD

1. Fill a small Mason jar halfway or less with dried Tulsi holy basil.
2. Pour in vodka to cover, leaving just a little room at the top.
3. Label and put the date on the jar.
4. Close the lid, store in a dark area.
5. Shake the bottle every day.
6. After two weeks, place a cheesecloth-covered strainer into a bowl and decant the contents of the jar. Gather the cheesecloth and squeeze the basil until all liquid is in the bowl.
7. Transfer the liquid into a dark jar, label and date.
8. Pour some of the liquid into a small dropper bottle; label and date the small bottle.
9. Adult dose is 6-10 drops in warm water. It can also be used in teas.
10. Tincture lasts for 2-3 years.

## *How to Grow Basil*

Basil is a highly fragrant and aromatic herb. There are numerous types of basil available. According to the variety, the color of the leaves may vary from green to purple, and the flavor may have a hint of lemon, cinnamon, jasmine, thyme or camphor in it. The seeds should be planted early spring in about a ¼-inch (.63 cm) of rich, moist soil. Plants should be spaced 10-12 inches (25-30 cm) apart. Germination requires 5-7 days, and thinning the plants is not necessary. Growth is rapid, and no special care other than the usual cultivation practices is required. Flowering shoots are pinched out to extend the useful life of plants.

**Sweet Basil:** A summer herb that can be grown successfully inside during the winter in a sunny window. It is plentiful during the summer months and available year-round in many markets. Choose evenly colored leaves with no sign of wilting. Refrigerate basil, wrapped in barely damp paper towels and then in a plastic bag, for up to 4 days or store a bunch of basil, stems down, in a glass of water with a plastic bag over the leaves. Refrigerate in this manner for up to a week, changing the water every 2 days.

To preserve fresh basil, wash and dry the leaves and place layers of leaves, then coarse salt, in a container that can be tightly sealed. Alternatively, finely chop the cleaned basil and combine it with a small amount of olive oil. Freeze in tiny portions to flavor sauces, salad dressings, etc. Dried basil, though it bears little resemblance in either flavor or aroma to the fresh herb, can be purchased in the spice section of most supermarkets. Store dried basil airtight in a cool, dark place for up to 6 months.

**Tulsi Holy Basil:** Plant types are Rama Tulsi, Krishna Tulsi and Vana Tulsi. Sow seeds outdoors in late spring or early summer, when the temperature reaches around 70°F (21°C). For an earlier start in spring, sow the seeds indoors in a greenhouse or on a sunny windowsill. Place the Tulsi holy basil seeds on top of the soil and tamp them for good soil to seed contact, cover the seeds with ¼-inch (.63 cm) layer of compost or soil. Water the seeds with a sprayer and place them where they receive partial morning sun. Keep the soil constantly moist until germination, which will take around 1-2 weeks.

When the seedlings have grown 2-3 sets of true leaves carefully transplant them in individual containers or outdoors, taking care not to disturb the roots. As Tulsi holy basil is a tropical plant you can grow it anytime in the tropics. Requirements of growing are similar to sweet basil. It grows well in loamy and fertile soil with good drainage; pH level of 6-7.5 is optimal. It thrives in full sun but grows in partial shade too, at least r hours of sunlight a day is required.

## *How to Grow Basil (continued)*

Water the plant when the top 1-inch (2.5 cm) of soil is dry. Do not water during rain. Reduce watering in the winter to prevent diseases. It is important to pinch off the tops of the plant when they are forming four or six pairs of leaves, this will make the plant grow bushier. Even the flower buds need to be removed when they appear. It grows more lush and full when seed production is prevented. It is also important to remove the faded, wilted or discolored leaves to encourage the growth of new foliage. Regular removal of old leaves and flower buds keeps the plant healthy.

Apply liquid fertilizer once every couple of weeks. Replacing the top 2-inch (5 cm) layer of soil with compost every 6 months to a year is also beneficial. Prune as needed throughout the year to control its size and promote bushier and more compact growth. Never remove more than half of the growth of stem while pruning.

Move plants indoors in the winter if you live below USDA Zone 10. Place the plant near a bright sunny window, where the temperature is kept above 50°F (10°C). Move the plant again outside after the danger of frost has passed.

To harvest, reap the aromatic leaves of your plant throughout the growing season. Once your plant reaches 12 inches (30 cm) in height, take a pair of scissors and depending on your needs, cut a large single leaf or a whole branch. Cutting just above a leaf will ensure continued growth on that branch. Use fresh leaves on the same day you harvest because they fade quickly. Store your Tulsi harvest for future use by drying out the leaves. Collect branches in a basket and place them in a dry spot away from sunlight and toss them 2-3 times every day until leaves become crispy.

### How to Make Basil Powder

To dry basil, strip the leaves from the stem and dry in a dark, airy location. Run them through a grinder mill to get powdered leaves. Store dried leaves whole in an airtight container.

CHAPTER THREE

# Ashwagandha

*(Withania somnifera)*

**Ashwagandha** is a beautiful and powerful plant with immense healing properties. It is considered a *Rasayana* (tonic) in Ayurveda. We have grown it successfully in our Northern California garden. In *Spice for Life*, we are carving a new niche for ashwagandha to be a spice due to its sweet earthy and slightly pungent flavor. It has synergistic benefits when added to turmeric, ginger, cinnamon and other spices. We encourage you to add ashwagandha to your daily regimen in tea, and use the root or powder as a booster food in cooking stock, soup, and sauces. We don't have to buy ashwagandha in capsules when we can cook with it and feel this *stallion-like* herb (translation of Ashwagandha) as food, stress buster and medicine.

I suggest you start by making an ashwagandha tea in the morning, either alone with honey to taste, or blended with equal amounts of fresh or powdered turmeric and ginger. After a few days you may notice more internal calmness, a better ability to manage stress and get a deeper and more satisfying sleep. After several weeks, you may find your energy and productivity picking up without feeling over stimulated.

Once you and ashwagandha are on familiar taste and energetic terms, you can begin to experiment by adding it to foods or perhaps making a homemade tincture providing a substitute for sugar and caffeine to make it through a long afternoon or evening of working late. As we age, taking adaptogenic (stabilizing) plants such as ashwagandha are a safe and effective way of not crashing and burning as the risk of injury, infection and illness increase in our world.

*Powdered ashwagandha is used in teas.*

*Ashwagandha capsules, powder and roots.*

*Ashwagandha roots and tincture*

## Background and Uses

*Withania somnifera,* commonly known as ashwagandha, is a member of the nightshade family. Other names include Indian ginseng, poison gooseberry, or winter cherry. In Sanskrit "Ashwa" means horse and "gandha" scent. Together ashwagandha connotes, the smell of a horse and powerful like a stallion. In Ayurveda, it is considered nature's gift to mankind. For centuries this herb has been used to treat a broad spectrum of conditions such as stress, anxiety, exhaustion, lack of sleep, infertility and more. With a powerful mix of antioxidants, iron and amino acids it is one of the most powerful herbs in Ayurvedic healing. In Ayurveda, it is classified as a rasayana, expected to promote physical and mental health, restore the body and increase longevity, working to calm and energize at the same time.

## Plant Specifics

It is an erect branching shrub that is covered in wooly hairs and thrives in the drier parts of India, West Asia and Northern Africa. It is a perennial herb often found as a roadside weed. This plant is short, 2-4 feet tall, and grows in the rainy season. The branches extend radially from a central stem. Leaves are green in color, long and spiky and grow in twos. A small cherry-like fruit grows in the center and its seeds are harvested when it turns red. While the stem is slim, the root is thick. The roots emanate a strong odor and hence the name "gandha." The roots are harvested and then dried. The longer and whiter the root is, the better. The medicinal properties of ashwagandha are primarily in the roots. It takes roughly seven months from seed to harvesting time which is peak for *withanolides* (steroidal saponins that have shown anti-inflammatory effects).

## Active Constituents

The biologically active chemical constituents of *Withania somnifera* include alkaloids (isopelletierine, anaferine, cuscohygrine, anahygrine, etc.), steroidal lactones (withanolides, withaferin) and saponins (Mishra, et al., 2004). Sitoindosides and acyl steryl glucosides in ashwagandha are anti-stress agents. Active principles of ashwagandha, for instance the sitoindosides VII-X and Withaferin-A, have been shown to have significant anti-stress activity against acute models of experimental stress (Bhattacharya, et al., 1987). Many of its constituents support immunomodulatory actions (Ghosal, et al., 1989). The aerial parts of *Withania somnifera* yielded 5-dehydroxy withanolide-R and withasomniferin-A (Atta-ur-Rahman, et al., 1991).

## Traditional Medicine

Ashwagandha is one of the most important herbs used in Ayurveda (the traditional system of medicine in India) used for millennia as a Rasayana for its wide-ranging health benefits. Rasayana is described as an herbal or metallic preparation that promotes a youthful state of physical and mental health and expands happiness (Singh, et al., 2010).

The root of ashwagandha is regarded as a tonic, aphrodisiac, narcotic, diuretic, anthelmintic, astringent, thermogenic and stimulant. It is commonly used in emaciation of children (when given with milk, it is considered the best tonic for children), debility from old age, rheumatism, vitiated conditions of vata, leucoderma, constipation, insomnia, nervous breakdown, goiter and more. (Sharma, et al., 1999). A paste is formed when roots are crushed with water and are applied to reduce the inflammation at the joints (Bhandari, 1970). It is also locally applied to carbuncles, for ulcers and painful swellings (Kritikar, et al., 1935). The root, in combination with other drugs, is prescribed for snake venom and a scorpion sting. It also helps in leucorrhoea, boils, pimples, flatulent colic, worms and piles (hemorrhoids) (Misra, 2004). Nagori Ashwagandha is considered supreme among all Ashwagandha varieties. Maximum benefit is achieved when fresh ashwagandha powder is used (Singh, 1983).

The leaves are bitter and are recommended for fever and painful swellings. The flowers are astringent, depurative, diuretic and aphrodisiac. The seeds are anthelmintic and combined with astringent and rock salt remove white spots from the cornea. Ashwagandharishta, a tonic prepared from it, is used in a number of ailments including hysteria, anxiety, memory loss and syncope (fainting). It also acts as a stimulant and increases sperm count (Sharma, 1938).

## Uses in Modern Medicine

Ashwagandha is compared to Siberian Ginseng *(Eleutherococcus senticosus)* and Chinese/Korean Ginseng *(Panax Ginseng)* in its adaptogenic properties, and hence it is popularly known as Indian Ginseng (Singh, et al., 2010). The extensive studies on the biological model of animals for the adaptogenic and anti-stress properties of ashwagandha (Abbas and Singh, 2006; Kalsi, et al., 1987; Singh, et al., 1983) have shown it to be effective in increasing stamina (physical endurance) and preventing stress-induced gastric ulcers, *carbon tetrachloride* (CCl4) induced hepatotoxicity and mortality. Ashawagandha showed similar anti-stress activity in rats (Namasivayam, 1999). An aqueous suspension of ashwagandha root was used at 100 mg/kg/oral dosage. The results indicate a significant increase in the plasma corticosterone level, phagocytic index and avidity index in rats subjected to cold swimming stress. In the rats pretreated with the drug, these parameters were near control values and an increase in the swimming time was observed. These results indicate that *Withania somnifera* used in the crude form is a potent anti-stress agent. The results of these studies lend support to the hypothesis of tonics, vitalizers and rejuvenators of Ayurveda which indicate clinical use of *Withania somnifera* in the prevention and treatment of many stress-induced diseases like arteriosclerosis, premature aging, arthritis, diabetes, hypertension and malignancy (Singh, 1995).

## Health Benefits of Ashwagandha

Please refer below for research citations:

### Adaptogenic

Brings equilibrium and homeostasis while balancing hormones.

### Relieves Stress

Traditionally, it had been administered to induce a soothing and calming effect on a person. The array of active ingredients responsible for this activity is still unknown, but various anti-stress properties have been observed in research experiments.

### Alleviates Insomnia

Insomnia is a disruption in the body's ability to regulate sleep-wake cycles. It is caused by chronic stress and deterioration in immunity, metabolism and hormonal balance. Ashwagandha does not act as a sedative but rather, reduces stress, improves vitality, and balances the nervous system, thereby helping to regulate sleep. While we are asleep, our body is repairing and rejuvenating. Sleep disorders increase the risk for other conditions such as high blood pressure, obesity, diabetes, depression and cancer.

### Relieves Anxiety and Depression

In India, ashwagandha has been traditionally used in Ayurveda to improve both physical and mental health. The effects, particularly on depression, were studied at the Institute of Medical Sciences at Banaras Hindu University, India. The study supported the benefits of Ashwagandha in relation to anxiety and depression.

### Improves Muscle Strength

Has been found to be useful in improving the muscular strength of limbs and helping people recover from weakness, while improving neuro-muscular coordination.

### Helps Endurance

Helps build muscle and improve body strength and conditioning. Studies have shown how people can build body strength and conditioning with Ashwagandha.

### Improves Fertility in Men

In addition to increasing libido, ashwagandha also helps improve semen quality. A recent scientific study indicated that ashwagandha did so by increasing the sperm count and sperm mobility. For many centuries, people have been using it to please their partner in bed.

### Improves Sexual Dysfunction in Women

Helps women who have a low libido whether they are young or in pre-menopause, during and post-menopause.

### Helps Manage Blood Sugar

Helps manage blood sugar. In Ayurveda ashwagandha is used to treat diabetes and studies have shown blood sugar levels go down when Ashwagandha has been taken for 4 weeks.

### Improves Hypothyroid Condition

Ashwagandha can be used to balance and stimulate the thyroid gland. The root extract, if taken on a daily basis, has been reported to increase the secretion of thyroid hormones.

### Alleviates Erectile Dysfunction

For those suffering from erectile dysfunction, ashwagandha may provide support. This plant is good for enhancing the libido in men. It is important that men consult a healthcare professional for dosage and duration of use.

### Supports Cancer Remission

In animal studies, ashwagandha is showing great promise of diminishing tumor cells in breast, prostate, medullary thyroid, cervical cancer, lung and colon cell studies.

## *Inflammatory Diseases: Select Clinical Data*

Ashwagandha has demonstrated benefits for a wide variety of conditions. Below are clinical trial data for its application in the remediation of common inflammatory syndromes, previously mentioned:

| DISEASE | DURATION | BENEFIT | STUDY DESIGN |
|---|---|---|---|
| **Stress** | **Human trial 60 days** | • The serum cortisol levels were substantially reduced in the ashwagandha group, relative to the placebo group.<br>• The findings of this study suggest that a high-concentration full-spectrum ashwagandha root extract safely and effectively improves an individual's resistance towards stress and thereby improves self-assessed quality of life. (Chandrasekhar, et al., 2012). | • 64 patients were randomized to either the placebo control group or<br>• Study drug treatment group were asked to take 1 capsule twice a day for a period of 60 days. Each capsule contained 300 mg of high-concentration full-spectrum extract from the root of the ashwagandha plant |
| **Male Infertility** | **Human trial 3 months** | • Measuring various biochemical and stress parameters before and after treatment, suggested a definite role of stress in male infertility and the ability of *W. somnifera* to treat stress-related infertility.<br>• Treatment resulted in a decrease in stress, improved the level of antioxidants and improved overall semen quality in a significant number of individuals.<br>• The treatment resulted in pregnancy in the partners of 14% of the patients (Abbas, et al., 2011). | • The study selected normozoospermic but infertile individuals (N = 60)<br>• The subjects were given root powder of *W. somnifera* at a rate of 5g/day for 3 months |

## *Inflammatory Diseases: Select Clinical Data (continued)*

| DISEASE | DURATION | BENEFIT | STUDY DESIGN |
|---|---|---|---|
| **Muscle Strengthening** | **Human trial 30 Days** | • The activity was assessed for exercise tolerance (by Cycle Ergometer), muscle strength (by Hand grip force, Quadriceps force, and Back extensor force), and body fat percentage and lean body weight (by measuring skin fold thickness at four areas such as Biceps, Triceps, Subscapular, and Suprailiac with a SkinFold Caliper in millimeters).<br>• The study demonstrates that WS, when given in the form of aqueous extract in capsules with gradual escalating doses from 750 to 1250 mg/day, was well tolerated.<br>• The formulation was found to be safe on hematological and biochemical organ function tests. This study has also demonstrated muscle strengthening, lipid lowering, and improved quality of sleep (Raut, et al., 2012). | • 18 volunteers (12 males and 6 females) in the ages of 18-30 years were enrolled for the study.<br>• WS extract was available as gelatine capsules in the sizes of 250 and 500 mg iu<br>• Each volunteer received 3 doses increased every 10 days.<br>• Thus, 750 mg/day (equivalent to 6g of crude pulverized roots of WS) was administered orally for first 10 days.<br>• 1,000mg/day (equivalent to 8g) for next 10 days, and 1250 mg/day (equivalent to 10g) for last 10 days.<br>• The dosing schedule was as follows:<br>250 mg in the morning and 500 mg at night<br>500 mg in the morning and 500 mg at night from Day 11 to Day 20; and<br>500 mg in the morning and 750 mg at night from Day 21 to Day 30. |
| **Sexual Dysfuntion in Women** | **Human trial 8 weeks** | • The study demonstrated that in healthy women the administration of HCARE can improve *female sexual dysfunction* (FSD).<br>• The study demonstrated that ashwagandha root extract can be used for the treatment of FSD. No side effects were observed (Dongre, et al., 2015). | • 50 patients in a placebo controlled study of ashwagandha *high concentration of root extract* (HCARE and KSM-66 the highest concentration extract)<br>• Dose was 300 mg twice daily or placebo |
| **Type II Diabetes and High Cholesterol** | **Human trial 30 days** | • Ashwagandha demonstrated hypoglycemic and hypolipidemic effects in non-insulin dependent diabetic and hypercholesterolemic patients (Andallu, et al., 2000). | • Total sample 12 |
| **Endurance in athletes** | **Human trial 8 weeks** | • There was significant improvement in the experimental group in all parameters, whereas the placebo group did not show any change with respect to their baseline parameters.<br>• Ashwagandha improved the cardiorespiratory endurance of the elite athletes (Shenoy, et al., 2012). | • Forty elite athletes, Indian cyclists, were chosen randomly and were equally divided into experimental and placebo groups.<br>• The experimental group received 500 mg capsules of aqueous roots of ashwagandha twice daily for 8 weeks, whereas the placebo group received starch capsules. |
| **Hypothyroid** | **Human trial 8 weeks** | • Ashwagandha treatment effectively normalized the serum thyroid indices during the 8-week treatment period in a significant manner (Sharma, et al., 2018). | • 50 patients: 25 extract, 25 placebo<br>• Ashwagandha root extract (600mg daily) or starch as placebo |
| **Parkinson's Disease** | **Mouse trial 9 weeks** | • Thus, the WS root extract have shown to counteract the pro-oxidants and their associated oxidative stress in the PD model studied here.<br>• The results clearly indicate the usefulness of Ws root extract in providing protection against MB-PQ induced nigrostriatal dopaminergic neurodegeneration (Prakash, et al., 2013). | • WS root extract for 3, 6 and 9 weeks |

## Cancer: Select Clinical Data

Ashwaganda has been cited as a valuable component in cancer prevention and treatment across a variety of cancer cell lines.

| THERAPEUTIC AREA | DURATION | BENEFIT | DOSAGE |
|---|---|---|---|
| **Breast Cancer** | **Rat study 5 months** | • Mammary tumors were not observed in control rats (no MNU). The carcinogen-exposed rats treated with the WS root extract developed 23% fewer tumors relative to rats dosed only with the vehicle; after 155 days of treatment, the rats receiving the root extract had an average of 3.47 tumors/rat, and those in the control group had 4.53 tumors/rat (Kamel, et al., 2013). | • 30 rats at a dose of 75 mg/kg body weight. The animals were randomized into two equal groups: Group 1, dosed with the root extract (150 mg/kg BW/day); and group 2, dosed with the vehicle (ethanol: polyethylene glycol 400, 10:90, v/v). |
| **Prostate Cancer** | **Mouse study 28 days** | • 70% Inhibition of tumor volume in WA-treated animals (Yang, et al., 2007). | • PC-3 tumor cells<br>• 4 or 8 mg/kg, i.p.<br>• daily for 28 days |
| **Medullary Thyroid** | **Mice study** | • 50% reduction in tumor volume by WA (Samadi, et al., 2010). | • DRO81-1 tumor cell xenograft<br>• 8 mg/kg, i.p. daily for 6 weeks; WA treatment started 2 weeks post tumor injection |
| **Cervical Cancer** | **Mice study** | • 70% reduction in tumor volume (Munagala, et al., 2011). | • CaSki tumor cell xenograft<br>• 8 mg/kg WA, i.p., q.o.d. for 6 weeks |
| **Lung Cancer** | **Mice study** | • 60% lower tumor volume by WA (Gupta, et al., 2012). | • A549 tumor cell xenograft<br>• Total dose= 4 mg/kg WA, i.p. or implant |
| **Colon Cancer** | **Mice study** | • 30% reduction in tumor volume by WA (Choi, et al., 2015). | • HCT116 cell tumor xenograft<br>• 2 mg/kg WA, i.p. 3 times/week, 32 days |

## Summary of Clinical Findings

The clinical studies show a very diverse group of diseases that ashwagandha can heal. It is a unique herb that can calm the mind, lower stress and energize the human body. It has been shown to be effective in managing insomnia, alleviating stress and anxiety, while at the same time improving energy building physical strength and enhancing endurance. Ashwagandha improves libido, and may be an agent in reversing infertility, erectile dysfunction and sexual dysfunction in both men and women. It supports blood sugar regulation, diabetic management, cardiovascular health, thyroid imbalances and neurodegenerative disease progression for Alzheimer's and Parkinson's diseases. Animal studies have been favorable in demonstrating the use of Ashwagandha in treating breast, prostate, cervical, medullary thyroid, lung and colon cancer.

The dose, duration, age and health status of the person will be significant in determining how quickly and to what extent a person will be helped by taking ashwagandha alone, or in combination with other botanicals, nutrients and medications. What a fabulous herb that has so many salutary properties. It is not a panacea, but is a wonderful natural booster food that enables the body to become stronger and more balanced with regular use. We look forward to reporting more human studies for the treatment of cancer in the future.

## Dosage Range

Doses of 300-1,250 mg of ashwagandha twice per day have been used in human studies.

## Contraindications

Having been granted *Generally Recognized as Safe* (GRAS) status in the United States by the *Food and Drug Administration* (FDA), ashwagandha is well tolerated by most people. While safe for short-term use, long-term safety is not known (webmd.com, 2018).

## Possible Side Effects

**Excitatory properties for some:** One interesting effect with ashwagandha, is that like the Western herb Valerian, a small percentage of people (maybe 10-20%) will experience stimulatory effects after taking it. If you take it before bed it could excite your nervous system and keep you awake all night long. If so, taking half dose or less is advised (Caldecott, 2018). In such cases take it in the morning hours. However, should you experience any interference with your nightly sleep, stop right away.

**Pregnancy and breast feeding:** It is best to avoid using ashwagandha during pregnancy and breast feeding (webmd.com, 2018). Excess use may cause miscarriage in highly sensitive individuals.

**Blood Sugar Control:** Ashwagandha tends to lower blood sugar. For persons with hypoglycemia and insulin treated diabetes it may lower blood sugar too much. If you are taking medicines for diabetes please monitor blood sugar closely (webmd.com, 2018).

**Thyroid Disorders:** Be cautious when taking ashwagandha for a person with fluctuating Hashimoto's Thyroiditis and taking thyroid medication.

**Stomach Ulcers:** Ashwagandha can irritate the *gastrointestinal* (GI) tract. Avoid using ashwagandha if you have stomach ulcers.

**Auto-immune Conditions:** If taken to excess, ashwagandha might cause the immune system to become more active, and this could increase the symptoms of auto-immune diseases. Avoid ashwagandha if *Multiple Sclerosis* (MS), *Rheumatoid Arthritis* (RA) or *Lupus* (SLE) are evident and being treated (webmd.com, 2018).

**Surgery:** In some, ashwagandha may slow down the central nervous system. Healthcare providers worry that anesthesia and other medications during and after surgery might increase this effect. Stop taking ashwagandha at least 2 weeks before a scheduled surgery (webmd.com, 2018).

**Drowsiness:** Ashwagandha may cause drowsiness during the day.

**Abdominal Discomfort:** May cause diarrhea. Large doses of ashwagandha can cause abdominal discomfort and diarrhea. Stop taking ashwagandha should you experience any such discomfort (webmd.com, 2018).

**Allergic Reactions:** Should you get an allergic reaction from taking ashwagandha such as hives, stop taking it immediately.

## Interactions From Taking Ashwagandha

**Immunosuppressants:** Ashwagandha boosts the activity of immune cells, hence taking it with other medications that lower immune cell activity may decrease the effectiveness of such medications (webmd.com, 2018).

**Sleep Medications:** Avoid taking ashwagandha with other sleep medications like Benzodiazepines and *central nervous system* (CNS) depressants as it may cause too much drowsiness and sleepiness (webmd.com, 2018).

## Toxicity

Ashwagandha has otherwise been tolerated well as some reports suggest. No significant toxicity has been reported following short- or long-term administration of ashwagandha extracts. However, it is important to note that the plant belongs to the nightshade family and people allergic to that plant group should monitor their intake closely for sensitivities. Large doses may cause abdominal discomfort.

## Supplementation

Ashwagandha is commonly available as dried powder. There are extracts and tinctures too. *KSM-66 Ashwagandha* is the best ashwagandha extract available in the market. KSM-66's extraction process entails pre-treating the ashwagandha roots with milk. For this reason, it contains milk constituents. Such pre-treatment is consistent with the process described by traditional Ayurvedic healers and texts. A milk-free vegan version is also available. KSM-66 is standardized to the highest percentage of withanolides in the world, >5% by HPLC, derived only from the roots of the plant. Standardization implies that an extract provides consistent dosage delivery and guaranteed potency. Standardization ensures that manufacturers and formulation developers can use a certain amount of extract and be assured of a commensurate number of active constituents without much random variation from batch to batch.

## *Kitchen Medicine*

Traditionally used as a powder, ashwagandha can be mixed with water or warm milk (cow/coconut/nut) and honey. Taken before bed, this mixture calms vata (air element) and fosters healthy sleep patterns, supports the reproductive system, and bolsters strength. A general serving is 1/4-1/2 teaspoon once or twice daily. Ashwagandha is traditionally taken with ghee and honey (equal parts), as an anupan (a medium for carrying herbs deeper into the tissues) for overall nourishment and rejuvenation. Taking ashwagandha with raw sugar adds a cooling effect and can even be substituted for the honey, particularly in the summer months. It can also be used with ghee and sugar as a supplement to support the female reproductive system and joints.

## *What is A2 Milk?*

Milk can cause discomfort for many people. Historically, through ages all cows naturally produced A2 milk protein, but over time a mutation occurred, and they have started producing A1 protein in their milk. Research has shown that A1 protein can be more difficult to digest. There are many cows that naturally produce A2 milk protein which is easier to digest.

The *A2 Milk®* brand company says they produce milk naturally free from the A1 protein. They say their cows have not been treated with growth hormones, rBST or antibiotics. All of their family farms are independently certified by the Validus Group to ensure they meet strict animal welfare guidelines. Our suggestion is to first test 2 ounces. If you find no digestive discomfort, then use the A2 milk. The milk is available in Australia, New Zealand, China, the U.S. and the United Kingdom. In the U.S. several grocery stores such as Whole Foods, Wegmans, Kroeger, Sprouts, Giant Foods and MOM's Organic Market stock A2 milk. Should you experience difficulty in digestion, please use nut milks instead.

## *Ashwagandha Supplementation*

This table describes Ashwagandha supplemental forms and dose range.

| TYPE OF SUPPLEMENT | ADULT | CONDITIONS | CHILD/ADOLESCENT |
|---|---|---|---|
| **Powdered Root (Caldecott, 2018)** | • High dose for acute conditions: 15-30g/day<br>• Ashwagandha is best prepared in A2-milk (casein-friendly cow's milk), taken warm with a little ghee and sweetener, on an empty stomach. | • Use in cases of severe exhaustion, fatigue, nervous stress, and acute insomnia. High doses, however, are typically used only for a short period, under proper supervision, until the patient has become stabilized. | • A typical traditional dosage of ashwagandha is 1-2g of the root (boiled in milk or water for 15-20 minutes) taken 3 times daily. |
| | • Medium for chronic conditions: 2-5g/day<br>• At these doses the powdered root can also be prepared with A2-milk or mixed with various anupana (vehicles) such as water, ghee, or honey, depending on the effect desired. | • More effective for chronic conditions that tend to wax and wane, like chronic insomnia or chronic anxiety, or long term during recuperative periods. | |
| | • Low for subtle effect:1-2g/day<br>• At these doses the powdered root can also be prepared with A2-milk or mixed with various anupana (vehicles) such as water, ghee, or honey, depending on the effect desired. | • Once again, it's the same ability of ashwagandha to promote balance, but at lower doses so as to match the nature of the signs and symptoms. This is also a good dosage range when taken long term to harness the anabolic strength of ashwagandha, helping with weight gain, or for its nootropic effects. | |
| **Tincture (Caldecott, 2018)** | • Prepared at a 1:1 ratio, or 1:3 ratio, with the dosage range between 2.5 mL (½ teaspoon) to 5 mL (1 teaspoon).<br>• Tinctures made at a 1:5 ratio will have to be dosed between 5-10 mL (1-2 teaspoon), and depending on the patient, this might seem like a lot of alcohol. | | |
| **Dried root extract (Axe, 2018)** | • Start with 300-500 mg 1-2 times/day with withanolides in a range 5-10%<br>• Going to a maximum of 1,000-1,500 mg 1-2 times/day<br>• Some sources are also suggesting 6000 mg as the optimal dose per day. | | |

# Ashwagandha Remedies

## Ashwagandha Tincture

*Here is an easy way to make your own long-lasting ashwagandha tincture.*

SERVES 1

**INGREDIENTS**

½ cup ashwagandha root powder
2 cups 80-100 proof vodka (non-GMO)

**METHOD**

1. Put ashwagandha root powder into a jar.
2. Pour vodka into the jar. The vodka must be 80-100 proof and non-GMO.
3. Cover the jar and place in a dark corner for 2 weeks to 4 months.
4. Shake the mixture every day.
5. When the tincture is done, carefully transfer into dark glass dropper bottles.
6. Add 40-50 drops of ashwagandha tincture to 4 ounces (120 ml) water and drink up to 3 times a day or as directed by your healthcare provider.

## Ashwagandha Tonic

*Drink once a day for a "pick-me-up." This is a good replacement for coffee or tea in the afternoon. To avoid clumping, mix the powder with boiling hot water before adding to milk.*

SERVES 1

**INGREDIENTS**

1 teaspoon ground ashwagandha root
2-4 oz. boiling hot water
1 cup A2 milk (digestion-friendly) nut milk
1 teaspoon raw honey/maple syrup
1 pinch cardamom

**METHOD**

1. Mix ashwagandha powder with 2-4 ounces of boiling hot water.
2. In a pot heat the milk then add ashwagandha mixture to warm milk.
3. Add raw honey or maple syrup and cardamom and mix well.
4. Simmer over low heat for 5 minutes, as it helps with the absorption.
5. Should you experience any clumping of ashwagandha powder, use a whisk.

NOTE: *You can also try the above recipe with goat milk or sheep milk.*

## Sleep Deep Tonic

*Ashwagandha is calming and can be relaxing at night. However, for some, it may have reverse effect due to individual biochemistry or interaction with other products.*

SERVES 1

**INGREDIENTS**

1 teaspoon ground ashwagandha root
1 cup hot water
2 heaping tablespoons nuts such as macadamia
1 date or one teaspoon raw honey
¼ teaspoon cinnamon (more for garnish)
1 pinch nutmeg
1 pinch clove
½ vanilla bean

**METHOD**

1. Whisk ashwagandha powder with boiling hot water.
2. Blend all the ingredients in a blender and then pour into a small pot.
3. Heat the decoction on low for 3-5 minutes.
4. To serve, pour into a cup and sprinkle some cinnamon on top.

# Ashwagandha Beverages

## Powerhouse Smoothie

*This is a potent tonic morning beverage. If the drink is too concentrated for your taste, add more nut milk or water.*

SERVES 2

**INGREDIENTS**

1 teaspoon ashwagandha root powder
1 teaspoon Tulsi holy basil leaves
1 tablespoon dandelion root powder
1 teaspoon ground turmeric
2 cups nut milk
1-2 teaspoons raw honey/maple syrup
1 teaspoon cacao nibs

**METHOD**

1. Take 5-7 cubes of ice and put in the bottom of the blender.
2. Add all the ingredients in the blender and blend for 1-2 minutes, starting with low to high.
3. Chill until ready to serve.
4. Sprinkle cacao nibs on top before serving.

**SOURCE:** Adapted from: https://www.curejoy.com/content/ashwagandha-recipes-tea-tincture-smoothie/

## Simple Ashwagandha Tea

*Tea is the simplest way to experience the benefits of ashwagandha. Add more water if the tea is too concentrated for your taste.*

SERVES 1-4

**INGREDIENTS**

3 grams or 3-6 teaspoons of ashwagandha root
3-5 cups water

**METHOD**

1. Soak roots in boiling water for 15 minutes
2. Strain and drink liquid once or twice daily.

## Honey Ashwagandha Tea

*Ashwagandha is a starchy root and it can get clumpy if dropped in a cold liquid. For a smoother brew, mix thoroughly with 1-2 ounces of boiling hot water first, then add to the preparation.*

SERVES 1

**INGREDIENTS**

½ teaspoon ground ashwagandha root
10 oz. boiling hot water, divided
½-1 teaspoon honey

**METHOD**

1. Heat all 10 ounces of water in a pot.
2. Place ashwagandha powder in a cup and stir in 1-2 ounces of boiling hot water. Mix well.
3. Add ashwagandha mixture back to pot with remaining water.
4. Let it simmer for 3-5 minutes.
5. Add honey and enjoy.

# Ashwagandha Soup

## Deep Healing Soup

*By combining ashwagandha with turmeric, ginger and pepper, and using it to infuse cauliflower and celeriac (celery root) in coconut milk base, we offer a velvety smooth, nourishing and protective soup. This soup is great for people dealing with high stress, a cold, flu, mold exposure, or undergoing chemotherapy.*

SERVES 4-6

### INGREDIENTS

1 head cauliflower, chopped
½ bulb celeriac, peeled and cubed
1½ tablespoons avocado oil
1 teaspoon salt, divided
½-1 teaspoon black pepper
1½ teaspoons ghee (clarified butter)
1 large shallot, minced
1-inch (2.5 cm) fresh ginger, peeled and minced
1-inch (2.5 cm) fresh turmeric, peeled and minced
1 cup full-fat coconut milk
4 cups low-sodium vegetable broth
1 teaspoon ashwagandha powder
1 lemon, juiced
1 teaspoon basil leaves, dill or chives per serving, minced
1 teaspoon toasted lightly salted sunflower or pumpkin seeds per serving

### METHOD

1. Preheat the oven to 400°F (232°C). Toss the cauliflower and celeriac with the oil and ½ teaspoon salt.
2. Spread evenly on a rimmed baking sheet. Roast for 30 minutes, until tender and beginning to brown.
3. Meanwhile, heat the ghee in a large pot set over medium heat. Saute the shallots, ginger and turmeric with ½ teaspoon salt and black pepper until soft.
4. Add the roasted cauliflower and celeriac, the coconut milk and vegetable broth. Simmer for 5-10 minutes.
5. Add the ashwagandha and lemon juice. Mix thoroughly.
6. Transfer to a high speed blender. Purée on high until completely smooth.
7. Add more salt and/or black pepper to taste.
8. Add extra water or broth to lighten the consistency, if so desired.
9. Serve warm, garnished with fresh green herbs and toasted seeds.

**SOURCE:** Adapted from recipe by Chef Alison Wu, wuhaus.com

# Ashwagandha Entree

## Steamed Fish in Clay Pot

*This Chinese inspired dish integrates the health benefits of ashwagandha cooked into a delicious broth, used to steam wild sea bass or red snapper. By adding black rice, mushrooms and vegetables to the clay pot this beautiful dish makes a complete main meal entrée, nicely complemented by a side green salad.*

SERVES 4

### INGREDIENTS

3½ cups fish stock, dashi, or low-sodium chicken broth
1½ cups black rice
¾ cup dry white wine or mirin (Japanese rice wine)
1 tablespoon ashwagandha powder
1 3 x 3-inch (7.5 x 7.5 cm) piece kombu seaweed
2 bay leaves
1 tablespoon dried seaweed (dulse, hijiki or arame)
½ teaspoon salt
½ teaspoon black pepper
2 6 oz. sea bass or red snapper fillets
1 cup shiitake mushrooms, halved, sliced if large
2 yellow or red sweet peppers, finely minced
2 tablespoons fresh mint or basil leaves, finely minced

### METHOD

1. Combine stock, rice, wine, ashwagandha, bay leaves, and seaweeds in a clay pot or small Dutch oven.
2. Bring to a boil and then reduce the heat to low.
3. Stir once, cover, and cook. Maintaining an active simmer add the rice and cook until it is tender and the stock is almost completely evaporated for 40-50 minutes.
4. Season fish with salt and pepper.
5. Uncover the pot or oven and lay the mushrooms over rice mixture.
6. Then lay fish, skin side up, over mushrooms.
7. Cover pot and steam for 6-8 minutes until fish is opaque and rice is beginning to crisp on the bottom of the pot.
8. Garnish with chopped sweet peppers and fresh mint or basil leaves.
9. Serve right from clay pot.

**SOURCE:** Adapted from a *Bon Appetit* recipe https://www.bonappetit.com/recipe/steamed-fish-in-clay-pot-with-ashwagandha/amp

# Ashwagandha Dessert

## A+ Chocolate

*Add ashwagandha to raw chocolate and other healthy ingredients for a guilt-free dessert.*

SERVES 4

**INGREDIENTS**

1 teaspoon ashwagandha root, ground
1-2 oz. boiling water
¼ cup maca powder
1-2 tablespoons cacao powder
1 teaspoon cinnamon
½ cup coconut butter
½ cup hemp butter
½ cup raw honey
¼ teaspoon sea salt

**METHOD**

1. Pour hot water over ashwagandha powder and mix well.
2. Place all the dry ingredients — maca powder, raw cacao powder, cinnamon and sea salt — in a bowl.
3. Add coconut butter, hemp butter, honey and ashwagandha with water to the bowl with dry ingredients and stir to combine well.
4. Pour mixture into a silicone mini muffin tray or chocolate mold.
5. Place in the freezer to set.
6. Store in a cool place.

**SOURCE:** Adapted from: https://www.curejoy.com/content/ashwagandha-recipes-tea-tincture-smoothie/

# Ashwagandha Dressing

## Lively Up Yourself Dressing

*Enjoy this salad dressing recipe to experience a mood boost from this unique spice combination.*

SERVES 4

**INGREDIENTS**

¼ cup vinegar
1 teaspoon ashwagandha
1 teaspoon Tulsi holy basil powder
1 tablespoon maple syrup
1-2 cloves garlic, minced
1 tablespoon green herbs
1 tablespoon chia seeds
½ teaspoon salt
1 teaspoon turmeric
½ cup extra-virgin olive oil

**METHOD**

1. Mix all the ingredients, except oil, in a blender. Turn blender on low and slowly add oil until emulsified.
2. Store in a glass container until ready to serve.

# How to Grow Ashwagandha

## Propagation and Planting

Ashwagandha is propagated from seeds. In India, it is cultivated in regions with low rainfall in hot and humid conditions with temperature around 75-85°F (24-30°C). It is a drought tolerant plant and grows in dry soil, once established.

For ashwagandha cultivation, plant seeds ¾-inch (2 cm) deep and 4 inches (10 cm) apart.

Seeds will germinate in two weeks. Water the seedlings well while they are establishing. Thin out the plants after a month of growing, leaving about 18-24 inches (50-60 cm) between plants.

## Soil

It needs sandy soil with good drainage and a pH level around 7.5-8, neutral to slightly alkaline. Growing Ashwagandha is not possible in soil that retains moisture.

## Watering

Watering should be economical and only when plant seems thirsty. Ashwagandha is a drought resistant herb and doesn't like wet feet.

## Temperature

Ashwagandha grows best when the temperature ranges between 70-95°F (21-35°C), below or above this it grows much slower.

## Fertilizer

Similar to ginseng, ashwagandha is not commonly fertilized probably due to the medicinal use of its roots. However, organic fertilizers can be used. You can apply aged manure or compost near the base of the plant.

## Overwintering

If you're growing ashwagandha in a cooler climate, overwinter it indoors. Keep it in temperatures around 50-60°F (10-15°C) or cultivate it as an annual plant in spring and summer.

## Pests and Disease

Pests, such as spider mites can attack the plant. Ashwangandha is also vulnerable to leaf spot diseases, and stem rot. When the plant is overwatered root rot is possible.

## Harvesting

Ashwagandha is ready to harvest in 150-180 days when flowers and berries start to form and the leaves begin to dry out.

Harvest ashwagandha roots by digging carefully using a small tool to prevent damaging the plant. Make sure the soil has some moisture while doing this.

After harvesting, roots and berries are separated from the plant. Roots are washed, cleaned and cut into small pieces of 2-4 inches (7-10 cm) and dried in the sun or shade.

Berries are also separated from the plant, dried and crushed to take out seeds.

## How to Make Ashwagandha Powder

Harvest ashwagandha plants when the berries turn red. Separate the roots from the plant. The more intense the odor of the root, the better the medicinal property. You may have to peel off some of the tough parts. Rinse the roots in clean water removing any dirt and chop into small pieces. Let the roots dry in the sun or part shade for a couple of days. The perfectly matured, clean and dried roots can then be ground in a blender or food processor until smooth. Store in a glass container and label with the date. It is important to use fresh powder as it is most potent in the first 6-8 months.

## CHAPTER FOUR

# Ginger

## *(Zingiber officinale Roscoe)*

**Ginger** is a great culinary and medicinal plant, in the same food family as turmeric. It has a bright flavor that is warming, pungent and aromatic. As such, ginger moves the blood and wakes up our metabolism. Fresh ginger is easy to find and lasts for a month or more refrigerated. I like grating ginger into hot water with lemon and honey. While this is a remedy for a sore throat, it is also a great wake-up or pick-me-up drink. I add ginger to green tea or Tulsi tea. Ginger harmonizes well with every herb, spice and food I have used it with.

Think of ginger as our body's metabolic symphony conductor. It promotes energy, digestion and cools inflammation. It can be used as a tea, smoothie, cooking spice, fresh root or dried powder. The powder is great in a sauce where the woodiness of a root would be unpalatable. Ginger is especially indicated for anyone who experiences coldness, excess moisture, mucous, and diminished circulation.

On my recent trip to India, I brought candied ginger, which is dehydrated ginger slices coated in sugar (not perfect, but acceptable) for motion sickness from long and windy bus rides. As I chewed the ginger candy, my nausea abated and my head cleared. I also found that munching on a bit of a fresh pungent ginger root helped me digest hotel buffet dinners where there were too many rich Indian dishes to sample, and a dessert table that was hard to resist. Ginger can be taken as a spice, tea, tincture, baked goodie and even confection to clear stagnation, congestion, inflammation and indigestion.

*Fresh ginger root*

*Slicing ginger root for tea.*

*Fresh ginger and powdered ginger*

## Background and Uses

Ginger *(Zingiber officinale Roscoe)* originated in Southeast Asia but is now valued around the world both as a spice and condiment for food and as a dietary supplement for numerous health conditions. The rhizome of ginger has also been used in traditional herbal medicine. The health-promoting perspective of ginger is attributed to its rich phytochemistry (Mashhadi, 2013). The Indians and Chinese have used ginger as a tonic dating back 5,000 years (Benzie, et al., 2011).

## Plant Specifics

Ginger is a member of the plant family Zingiberaceae that includes cardamom and turmeric. Its aromatic flavor and scent is mainly due to the presence of ketones, especially the gingerols, which appear to be a primary focus of studies on ginger in health-related scientific research. The rhizome, which is the horizontal stem from which the roots grow, is the main portion of ginger that is consumed (Benzie, et al., 2011). Compared to other herbs, ginger grows relatively slowly. It will eventually reach a height of 24 inches (61 cm) or more in a container and may reach a height of 24-36 inches (61-91 cm) in the garden. Ginger grows with narrow bladed reed-like leaves that are mostly vertical. The ginger rhizomes will tend to grow out and up.

## Active Constituents

At least 115 constituents in fresh and dried ginger varieties have been identified by a variety of analytical processes. Gingerols, the major polyohenols of fresh ginger, are slightly reduced in dry ginger. Whereas the concentrations of shogaols, which are pungent constituents of ginger, are more abundant (Jolad, et al., 2005) in dry ginger than in fresh ginger. At least 31 gingerol-related compounds have been identified from the methanolic crude extracts of fresh ginger rhizome (Jiang, Solyom, et al., 2005). Ginger has been fractionated into at least 14 bioactive compounds, including [6]-gingerol, [8]-gingerol, [10]-gingerol, [6]-paradol, [14]-shogaol, [6]-shogaol, 1-dehydro-[10]-gingerdione, [10]-gingerdione, hexahydrocurcumin, tetrahydrocurcumin, gingerenone A, 1,7-bis- (4′ hydroxyl-3′ methoxyphenyl) -5-methoxyhepthan-3-one, and methoxy-[10]-gingerol (Koh, et al., 2009) (Benzie, et al., 2011).

## Traditional Medicine

Both fresh and dry ginger is used regularly in Ayurveda but they have slightly different qualities and effects on the body. From an Ayurvedic perspective, ginger is a superfood particularly for digestion, respiration and the joints. It is reputed to destroy toxins, enkindle the digestive fire, improve the secretion of digestive enzymes, prevent nausea and stop hiccups. It also improves peripheral circulation and warms up the body, reducing feelings of cold and pain — perfect for Vata (airy) or Kapha (earthy) folk in cold climates. It can even be helpful in congestive-types of cardiac disorders when used at a high dosage. Ginger clears phlegm in the lungs, alleviating coughs, colds and breathing difficulties. Despite its warming quality, it also reduces inflammation by inhibiting the activity of prostaglandins so is used in many traditional formulations to treat arthritis. For the same reason, hot, fresh ginger tea is also a great medicine for menstrual cramps. Ginger also has a rejuvenating effect on the body/mind and is considered Sattvic, helping to promote a calm, peaceful mind.

## Uses in Modern Medicine

The phenolic compounds that give ginger its unique flavor and fragrance are collectively known as 6-gingerol which is known to have anti-cancer, anti-inflammatory and antioxidant properties. Ginger has been shown to reduce nausea post-surgery and in cancer patients on chemotherapy, to reduce the day-to-day progression of muscle pain and to reduce the symptoms of osteoarthritis. In a relatively small study it was also shown to reduce fasting blood sugar and improve major risk factors for heart disease. It has also been shown to reduce cholesterol or blood lipid levels, to ease chronic indigestion, referred to as dyspepsia, and reduce menstrual pain as effectively as ibuprofen.

## *Health Benefits of Ginger*

### Improved Digestion

The phenolic compounds in ginger are known to help relieve *gastrointestinal* (GI) irritation, stimulate saliva and bile production, and suppress gastric contractions as food and fluids move through the GI tract. Ginger has been reported to have beneficial effects on the enzymes trypsin and pancreatic lipase, and to increase motility through the digestive tract, suggesting that ginger could help prevent colon cancer and constipation.

### Anti-nausea

Drinking ginger tea is a common home remedy for nausea during cancer treatment. It is also available in the form of lozenges and chewing gum. Taking ginger for motion sickness seems to reduce feelings of nausea and the incidence of vomiting. Ginger is also safe to use during pregnancy, to relieve nausea.

### Cold and Flu Relief

During cold weather, drinking ginger tea is a good way to keep warm. It is diaphoretic, which means that it promotes sweating, working to warm the body from within. This makes ginger a soothing natural remedy for a cold or flu.

### Pain Reduction

A study involving 74 volunteers carried out at the University of Georgia found that daily ginger supplementation reduced exercise-induced muscle pain by 25%. Ginger has also been found to reduce the symptoms of dysmenorrhea, the severe pain that some women experience during a menstrual cycle.

### Inflammation

Ginger has been used for centuries to reduce inflammation and treat inflammatory conditions. Ginger has also been found to be "modestly efficacious and reasonably safe" for treating inflammation associated with osteoarthritis.

### Cardiovascular Health

Ginger, either alone or with other herbs and spices, may reduce cholesterol, lower the risk of blood clotting, and help maintain healthy blood sugar levels.

### Cancer

Ginger is known to be anti-inflammatory, antioxidant and anti-proliferative which suggests a potentially promising role as a cancer preventive agent. Evidence from in vitro, animal, and human studies suggests that ginger and its active constituents suppress tumor growth and induce apoptosis of a variety of cancer types including skin, ovarian, colon, breast, cervical, oral, renal, prostate, gastric, pancreatic, liver, and brain cancer.

## *Cancer: Select Clinical Data*

Below are findings on the benefit of ginger for people undergoing conventional cancer therapy.

| DISEASE | DURATION | BENEFIT | STUDY DESIGN & DOSAGE |
|---|---|---|---|
| **Breast Cancer** | **3 days prior to chemo-therapy and 6 days after** | • *Chemotherapy-induced vomiting* (CIV) is a common complaint in patients with cancer, despite receiving numerous antiemetic drugs.<br>• A study conducted to evaluate the effect of ginger plant on chemotherapy-induced vomiting in breast cancer patients found that vomiting cases were significantly lower in the ginger group.<br>• Taking ginger capsules for 3 days prior and 6 days after chemotherapy along with routine antiemetic treatment could relieve chemotherapy-induced vomiting in all phases (Parsa Yekta, et al., 2012). | • Study sample was 80 women undergoing chemotherapy for breast cancer.<br>• The treatment group received 250 mg ginger powder capsules *(Zintoma)* and placebo group 250 mg starch capsules 4 times a day (1g/day) for 3 days prior and 6 days after chemotherapy session. |
| **All Types of Cancer** | **3 days prior to chemo-therapy and 6 days after** | • All doses of ginger significantly reduced acute nausea severity compared to placebo on Day 1.<br>• The largest reduction in nausea intensity occurred with 0.5g and 1.0g of ginger. Ginger supplementation at daily dose of 0.5g-1.0g significantly aids in reducing the severity of acute chemotherapy-induced nausea in adult cancer patients (Ryan, et al., 2011). | • In this double blind, multicenter trial, 744 cancer patients to four arms:<br>placebo<br>0.5g ginger<br>1.0g ginger<br>1.5g ginger<br>Plus, antiemetic drugs |
| **Colorectal Cancer** | **28 days** | • Pilot study results suggest that ginger may reduce proliferation in the colorectal epithelium and increase apoptosis or cell death rather than proliferation of cancer cells.<br>• The findings support a larger study to further investigate these results (Citronberg, et al., 2013). | • Pilot randomized control trial with 20 persons with increased risk of colorectal cancer.<br>• 2g of ginger standardized to 5% gingerols for 4 weeks daily to control group and placebo pill to placebo group was evaluated for 28 days. |
| **Gastric Cancer** | **Preclinical cell study** | • Pre-clinical studies have shown that ginger extract and its constituents possess chemopreventive and antineoplastic properties in gastric cancer. In vitro study showed that 6-gingerol induces apoptosis of gastric cancer cells (Ishiguro, et al., 2007). | • 6-gingerol standardized formulation used to measure apoptosis. |
| **Liver Cancer** | **Preclinical cell study** | • In vitro studies reveal that ginger components are effective against liver cancer. In a study, 6-shogaol has been reported to induce apoptotic cell death of Mahlavu hepatoma cells via an oxidative stress-mediated caspase dependent mechanism. (Chen, et al., 2007). | • Mahlavu cells Activate caspases 3/7 resulting in the DNA fragmentation |
| **Pancreatic Cancer** | **Preclinical cell study** | • Ginger and its constituents are also effective against pancreatic cancer. Park, et al., [27] have shown that 6-gingerol inhibits the growth of pancreatic cancer HPAC and BxPC-3 cells through cell cycle arrest at G1 phase and independent of p53 status. (Park, et al., 2006). | • pancreatic cancer HPAC and BxPC-3 cells |
| **Prostate Cancer** | **Mice study** | • The study showed that whole *ginger extract* (GE) exerts significant growth-inhibitory and death-inducing effects in a spectrum of prostate cancer cells.<br>• GE-treated mice showed reduced proliferation and apoptosis compared with controls. This study demonstrated the in vitro and in vivo anticancer activity of whole GE for the management of prostate cancer. (Karna, et al., 2011). | • Daily oral feeding of 100 mg/kg body weight of GE |

## *Other Diseases: Select Clinical Data*

Below are clinical data for the use of ginger in managing select disease states.

| DISEASE | DURATION | BENEFIT | DOSAGE |
|---|---|---|---|
| **Nausea and Vomiting in Early Pregnancy** | **15 clinical studies and 3 prospective studies** | • A review to assess effectiveness and safety of ginger consumption during early pregnancy through December 2017 was conducted.<br>• Results show a significant decrease in nausea and vomiting and no risk for the mother or her future baby The available evidence suggests that ginger is a safe and effective treatment for NVP (Stanisiere Jet, et al., 2018). | • 1g of fresh ginger root per day for 4 days |
| **Menstrual Cramps** | **3-4 days** | • The meta-analysis of 29 articles showed ginger significantly reduced pain scores on a visual analogue scale for subjects having primary dysmenorrhea<br>• The meta review shows effectiveness of 750-2000 mg ginger powder during the first 3-4 days of menstrual cycle for primary dysmenorrhea (Daily, et al., 2015). | • 750-2000 mg ginger powder administered during the first 3-4 days of menstrual cycle |
| **Sea Sickness** | **5 weeks** | • Ginger root reduced the tendency of vomiting and cold sweating significantly better than the placebo (Grontved, et al., 1988). | • Double-blind randomized placebo trial, the effect of the powdered rhizome of ginger *(Zingiber officinale)* was tested on seasickness. Eighty naval cadets<br>• Symptoms of seasickness tested every hour for 4 consecutive hours after ingestion of 1g of ginger or placebo |
| **Cardiovascular Health** | **8 weeks** | • A review of several studies shows the potential of ginger to treat many aspects of cardiovascular disease such as anti-inflammatory, antioxidant, anti-platelet, hypotensive and hypolipidemic effects in in vitro and animal studies.<br>• While human trials have been few, dosages of 5g or more demonstrated significant anti-platelet activity. More human trials are needed to determine appropriate dosage of a standardized extract. Should these prove positive, ginger has the potential to offer not only a cheaper natural alternative to conventional agents but one with significantly lower side effects (Nicoll, et al., 2009). | • 5g or more |
| **Diabetes** | **10 studies** | • Meta search of 10 studies across multiple databases suggest Ginger showed a significant beneficial effect in glucose control and insulin sensitivity.<br>• Ginger may be a promising adjuvant therapy for T2DM and MetS (Zhu, et al., 2018). | • 490 individuals |
| **Anti-inflammatory** | **8 weeks** | • In the study, the analgesic and anti-inflammatory effects of [6]-gingerol, which is the pungent constituent of ginger, were performed.<br>• The swelling and inflammation were reduced from the ginger. These results suggested that [6]-gingerol possessed analgesic and anti-inflammatory activities. (Young, et al., 2005). | • Intraperitoneal administration of [6]-gingerol (25-50 mg/kg) to (50-100 mg/kg) |

## Summary of Clinical Findings

The underlying actions and clinical effects of ginger indicate anti-inflammatory, anti-oxidant, anti-nausea, anti-cancer, and anti-tumor properties. The clinical trial data suggests that ginger alone or in combination with conventional modalities reduces morbidity or mortality from several disease states.

Ginger is a valuable anti-nausea agent either after chemotherapy, for morning sickness in pregnancy or sea sickness, either alone or in combination with anti-emetic drugs. It is also a natural remedy of choice for pain from menstrual cramps and arthritis. Ginger has been shown to be beneficial for metabolic syndrome, diabetes, cardiovascular health, cancer prevention, and integrative oncology.

## Dosage Range

Doses of 750-2,000 mg of ginger per day have been used in human studies shown in these tables.

## Contraindications

Ginger is recognized by the *Food and Drug Administration* (FDA) as a food additive that is *Generally Recognized As Safe* (GRAS).

In moderation, ginger is generally safe and unlikely to cause any adverse side effects in most people. Common symptoms reported include stomach discomfort, heartburn and diarrhea.

Although rare, some people may have an acute, IgE mediated allergy to ginger. If one experiences hives, swelling or difficulty breathing, stop use immediately and consult with your health professional.

When applied to the skin, ginger essential oil may cause skin irritation. If highly sensitive, dilute ginger essential oil in olive oil, and try a skin patch test by applying a small amount of diluted oil on the inside of your wrist to observe tolerance or reactivity. If taking ginger capsules, start with a low dose and work your way up to assess your tolerance. Adhere to the recommended dosage and decrease as needed if you have any negative symptoms (Dr.Axe.com).

## Toxicity

No significant toxicity has been reported following short or long-term administration of ginger extracts at standard doses.

## Supplementation

Ginger root fresh, dried and extract are healthy options to take daily. Consult with your healthcare provider to determine whether to use ginger as a spice, tea, tincture, capsule and/or body poultice.

## Kitchen Medicine

Ginger is used in numerous forms, including fresh, dried, pickled, preserved, and powdered or ground. You can add fresh ginger to teas, smoothies, juices, curries, stir-fry and soups. It adds a zing to the flavor with its sweet, spicy and even hot notes. Dried ginger can be used in soups, baking and to make a tincture. Dried ginger complements nutmeg in pumpkin dishes.

## *Supplementation: Ginger (Ginziber Officinale Roscoe)*

Below is information on supplemental ginger forms and dose ranges.

| TYPE OF SUPPLEMENT | ADULT | DOSAGE | CHILD/ADOLESCENT |
|---|---|---|---|
| **Dried powdered root extract** | **For an anti-inflammatory use** | 2 grams of ginger root extract for 28 days by mouth | A typical traditional dosage of ginger would be half the adult dose. |
| | **For chemotherapy-induced nausea and vomiting** | Liquid ginger root extract in doses of 0.5 grams, 1 gram, and 1.5 grams divided doses over the first 3 days of chemotherapy | |
| | **For gastrointestinal motility** | 1 gram of ginger powder diluted in 100 milliliters of distilled water | |
| | **For indigestion** | 1.2 grams of ginger root powder taken by mouth as a single dose | |
| | **For motion sickness or seasickness** | 1-2 grams of ginger daily by mouth in divided doses | |
| | **For nausea and vomiting after surgery** | 0.5-1 gram of ginger one hour prior to surgery | |
| | **For pain relief** | 30 mg-2 grams of ginger, root powder taken orally in single or divided doses for exercise-induced muscle pain, osteoarthritis pain, pain during menstruation | |
| | **For rheumatoid arthritis** | 1-4 grams of powdered ginger or ginger extract taken by mouth daily | |
| | **For weight loss** | 2 grams of dried ginger powder dissolved in 6 ounces of hot water by mouth as a single dose | |
| **Dried root Extract** | **For an anti-inflammatory use** | Eight 250 mg capsules, in divided doses | |
| | **For chemotherapy-induced nausea and vomiting** | Ginger root powder capsules in doses of 1 or 2 grams by mouth daily over the first 3 days of chemotherapy | |
| | **For exercise recovery** | 6 capsules totaling 2 grams of raw or 2 grams of heat-treated ginger by mouth daily for 11 days | |
| | **For high cholesterol** | 3 grams of ginger capsules orally in 3 divided doses for 45 days | |
| | **For nausea and vomiting after surgery** | 2-3 capsules of ginger (each containing 0.5 grams of ginger powder) have been taken by mouth one hour before a gynecological laparoscopy. Ginger use during surgery should be approached cautiously. | |
| | **For nausea and vomiting during pregnancy** | 0.5-2 grams of ginger extract or powder for up to 3 weeks in capsule or syrup form in single or divided doses<br>Consumption of ginger in amounts greater than those commonly found in food (<1 gram of dry weight daily) is not recommended during pregnancy. | |
| | **For painful menstruation** | One capsule containing 250 mg of ginger root powder orally by mouth 4 times daily for 3 days from the start of the menstrual period | |

## Supplementation: Ginger (Ginziber Officinale Roscoe) (continued)

| TYPE OF SUPPLEMENT | ADULT | DOSAGE | CHILD/ADOLESCENT |
|---|---|---|---|
| **Fluid Extract** | For general use | • droppers (2mL) of liquid extract<br>• 2 teaspoons (10mL) of syrup | |
| | For painful muscles and joints | Mix 2-3 drops of the tincture with a neutral massage oil and rub painful muscles and joints with it. | |
| | • Use for nausea due to pregnancy, chemo or other such as motion sickness.<br>• Helpful also for digestion, arthritic pain, IBS, cold relief, and fibromyalgia | Adult dose of ginger root herbal tincture is 3 ml added to warm water as needed. | |

**SOURCES:** https://www.wellness.com/reference/herb/ginger-zingiber-officinale-roscoe/dosing-and-safety
https://examine.com/supplements/ginger
http://epicureandigest.com/2014/04/04/dosage-and-method-ginger

# Ginger Beverages

## Ginger Power Smoothie

*This is a variation of our "go to" workout recovery drink. Fresh ginger and turmeric add a peppery taste.*

SERVES 1

**INGREDIENTS**

1 medium apple
4 oz. celery
4 oz. dandelion greens
1-inch (2.5 cm) fresh ginger
1-inch (2.5 cm) fresh turmeric
2 tablespoons flax seeds
1 scoop protein powder
6 oz. kefir
Water to dilute, if desired

**METHOD**

1. Wash all the ingredients. Peel the skin of the ginger and turmeric.
2. Roughly chop the apple, celery, dandelions greens, ginger and fresh turmeric.
3. In a blender, place a few ice cubes (optional) at the bottom, add all the ingredients and blend until smooth.
4. Add water to dilute if the drink is too concentrated for your palatability.

## Eaters Digest Tea

*A morning cup to awaken digestion and soothe the gut.*

SERVES 1

**INGREDIENTS**

1 tablespoon fresh ginger
1-1½ cups water
1 teaspoon honey
Squeeze of fresh lemon juice (optional)

**METHOD**

1. Chop a 1-inch (2.5 cm) slice of fresh ginger into smaller pieces.
2. Place water in a pot and add the ginger.
3. Bring to a boil and brew for 10 minutes.
4. Strain into a cup and stir in honey and lemon if using.

**SOURCE:** http://muditainstitute.com/blogs/happybelly/ginger.html

## *Best Masala Chai*

*Masala chai is our "go to" beverage for the winter. The spices making it healing and warming. People in India drink variations of masala chai all year round.*

SERVES 1

### INGREDIENTS

1 cup hot water
1 teaspoon fresh ginger, chopped
2 large cardamom pods
1 cinnamon stick whole
1 teaspoon black tea
1 teaspoon honey
Milk to taste (A2/Nut Milk) optional

### METHOD

1. Put water in a pot with ginger, cardamom and cinnamon.
2. Bring to a boil for about 5-7 minutes.
3. After boiling, turn the stove off, add the black tea and cover.
4. Allow to steep for 3-5 minutes before straining into a mug.
5. Stir in honey and milk if using and enjoy warm.

## *Relax and Refresh Tea*

*I (SM) drink this combination at least once daily. It is calming and caffeine-free.*

SERVES 1

### INGREDIENTS

½-1 teaspoon dried Tulsi holy basil or 2 tablespoons fresh Tulsi leaves
¼-½ teaspoon dried ginger or ½-1 teaspoon fresh ginger
1 cup water
½-1 teaspoon freshly squeezed lemon to taste (optional)
½-1 teaspoon honey (optional)

### METHOD

1. Boil the ginger root or powder for 3-5 minutes.
2. Add the dried or fresh Tulsi leaves and steep 3-5 minutes.
3. Strain the solids and drink hot.
4. Add lemon and honey if you wish or store in the refrigerator for a cool drink in the summer.

NOTE: *Finer powdered tulsi will yield a stronger brew than coarse tulsi leaves.*

# Ginger Dressing, Salads & Pickling

## Ginger Power Dressing

*This salad dressing is a spicy substitute for any dish calling for mayonnaise.*

SERVES 4

### INGREDIENTS

¼ cup vinegar
1 tablespoon maple syrup
1-2 cloves garlic, minced
1 tablespoon green herbs
1 tablespoon chia seeds
½ teaspoon salt
1 teaspoon turmeric powder
1 teaspoon ginger powder
½ cup extra-virgin olive oil

### METHOD

1. Mix all the ingredients except the oil in a blender.
2. With the motor on low, slowly add the extra-virgin olive oil until emulsified.
3. Store in a glass container until ready to use.

## Seaweed Carrot Kale Salad

*If you are new to sea vegetables or are looking for a festive way to prepare them, try this Asian inspired salad.*

SERVES 6

### INGREDIENTS

1½ oz. dried arame seaweed
Warm filtered water
⅜ cup rice vinegar
2 tablespoons tamari sauce
2 tablespoons toasted sesame oil
2 teaspoons raw honey
¼ teaspoon red pepper flakes
2 teaspoons ginger, finely grated
1 tablespoon garlic, minced
½ teaspoon sea salt
1 large bunch Tuscan or Dino kale, chiffonade (sliced into ribbons)
2 cups carrots, shredded
4 scallions, finely sliced
1 cup Daikon radish, shredded
½ cup cilantro, chopped
Sea salt to taste
2 tablespoons sesame seeds, toasted

### METHOD

1. Soak seaweed in a medium bowl with warm, filtered water. Cover and allow to rehydrate for 15 minutes. Drain, rinse and strain, squeezing out excess water.
2. Whisk together the vinegar, tamari, sesame oil, raw honey, pepper flakes, ginger and garlic until honey is dissolved.
3. Place the cut kale in a large bowl and massage with ½ teaspoon sea salt until leaves soften and take on a shiny emerald green color.
4. Add shredded carrots, scallions, daikon, and cilantro to kale and toss together. Then pour dressing over vegetables and toss again until thoroughly combined. Taste and add more salt if needed.
5. Sprinkle with sesame seeds and serve.

## Ginger Dressing, Salads and Pickling (continued)

# Open Sesame Salad

*This beautiful poached chicken salad recipe is easy to prepare and quite tender and flavorful.*

SERVES 4

### INGREDIENTS

4 organic chicken breasts
1 quart chicken stock
2-inch (5 cm) piece fresh ginger, sliced into coins
3 tablespoons tamari
1 teaspoon toasted sesame oil
2 cups Savoy cabbage, shredded
4 cups romaine hearts, torn
2 carrots, orange and purple, grated
1 red pepper, diced medium
1½ cups mung bean sprouts
⅓ cup mint, torn
⅓ cup cilantro, chopped
⅓ cup basil, chopped
1 orange, supremed (carefully cut between slices without pith)
½ Asian pear, thinly sliced
⅓ cup pumpkins seeds, toasted

### DRESSING INGREDIENTS

¼ cup tahini
2 tablespoons tamari
6 oz. kefir
4 oz. water
¾ cup rice vinegar
½ teaspoon garam masala powder
¼ teaspoon sea salt, or to taste
⅛ teaspoon white pepper
1 small shallot, minced
2 green onions, thinly sliced
2 tablespoons mint, chopped
4 medium basil leaves, chopped
1 tablespoon ginger, minced

### METHOD

1. Poach chicken breasts in broth, ginger, tamari and sesame oil. Allow to cool, drain and cube into bite-sized pieces.
2. Toss together cabbage, romaine, carrots, red pepper, mung bean sprouts, mint, cilantro, and basil.
3. To make the dressing whisk together tahini, tamari, kefir, water and rice vinegar with garam masala, salt and pepper.
4. Add remaining dressing ingredients. Taste and adjust seasonings.
5. Toss salad with about half the dressing. Taste and add more if needed.
6. Divide salad between four plates and garnish with pears, orange slices and pumpkin seeds.

**SOURCE:** Chef Lizette Marx

# ABC: Amazing Beet Condiment

*Here is a great way to ferment ginger, which settles your stomach and produces friendly flora for your gut.*

SERVES 2

### INGREDIENTS

1 small red beet
4 oz. ginger, peeled and cut into very thin 1-inch (2.5 cm) matchsticks
¼ cup rice vinegar
1 tablespoon kosher or sea salt

### METHOD

1. Put beet in a small saucepan with 1-inch (2.5 cm) water covering it. Bring to a boil, then simmer until tender when pierced with the tip of a small knife, about 25 minutes. Drain. When cool enough to handle, peel and cut into quarters.
2. Combine rice vinegar and salt with 1 cup water in a small bowl, stirring to dissolve salt. Add ginger and beet, cover, and chill overnight.
3. Make ahead, keeps up to 2 weeks refrigerated.

**SOURCE:** https://www.myrecipes.com/recipe/pickled-ginger

# Ginger Entrees

## Palak Paneer

*Our favorite Indian main dish that contains greens with cubes of paneer, which in India is made from creamy buffalo milk. This makes a great meal served with rice, raita (yogurt cucumber salad) and warm garlic naan bread.*

SERVES 4

**INGREDIENTS**

8 oz. paneer (mild Indian cheese made with whole milk)
1 tablespoon extra-virgin olive oil or extra-virgin coconut oil
1 cup onions, diced small
1 small green Indian chile, thinly sliced
1 teaspoon fresh ginger, grated
2 cloves garlic, minced fine
1 teaspoon ground turmeric
¼ teaspoon cayenne pepper
1 teaspoon ground cumin
1 teaspoon ground coriander
1 medium tomato, seeded and diced small
16 oz. fresh spinach, roughly chopped
1 tablespoon cilantro leaves
Sea salt to taste

**METHOD**

1. Cut the paneer in ½-inch (1.27 cm) cubes and set aside.
2. In a large pot or sauté pan, heat the oil to medium heat and add the onions.
3. Sauté until golden and add green chilies. Cover the pan to allow peppers to soften.
4. Add ginger and garlic and stir for about a minute.
5. Stir in turmeric, cayenne, cumin and coriander for another minute.
6. Add diced tomatoes and cook until they start to break down, about 10 minutes.
7. Add spinach next, stir and cover for about 2 minutes until wilted.
8. Reduce heat to low and stir in paneer until heated through.
9. Turn off heat and add cilantro and sea salt to taste.

## So Thai, So Good Chicken (Gai Pad Khing)

*The blending ginger, spices and fish sauce, and at times, shrimp paste, distinguishes Thai from India stir fry or curry.*

SERVES 2

**INGREDIENTS**

2 tablespoons fish sauce
1 tablespoon oyster sauce
1 tablespoon coconut sugar
1 tablespoon extra-virgin coconut oil
8 oz. boneless, skinless chicken breasts or thighs, cut into bite-sized pieces, ¼-inch (.63 cm) thick
½ cup onions, sliced
½ cup scallions, minced
2 tablespoons fresh ginger, sliced into matchsticks
2 cloves garlic, minced
½ cup bell peppers, sliced
A couple lettuce wraps
Sea salt to taste

**METHOD**

1. Place the fish sauce, oyster sauce, and sugar in a small bowl and stir to combine. Keep near the stove, along with the chicken and vegetables.
2. Heat a wok or large skillet over high heat until very hot.
3. Add the oil and swirl the pan to coat the bottom.
4. Add the chicken in an even layer and sear, undisturbed, for about 1 minute. Chicken will be lightly browned, but not cooked through. Flip to cook the other side.
5. Add the onions, scallions, ginger, garlic, peppers and sauce.
6. Stir-fry for 3-4 minutes, until the chicken is cooked through and the bell peppers and onions are crisp-tender.
7. Serve with brown rice.

**SOURCE:** Adapted from www.thekitchn.com/recipe-thai-ginger-chicken-stirfry-recipes-from-the-kitchn-189644

# *Channa (Chickpea) Masala*

*This North Indian inspired creation is a staple of the region and is well loved by vegetarian restaurants and yoga centers.*

SERVES 4

**INGREDIENTS**

1 cup dried channa (chickpeas) or 2 cans
2 tablespoons ghee or extra-virgin coconut oil
1 teaspoon cumin seeds
½ cup onions, diced
1 tablespoon ground turmeric
1 teaspoon cumin powder
1 teaspoon coriander powder
1 pinch red chili powder
1 green Indian chile, diced small
2 cloves garlic, minced fine
1 teaspoon fresh ginger, minced
1 medium tomato, seeded and diced
A handful of fresh cilantro, chopped
Sea salt to taste

**METHOD**

1. Soak the channa overnight or at least 7 hours. Rinse off the channa with fresh filtered water. Boil in filtered water for about 30-45 minutes. You can also use canned chickpeas.
2. Heat the ghee or oil in a large pot and add the cumin seeds. Stir until they start to pop. Boil in 4 cups of filtered water until tender but firm, about 30-45 minutes.
3. Add the onions next, sautéing until golden.
4. Stir in the dried spices, turmeric, cumin, coriander and red chili powder for 30-60 seconds.
5. Add the green chile, garlic, ginger and tomato. Cover and sauté for a few minutes.
6. Add the cooked chickpeas and let simmer for a few minutes.
7. Stir in cilantro and turn off the heat.
8. Add sea salt to taste.

## *Ginger Entrees (continued)*

# *Poached Cod*

*Cod's firm texture and delicate sweetness makes it excellent for poaching. In this recipe, aromatic herbs are simmered slowly in broth before the fish is immersed and allowed to infuse the flavors.*

SERVES 4

### INGREDIENTS

6 cups vegetable stock
4 sprigs Italian parsley
3 sprigs fresh thyme
3 strips lemon peel, no pith (use potato peeler)
4 cloves garlic, peeled, chopped
1 tablespoon fresh ginger, chopped
1 tablespoon dried basil
1 bay leaf
1/4 teaspoon ground black pepper
1/4 teaspoon white pepper
1/8 teaspoon sea salt per filet
4 leeks, (light green and white parts) sliced 1/3-inch (.83 cm) thick
4 servings of 4 oz. cod fillets
1 whole lemon, thinly sliced

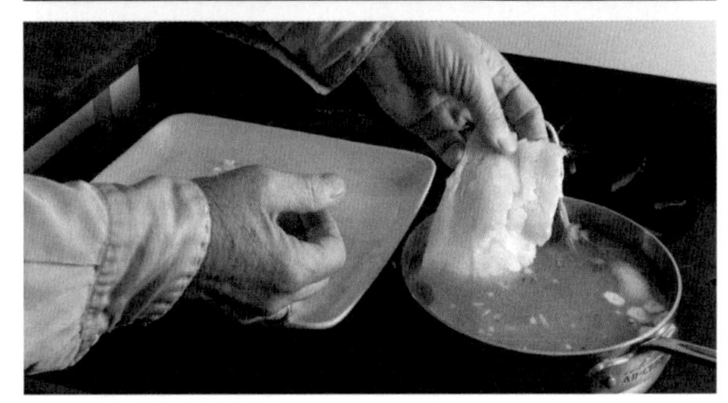

### METHOD

1. Bring stock to a low simmer in a shallow pan large enough to accommodate the cod fillets.
2. Tie the herbs together in a bundle and add to the stock along with lemon peel. Add garlic, ginger, basil, bay leaf, pepper and salt. Let all this simmer while you prepare the leeks.
3. Separate the rounds of leeks with your fingers and wash them well in a bowl of cold water, letting any grit or soil fall to the bottom of the bowl.
4. Scoop the leeks out with a slotted spoon or strainer and add them to the simmering broth and simmer for 5 minutes or so.
5. Slide the fillets into the stock and bring it to a simmer again. The stock should be barely moving.
6. Cook until fish is tender, 5-6 minutes on each side, depending on the size of the piece.
7. Discard the herb bundle and other aromatics.
8. Transfer the fish to a cutting board and lift the leeks out of the broth with a slotted spoon.
9. Season the leeks, if desired, with a pinch of salt and freshly ground pepper and set aside.
10. Arrange cod on plates and top with lemon slices and leek rings or a light pesto sauce.

## *Uptown Green Beans*

*This ginger infused green bean stir fry receives an health and flavor boost by combining it with gremolata.*

SERVES 4

**INGREDIENTS**

1 tablespoon sesame oil
3 large shallots, finely chopped
½ teaspoon fresh ginger root, grated
1 teaspoon sea salt, divided
¾ pound fresh green string beans, stem ends snapped off and strings removed
2 tablespoons ghee or unsalted butter

**METHOD**

1. Gently heat a large pan or wok, add oil and sauté shallots and ginger with ¼ teaspoon salt for 2 minutes.
2. Add green beans and stir to combine, then add ¼ cup water and another ¼ teaspoon of sea salt. Cover and steam until green beans are crisp, but tender, about 8 minutes. Remove cover and allow remaining water to evaporate slightly.
3. Add ghee or butter and stir until green beans are coated evenly.
4. Toss in ¼ cup of the turmeric gremolata (see below).
5. Taste and add remaining sea salt if needed and serve immediately.

NOTE: *Add more gremolata to taste is desired.*

## *Turmeric Gremolata*

*This potent garnish can be added to meat or vegetarian main dishes. Note: a little dab will do you.*

SERVES 4

**INGREDIENTS**

1 small bunch fresh parsley, washed and dried (enough to make 1 cup loosely-packed)
1 garlic clove, papery skin removed
2 lemons, washed and dried
1 2-inch (5 cm) piece fresh turmeric, peeled and grated (if unable to find fresh turmeric, use ¼ teaspoon turmeric powder)

**METHOD**

1. Gather parsley leaves together on a large cutting board and chop fine. The chopped parsley should measure about 1 cup.
2. Grate garlic clove, lemon zest from 2 lemons and turmeric over parsley. Stir until all ingredients meld together.
3. Use gremolata immediately or store in an airtight container in the refrigerator. Gremolata will keep for 1 day only.

**SOURCE:** Adapted from *Flavors of Health Cookbook* by Chef Lizette Marx and Dr. Ed Bauman

# Ginger Tincture

## Ginger Tincture

*Making a tincture is a convenient way to reap the benefit of ginger's health properties.*

SERVES 1

### INGREDIENTS

One whole ginger root, peeled
1 cup 80-100 proof vodka (non-GMO)

### METHOD

1. Chop a whole, peeled ginger root into small pieces and place in a jar with a secure lid.
2. Pour neutral alcohol such as vodka over the ginger root until completely covered.
3. Cover the jar and place in a dark corner for two weeks, shaking the jar every two days.
4. After two weeks, strain into a dark bottle, label and date. It will keep for several years.

### DOSE/USE OF TINCTURE:

1. Mix 2-3 drops of the tincture with a neutral massage oil and rub painful muscles and joints with it.
2. Adult dose of ginger root herbal tincture is 3 ml added to warm water as needed. Use for bouts of nausea, including due to pregnancy, chemotherapy or motion sickness. Half the dose for children over the age of 6. Helpful also for digestion, arthritic pain (anti-inflammatory, analgesic) IBS, cold relief or fibromyalgia.

## How to Grow Ginger

Ginger is not commonly grown from seeds because it is much faster and easier to use a rhizome. There are many varieties of ginger and they vary by region, some ornamental, and others medicinal. Zingiber officinale Roscoe is the species that we recommend with the most medicinal benefits. Simply place the rhizome with the growing bud (eye) facing up in soil about 1-inch (2.5 cm) deep. Ginger is not a fan of too much sun or water. Plant in full to part shade in well-draining soil.

### Cultivating Ginger

If you live in a cooler climate, the plant will need to be moved inside when there is any danger of frost. Allow the plant to yellow and trim the leaves off of the plant. Water the soil once a month (or less) to keep the roots viable and then set the plant out again in the spring when danger of frost has passed. If the roots are too wet, they will rot. With any luck the plant should come back the following year. If stored properly, rhizomes should remain viable for up to 2 years.

### Where to Grow Ginger

Ginger is a perennial herb that likes a warm, humid climate and filtered sunlight. It is a tropical plant. Colder regions will have to start their ginger indoors, or under some sort of cover, but you can have it out in the garden between USDA Zones 7 and 10. Ginger does well in pots and containers so this should not present much of a problem to those growers in colder regions. Ginger also does quite well with a hydroponic system.

### Soil for Ginger

Ginger likes soil rich with organic matter, free of rocks, and in a location that drains well. Proper hilling is important, so it should either be planted over a trench, or have sufficient soil nearby to facilitate hilling. It does best with a soil pH of 5.5-6.5.

### *How to Grow Ginger (continued)*

To increase yields supplement your ginger with fertilizer. We recommended a fertilizer with a 5-5-5 ratio (5% nitrogen, 5% phosphorus and 5% potassium). If your ginger leaves begin to yellow or look burnt at the edges, or if the leaves improperly begin to unfurl, assess water schedule and add an extra feeding. These are symptoms of insufficient nutrients due to overwatering and/ or underfeeding. You can also amend soils with gypsum.

A drip system is the recommended method of irrigation for ginger; this is the best way to ensure it is consistently and adequately watered. Be careful not to overwater just after transplanting. If your site is arid, misting the canopy may increase yields. Additional watering will also wash away nutrients, so make sure you are not watering excessively.

Hilling ginger plants may also increase yields. As the shoots begin to grow, the base of the shoot will be bright white. When the base of the shoot turns from bright white to bright pink, it's time to hill the crop about 4 inches (10 cm). This should occur roughly after 4-6 weeks at which time it is recommended to add fertilizer. Hilling simply means covering the rhizomes with an additional amount of soil and pulling out any weeds.

#### Harvesting Ginger

Baby ginger can be harvested within 4-6 months after sprouting. It will be very different from the mature ginger you buy in the supermarket with tender flesh, no skin to peel, nor stringy fibers. I will also have a milder flavor. The rhizomes should be cream colored with pink scales when ready to harvest. For stronger flavored ginger let your plants mature within about 10-12 months, or after the leaves die back in the fall/winter. You can choose to harvest the entire plant or you can just cut off what you need and allow the plant to continue growing. If storing some of your rhizomes over winter, make sure they stay above 55°F (12°C) to ensure they will remain viable next year.

#### Storage

Place ginger in the crisper drawer of your refrigerator for approximately 3 weeks. It can also be wrapped in wax paper and placed in a sealed plastic bag in the freezer for approximately 3 months.

## *How to Grow Ginger (continued)*

### How to Make Ground Ginger Powder

1. Rinse the ginger root to remove dirt and debris.
2. Peel off the skin using a peeler or spoon.
3. Cut the root into thin slices.
4. Place the sliced ginger pieces onto a single layer baking sheet.
5. Place the baking sheet with ginger root by a sunny window or outside in the sun. If you live in a sunny and dry climate it may take from 3 days up to a week. Alternately for faster drying, place the sliced ginger root in a food dehydrator at 95°F (35°C) for 1-3 hours.
6. Store dried ginger in an airtight container in a cool, dry and dark place.
7. When ready to use, grind into a powder using a coffee grinder or food processor.

**SOURCE:** https://www.livestrong.com/article/232697-how-to-dry-ginger-root

CHAPTER FIVE

# Cinnamon

*(Cinnamomum zeylanicum)*

*Cinnamon bark*

**Cinnamon** has been used as a spice in daily life for well over a thousand years. It comes from the bark of a tropical Asian tree that is now facing sustainability issues. Be sure the cinnamon you are buying is true cinnamon, which costs more than "cassia" a common cinnamon substitute with no health benefit. Artificial cinnamon flavoring, a so-called better-living-through-chemistry invention (not!) is found in commercial cereal, desserts and beverages to provide a familiar, pleasant taste.

The wonderful taste and properties of cinnamon bark come from its essential oils, phenolic compounds, and complex natural constituents. Each of the properties in fresh cinnamon synergistically supports our well-being. Most of us enjoy the taste and smell of cinnamon without knowing of its antioxidant, anti-microbial, anti-inflammatory, anticancer, and anti-diabetic value. Cinnamon's role in managing blood sugar regulation is becoming better appreciated. A half to full teaspoon of cinnamon is the dose needed to improve insulin sensitivity, so feel empowered to add cinnamon to all forms of sweets, including fruit salad, cookies, cakes, cereals and smoothies.

*Cinnamon bark is used to stir tea.*

Like ginger, cinnamon blends well with other spices, including the savory ones, as it can help balance a spicy dish without adding sugar. Powdered cinnamon that has been on a shelf for months oxidizes in the presence of heat and light and is not health promoting or good tasting. It is best to store your cinnamon in a cool, dark place rather on top of your stove top. I buy cinnamon sticks and grind them right before using to get the best taste and freshest constituents in the cinnamon granules I make in my own kitchen. Cinnamon sticks are delightful as a tea with honey and lemon, or compounded with the spices we have discussed so far. Use it liberally to enjoy the benefit of the highly protective eugenol phenolic compound, also found in cloves. I finish my Thai curry dishes with a dusting of cinnamon to create a pleasant taste, aroma and secret ingredient.

*Cinnamon bark and powdered cinnamon*

## Background and Uses

Cinnamon is a ubiquitous ingredient in pantries around the world due to its distinctive warming flavor and ambrosial aroma. It is used as a condiment and flavoring additive in sweet and savory dishes. The spice comes from the inner bark of a tropical evergreen tree. The bark is one of the most important and popular spices not only for cooking but also in traditional and modern medicines. Approximately 250 species have been identified among the cinnamon genus, which is a member of the laurel family, but only two are used commercially: Ceylon and Cassia.

Cinnamon was one of the most sought after commodities in the early days of the spice trade because it was very expensive and highly treasured. The quest for spices was the driving force behind world exploration in the 15th century. It was the motivation behind Christopher Columbus's voyage which led to the discovery of the new world and for Vasco da Gama's exploration of South India and Sri Lanka. Ceylon cinnamon (a.k.a. true cinnamon) was found in Sri Lanka (formerly Ceylon). Colonization followed as it became evident that any country which could hold that area captive, had control over the world's cinnamon trade and would ultimately reap immense profits. Initially the Portuguese ruled, who were later over-powered by the Dutch, followed by the British in 1815. Now it's cultivated by an independant Sri Lanka along the coastal belt from Negombo to Matara.

The bark, leaves and root are the primary parts used for medicinal and culinary purposes. The volatile oils obtained from the bark, leaf, and root vary significantly in chemical composition, which suggests that they might vary in their pharmacological effects as well. The different parts of the plant possess the same array of hydrocarbons in varying proportions, with primary constituents such as; *cinnamaldehyde* (bark), *eugenol* (leaf) and *camphor* (root).

## Active Constituents

The most important constituents of cinnamon are *cinnamaldehyde* and *trans-cinnamaldehyde* (Cin), which are present in the essential oil, thus contributing to the fragrance and to the various biological activities observed with cinnamon. A study on *Cinnamomum osmophloeum (C. osmophloeum)* indicated that the essential oil from cinnamon leaves contains a high level of Cin. Consequently, *C. osmophloeum* is also used as an alternative spice for *C. cassia*. One of the major constituents of essential oil extracted from *C. zeylanicum* named (E)-cinnamaldehyde has an anti-tyrosinase activity, while cinnamaldehyde is the principal compound responsible for this activity. Cinnamon bark contains procyanidins and catechins. The components of procyanidins include both procyanidin A-type and B-type linkages. These procyanidins extracted from cinnamon and berries also possess antioxidant activities.

## Traditional Medicine

As far back as 2800 BC, our ancestors had a variety of uses for cinnamon including anointment, embalming and treating various ailments. The Romans used it for its medicinal properties in treating digestive and respiratory ailments. They also used it for funerals in order to fend off the odor of dead bodies. It was used in Egypt for embalming mummies as well as for its fragrance and flavoring properties.

## Uses in Modern Medicine

Recently many trials have explored the beneficial effects of cinnamon in treating Parkinson's, diabetes as well as diseases of the blood, and brain. Data were collected regarding its antioxidant, anti-inflammatory, anti-lipemic, anti-diabetic, anti-microbial, and anticancer effects. This systematic review underlines the surplus health benefits of this clandestine ingredient and the scope of further research in these clinical scenarios.

## Health Benefits of Cinnamon

### Antioxidant

Methanol extract is said to have maximum antioxidant properties as compared to ethanolic and water extracts (Mancini-Filho, et al., 1998). The antioxidant property is due to the eugenol component which inhibited peroxynitrite-induced nitration and lipid peroxidation in in vitro models. The oil is said to form a phosphomolybdenum complex which is responsible for its antioxidant activity.

### Anti-inflammatory

The multi-faceted nature of cinnamon has incited researchers to look further into its likely uses. Cinnamon water extract possesses an anti-inflammatory effect in vitro ascribed to a fall in the levels of tumor necrosis factor α and Interleukin 6 (Hong, et al., 2012). Twigs of *C. osmophloeum* contain compounds such as trans-cinnamaldehyde, caryophyllene oxide, eugenol, L-borneol which possesses anti-inflammatory activity.

### Anti-diabetic

Management of the glycemic index in a diabetic is one of the foremost challenges confronted by the physicians in daily practice. Various known studies have demonstrated that meticulous control with intensified insulin treatment and sulphonylureas can result In a decrease in microvascular complications as well as hospitalization costs (Reichard, et al., 1993; Menzin, et al., 2010; UK prospective Diabetes Study, no authors listed, 1998).

### Anti-microbial

The cinnamaldehyde component of cinnamon is responsible for its antimicrobial activity. It can inhibit the growth of Listeria and Escherichia coli in food products thereby potentiating their shelf life (Muthuswany, et al., 2008). In one of the studies, the effect of cinnamon was studied against various organisms like bacteria such as *Staphylococcus aureus,* fungi like *(Aspergillus flavus, Mucor plumbeus)* and yeast species such as *(Candida lipolytica)*.

### Cardiovascular

An animal study on Sprague Dawley rats evaluated the effect of *C. cassia* on Ischemic Heart Disease (Song, et al., 2013). The active components cinnamaldehyde and cinnamic acid are said to be cardio-protective due to their ability to produce nitric oxide as well as the associated anti-inflammatory property. Its vasorelaxation effect has also been attributed to the cinnamaldehyde component which inhibits the L type calcium channels.

### Anti-cancer

Several studies have shown strong anti-proliferative potential of cinnamon against different cancer cells. Extract of cinnamon as a whole and its different active compounds exhibit significant alteration in the rate of apoptosis in different types of cancer (Kwong, et al., 2010).

## *Cancer: Select Clinical Data*

Cinnamon is being studied for use with several types of cancer. Pre-clinical studies show promise for future application.

| DISEASE | DURATION | BENEFIT | DOSAGE |
|---|---|---|---|
| **Blood Cancer** | **Cell Study 24 hours** | • Significant antiproliferative action of cinnamon extract has been observed in 3 different hematologic tumor cell lines.<br>• This establishes cell-specific differential potential of cinnamon in controlling cell proliferation (Schoene, et al., 2005). | • Tested on Wurzburg cells<br>• Doses evaluated were *Cinnamon Extract* (CE) between 0.05 to 0.2 mg/mL<br>• Duration 24 hours |
| **Cervical Cancer** | **Cell Study 24 -72 hours** | • A cervical cancer cell line also showed antiproliferative action of cinnamon extract when treated with different concentrations for each group.<br>• Observed a dose-dependent decrease in the growth kinetics with a two-fold decrease at a concentration around 80 ug/ml of CE treatment in comparison to the untreated cells (Koppikar, et al., 2010). | • Tested on SiHa cells<br>• Doses evaluated were *Cinnamon Extract* (CE) tested 10, 20, 40, and 80 ug/ml<br>• For 3 different time durations of 24, 48, and 72 hours |
| **Colon Cancer** | **Cell Study** | • Cytotoxic effect of eugenol has also been observed against colon cancer cells HCT-15 and HT-29 where HCT-15 cells were found to be more sensitive than HT29 cells towards eugenol (Jaganathan, et al., 2011). | • Tested on HCT-15 and HT-29 cells |
| **Leukemia** | **Cell Study** | • The study, investigated the effects of eugenol on the cytotoxicity, induction of apoptosis, and the putative pathways of its actions in *human promyelocytic leukemia cells* (HL-60)<br>• Eugenol exhibited remarkable anti-proliferative efficiency against promyelocytic leukemia cell (Yoo, et al., 2005). | • Cells evaluated HL-60<br>• Eugenol is a major component of essential oil isolated from the *Eugenia caryophyllata* (Myrtaceae), (CE) used in concentration of 23.7 mM |
| **Breast Cancer** | **Cell Study 6 hours** | • In breast cancer (MCF7) cells, significantly hindered the constitutive activation of PI3K and serine/threonine protein kinase AKT which directly decreases the rate of cell proliferation (Park, et al., 2011) | • Cells evaluated MCF7 cells<br>• Doses evaluated (10, 30, and 50 uM)<br>• Duration of *caryophyllene* (CPO) for 6 hours |
| **Liver Cancer** | **Cell Study 6-24 hours** | • Cinnamaldehyde exhibited potent antiproliferative effect on a liver cancer cell line, HepG2, in a dose- and time-dependent pattern where a concentration of 30uM of cinnamaldehyde inhibited approximately 71% of cell proliferation [8]<br>• Similarly, PLC/PRF/5 cells treated with the same compound, showed decreased cell viability in a timely manner (Wu, et al., 2005). | • Cells evaluated HepG2 and PLC/PRF/5 cells<br>• Dose evaluated were 30uM of cinnamaldehyde<br>• Duration times of 6, 12, and hours |
| **Prostate Cancer** | **Cell Study** | • Sensitizing effect of eugenol has also been observed in human prostate cancer cells where eugenol in combination with *2-methoxyestradiol* (2ME-2) synergistically enhances its cytotoxicity against androgen independent PC-3 cell line compared to either of their individual effects.<br>• IC50 of both 2-ME2 and eugenol when applied in combination exhibited 50% growth inhibition (Ghosh, et al., 2005). | • Cells tested were PC-3 cancer cells<br>• Eugenol in combination with *2-methoxyestradiol* (2ME-2)<br>• IC50 of both 2-ME2 and eugenol were evaluated between 1 uM and 82 ug/ml |

## *Other Inflammatory Diseases: Select Clinical Data*

While cinnamon has demonstrated potential for a wide variety of conditions, below are clinical trial data for its benefits in the treatment of select inflammatory disease states.

| DISEASE | DURATION | BENEFIT | DOSAGE |
|---|---|---|---|
| **Diabetes** | **Human Trial 4 months** | • Role of cinnamon in regulating glucose levels in the body has been implied in numerous small randomized control trials. A meta-analysis by Allen, et al. done for 10 randomized controlled trials leads to a statistical decrease in levels of fasting plasma glucose along with an improvement in the lipid profile (Allen, et al., 2013). | • 543 patients taking cinnamon, dose of 120 mg/day to 6g/day for 4 months |
| **Anti-inflammatory** | **Mouse Study 24 hour** | • Cinnamon water extract produces an anti-inflammatory effect in vitro and the findings demonstrate that the leaf essential oils and their constituents of *C. osmophloeum* have excellent anti-inflammatory activities. (Hong, et al., 2012). | • RAW 264.7 cells, a murine macrophage cell line was used to test the effects<br>• *Cinnamomum osmophloeum Kaneh.* (Lauraceae) is one of the indigenous tree species in Taiwan. |
| **Heart Diseases** | **Rat Study 15 days** | • An animal study on Sprague Dawley rats evaluated the effect of *C. cassia* on Ischemic Heart Disease.<br>• The active components *cinnamaldehyde* (CA) and *cinnamic acid* (CD) are said to be cardio-protective due to their ability to produce nitric oxide as well as the associated anti-inflammatory property.<br>• The protection was attributable to anti-oxidative and anti-inflammatory properties, as well as increased nitric oxide. The results support further study of CA and CD as potential treatments for ischemic heart disease. (Song, et al., 2013). | • *Cinnamic aldehyde* (CA) and *cinnamic acid* (CD) isolated from Cinnamomum cassia against myocardial ischemia produced in rats by *isoproterenol* (ISO)<br>• Ninety male Sprague-Dawley rats were randomized equally to 9 groups: a control group, an untreated model group, CA (22.5, 45, 90 mg/kg)<br>• or CD (37.5, 75, 150 mg/kg) treatment, or propranolol (30 mg/kg). Rats were treated for 14 days and then given ISO, 4 mg/kg for 2 consecutive days by subcutaneous injection. |
| **Lipid Lowering** | **Albino Rat Study** | • Cinnamon is also known to have a lipid lowering effect. An in vitro study proved to be as effective as simvastatin.<br>• However, this study needs evaluation in humans (Javed, et al., 2012). | • *C. zeylanicum extract* (0.75g/kg bark powder)<br>• or as effective as Simvastatin (0.6 mg/kg body weight). |
| **Blood Pressure** | **12 weeks** | • With respect to diabetes and its role in maintenance of *blood pressure* (BP).<br>• Consumption of cinnamon (short-term) is associated with a notable reduction in SBP and DBP. Although cinnamon shows hopeful effects on BP-lowering potential.<br>• A systemic review done between 2000-2012, 3 studies have suggested that cinnamon can cause a significant fall in systolic as well as diastolic BP (Akilen, et al., 2013). | |

## Summary of Clinical Findings

Cinnamon is anti-inflammatory, anti-microbial, anti-oxidant, anti-diabetic, anti-cancer, anti-lipemic and cardio-protective. The eugenol oil in cinnamon has been shown, in animal cell studies, to control cell proliferation and support apoptosis of cancer cells. In human studies, cinnamon has demonstrated potential for lowering glucose levels and blood pressure. Much more clinical trial data are needed to determine optimum dose for various health conditions including diabetic health and cardio protection to determine optimal dosing. Using cinnamon as a culinary spice and as a medicinal agent may be recommended due to the potential beneficial effects.

## Dosage Range

Doses of cinnamon used in the select trials listed above are between 120 mg and 6,000 mg of cinnamon per day in human studies.

## Contraindications

Having been granted *Generally Recognized as Safe* (GRAS) status in the United States by the *Food and Drug Administration* (FDA), cinnamon is well tolerated by most people. Avoid cinnamon during pregnancy. Not for use in pregnancy unless otherwise directed by a qualified expert.

## Toxicity

No significant toxicity has been reported following short- or long-term administration of cinnamon extracts at standard doses.

## Supplementation: Cinnamon (Cinnamomum Zeylanicum)

Cinnamon is a great spice to use in the kitchen. You can also use it as a supplement. The amounts are below:

| TYPE OF SUPPLEMENT | ADULT | CHILD ADOLESCENT |
|---|---|---|
| **Cinnamon** | *Daily Intake* (TDI) for coumarin of 0.1mg/kg body weight/day recommended by the *European Food Safety Authority* (EFSA) | 38% of adult dose |
| **Dried powdered root** | 1-3g per day or 1 teaspoon per day | |
| **Standardized powder (cinnamon** | 120 mg per day | |
| **Fluid extract** | (1:1) 30-90 drops a day | |
| **Tincture** | (1:2): 15-30 drops, 4 times per day | |

## Kitchen Medicine

Cinnamon can be used in whole stick form or ground into a powder for dishes that are savory or sweet. It is most commonly used for baking desserts but is also found in savory entrees as well as teas, soups and other beverages. Cinnamon is a great flavoring agent that can blend well with other spices from diverse geographic regions as its use has expanded beyond South Asia to all parts of the globe and incorporated into their local cuisines.

# Cinnamon Beverages

## Holiday Egg Nog

*For the holiday season try an egg free egg nog. This recipe is made from a delicious mixture of fruit, nuts mixed spices.*

SERVES 4

**INGREDIENTS**

1 cup cashews, soaked overnight
1 ½ ripe bananas, peeled, cut into chunks and frozen overnight on a parchment lined sheet
1 teaspoon vanilla extract
1 tablespoon cinnamon
½ teaspoon nutmeg
½ cup maple syrup
3 cups water or chamomile tea
Grated nutmeg and allspice to garnish

**METHOD**

1. Drain the cashews and place in the blender with all the other ingredients except for the garnish.
2. Blend until smooth.
3. Garnish with grated allspice and nutmeg.
4. Serve immediately.

## Cool Down Mint Julep

*A hit at parties or in the heat of the day.*

SERVES 4

**INGREDIENTS**

1 cup fresh spearmint
1 cup ice
4 cups fresh, organic apple juice
1 tablespoon cinnamon
¼ cup fresh squeezed lime juice

**METHOD**

1. In a large pitcher, muddle or gently mash the mint leaves.
2. Stir in apple juice, lime juice and cinnamon.
3. When blended, add ice and serve with a sprig of mint.

## Ah Cha' Mango Lassi

*Spice up your lassi with a dash of cinnamon to get a distinctive flavor.*

SERVES 4

**INGREDIENTS**

2 cups brewed unsweetened Chai tea
1 cup kefir
1 ½ cups fresh or frozen mango
1 teaspoon cinnamon, plus more for garnish
1 tablespoon maple syrup

**METHOD**

1. Add all ingredients to a blender and blend until smooth.
2. Pour into 8 ounce glasses and sprinkle cinnamon on top.

# Cinnamon Entrees

## Butternut Yum Soup

*Butternut squash soup is a favorite for the fall and winter. It brings rich flavors to keep you warm and well nourished.*

SERVES 4

### INGREDIENTS

1 medium butternut squash
2 tablespoons extra-virgin olive oil, divided
Sea salt
Black pepper
1 medium red onion, diced small
4 large cloves garlic, minced
½ teaspoon cinnamon
½ teaspoon dried ginger
½ teaspoon nutmeg
½ teaspoon allspice
1 cup parsley, chopped fine
6 cups vegetable stock

### METHOD

1. Preheat the oven to 425°F (218°C).
2. Remove stem and slice the butternut squash in half lengthwise. Scoop out seeds with a spoon.
3. Brush the insides with 1 tablespoon of olive oil and sprinkle with salt and pepper. Lay the squash cut side down on a parchment lined baking sheet.
4. Bake for 30-40 minutes or until the skin gives when pressed with a fork. Don't worry if it browns.
5. In a large pot over medium heat, add remaining tablespoon of oil and sauté the onions until translucent. Stir in garlic and sauté for another minute.
6. Stir in cinnamon, ginger, nutmeg, allspice and fresh parsley. Cook for about a minute.
7. Pour in stock and bring to a slow simmer for about 5 minutes.
8. Remove butternut squash from the oven and set aside to cool. When cool enough to handle, scoop out the pulp, and roughly chop if needed. Add squash to the soup pot. Bring back to a low simmer for a few more minutes to let flavors meld.
9. Use a stick blender in the pot, or blend in an upright blender (in batches) to a smooth consistency.
10. Return soup to the pot and add salt and pepper to taste before serving.

## Conscious Consommé

*This cinnamon spice vegetable consommé can be enjoyed warm or cool.*

SERVES 4

**INGREDIENTS**

2 cups onions, diced
2 cups carrots, diced
2 cups organic potato peels (not inside of the potato), chopped
1 strip of seaweed, such as kombu or wakame
3 sprigs fresh oregano
3 sprigs fresh thyme
2 cinnamon sticks
6 peppercorns
½ tablespoon sea salt
2 quarts water

**METHOD**

1. Put all the ingredients in a large pot and bring to a boil. Turn heat down to low and simmer gently for at least 30 minutes. Taste and adjust seasonings.
2. Strain and serve hot, warm or cool.
3. Leftover potatoes can be covered with water and refrigerated for 2 days until ready to use.

# Cinnamon Desserts

## Baked Apple Eddie

*This simple dessert, served warm with toppings, is delightfully satisfying on a fall day. Warming spices with added flax seeds give a flavorful twist on an old favorite comfort food, Apple Betty.*

SERVES: 4

**INGREDIENTS**

4 apples, cored and cut into ½-inch (1.27 cm) rounds
1 tablespoon lemon juice
⅛ teaspoon sea salt
1 teaspoon ground cinnamon
¼ teaspoon ground cardamon
½ teaspoon ground ginger
½ tablespoon orange rind, finely grated
2 tablespoons maple syrup
2 tablespoons butter, melted
"Walnut Flax Crumble" *(See recipe below)*

**METHOD**

1. Preheat oven to 350°F (176°C).
2. Place apple rounds in a bowl and toss with lemon juice, salt, spices, maple syrup, and butter.
3. Line medium baking pan with parchment paper and lay apple rounds in it. Bake 30-35 minutes.
4. Arrange apples in a pretty dessert dish and top with "Walnut Flax Crumble."

## Walnut Flax Crumble

*The cinnamon and ginger coats the walnuts deliciously.*

YIELDS: 3/4 CUP

**INGREDIENTS**

¾ cup walnuts, toasted and chopped
1 cup apple cider
2 quarter-size ginger slices
1 cinnamon stick
2 tablespoons flax seeds

**METHOD**

1. In a small sauce pan, cook apple cider over medium high heat with ginger slices and cinnamon stick until juice is reduced to ¼ cup. Sauce should coat the back of spoon.
2. Remove ginger and cinnamon. Add walnuts and flax seeds to sauce.
3. Spread nut and seed mixture on parchment-lined baking sheet and cool. Crumble for use as topping for "Baked Apple Eddie."

## *Cinnamon Desserts (continued)*

# *I Dream of Peaches Cobbler*

*Enjoy this yummy cobbler made with nut and grain flours, fresh or frozen fruit and aromatic, spices.*

SERVES 4

### COBBLER TOPPING INGREDIENTS

3 tablespoons coconut oil or butter
¼ cup coconut, palm or date sugar
⅔ cup quick whole oats
½ cup almond flour
½ cup walnuts, or nuts of your choice, chopped
¼ cup arrowroot powder or tapioca starch
½ teaspoon sea salt
1 teaspoon baking powder
1 tablespoon cinnamon
½ cup almond milk
¼ teaspoon vanilla
3 tablespoons flax seeds

### FRUIT FILLING INGREDIENTS

2 teaspoons arrowroot powder
1 tablespoon coconut or date sugar
1 tablespoon cinnamon
½ teaspoon lemon juice
2 cups berries, any combination of blackberries, raspberries, blueberries
2 cups peaches, sliced or cut into bite-sized pieces

### METHOD

1. Preheat the oven to 350°F (176°C).
2. Using a mixer, cream together coconut oil and sugar until light and fluffy.
3. In a separate bowl, sift together dry ingredients: rice flour, almond flour, nuts, arrowroot, cinnamon, sea salt and baking powder.
4. Alternately add sifted dry ingredients and almond milk into creamed coconut oil and sugar mixture, beginning and ending with dry ingredients. Add vanilla and mix batter until all ingredients are well incorporated. Fold in flax seeds.
5. Wash and dry berries and place into a bowl. Add peaches. Sprinkle fruit with arrowroot powder, sugar, cinnamon and lemon juice. Gently but thoroughly mix until combined.
6. Spread fruit into a greased baking dish.
7. Spoon cobbler batter over fruit and bake for 30-40 minutes until crisp and bubbling.

## *Dessert Crepes to Live For*

*Buckwheat crepes or Gallete de Sarrasin as the French like to call them are usually reserved for savory ingredients. In this rendition we've sweetened them a bit and filled them with a Bing cherry and ricotta filling.*

SERVES 4-6

### INGREDIENTS

3 tablespoons coconut oil or unsalted butter
¾ cup buckwheat flour
¼ cup sorghum flour
¼ cup arrowroot starch
1 tablespoon cinnamon, more for garnish
½ teaspoon sea salt
1 tablespoon coconut sugar
3 large eggs
1 teaspoon coconut oil to brush on crepe pan
1½ cups fresh goat milk or nut milk
1 pint fresh cherries, pitted and halved
2 cups fresh ricotta cheese

### METHOD

1. Melt the butter in a small saucepan and set aside to cool.
2. In a large bowl, sift together the buckwheat flour, sorghum flour, arrowroot, cinnamon, sea salt and sugar. Make a well in the center.
3. Crack eggs into the well and begin whisking eggs and flour until thoroughly mixed. Batter will be thick.
4. Slowly add half the milk to the flour and egg mixture, whisking constantly until batter is smooth.
5. Stir in half of the melted butter and half of the remaining milk. Allow to stand for 2 hours.
6. Just before cooking, stir and check the consistency of the batter. It should be like thin cream. If necessary, add more milk to achieve the right consistency. Use the remaining oil or butter to coat the pan.
7. Heat an 8-inch (20 cm) crepe pan or skillet over medium-high heat. Sprinkle a few drops of water on the pan; if they sizzle, the pan is ready to use. Brush with oil or butter.
8. Using a ¼ cup measuring cup, fill it with batter and pour it into the skillet. Immediately pick up the pan and tilt and swirl it so that the batter covers the entire bottom of the pan.
9. Loosen the edges of the crepe with a spatula and quickly flip it over.
10. Cook on the other side until lightly brown (usually less than a minute) and slide it out onto a plate. Cover with waxed paper. Repeat with the remaining batter.
11. Fill with cherries and ricotta cheese.
12. Sprinkle a little cinnamon on top.

## *Cinnamon Desserts (continued)*

# *Fondue Fantastique*

*This fruit and chocolate fondue is a party pleaser like none other. Make it for dinner parties to delight your family and friends.*

SERVES 4-6

### INGREDIENTS

1 pound premium dark chocolate (70% cacao or higher)
1 cup coconut milk
1 teaspoon ground cinnamon
½ teaspoon ground ginger
½ teaspoon vanilla extract
4 medium green apples, sliced

### METHOD

1. Melt the chocolate in the small double boiler and stir in the coconut milk.
2. Add cinnamon, ginger and vanilla.
3. Once combined, dip the apple slices with a fondue fork and enjoy.

# I Can See Clearly Maca Balls

*Instead of buying protein bars, consider making your own! When you make your own, you have full control over the ingredient. Maca root is a cruciferous vegetable native to the Andes of Peru and Bolivia. It resembles a turnip or parsnip and is sun-dried and ground into a powder. Blended with nuts, seeds and cacao, this snack elevates energy and mood and supports blood sugar and hormone balance.*

SERVINGS: 15-20 BALLS

## INGREDIENTS

½ cup medjool dates
¼ cup dried cherries (or raisins, or blueberries)
¼ cup dried figs
I cup lightly toasted nuts (walnuts, pecans, almonds, brazil nuts)
2 tablespoon flax seeds
2 tablespoon unsweetened carob powder or cacao powder
1 scoop protein powder
1 teaspoon maca powder
½ teaspoon ground cinnamon
¼ teaspoon freshly ground nutmeg
1 tablespoon fresh orange zest
2 tablespoons filtered water (or as little is needed)
1 cup unsweetened coconut, shredded

## METHOD

1. Soak the dried fruits in warm water for 15 minutes, strain and roughly chop them.
2. Using a food processor, pulse the nuts and flax until finely ground.
3. Add the chopped fruits to the food processor, along with the carob or cacao powder, protein powder, maca powder, spices and orange zest.
4. Pulse mixture until it forms a ball. If it's too dry add a little water and pulse again.
5. Transfer mixture into a bowl.
6. With wet hands, scoop about a tablespoon of the mixture and form into round balls.
7. Place the coconut flakes into a dish with sides and roll each ball in coconut until coated.
8. Place the finished balls on a parchment lined baking sheet and chill in the refrigerator for at least an hour before serving.
9. Transfer unused balls into a container and store in the refrigerator for up to 2 weeks.

**SOURCE:** Modified from *Flavors of Health Cookbook*. Dr. Ed Bauman and Chef Lizette Marx, Bauman College, Penngrove CA, 2012.

## *Cinnamon Desserts (continued)*

# *A Cookie for Your Thoughts*

*These cookies are tasty, healthy and great with a cup of tea or chai.*

SERVES 4-6

### INGREDIENTS

1 cup butter
½ cup coconut, palm or monk fruit sugar
2 eggs
1 tablespoon vanilla extract
1 tablespoon cinnamon
2 cup rolled oats
1 cup almond flour
1 cup coconut flour
1 teaspoon baking soda
¾ teaspoon baking powder
1 teaspoon sea salt
1 cup cranberries
1 cup raisins

### METHOD

1. Preheat the oven to 350°F (176°C).
2. Beat the butter and sugar until light and fluffy.
3. Add eggs and vanilla to the mixing bowl and beat until well combined.
4. In a separate bowl combine cinnamon, oats, flours, baking soda baking powder and salt.
5. Gradually add dry ingredients to mixing bowl and beat on low setting until well combined.
6. Add raisins and cranberries and mix for 2 more minutes.
7. With your hands roll about a tablespoon of the mixture into 1-inch (2.5 cm) balls and place them on a parchment lined baking sheet.
8. Bake for 10-12 minutes.

## How to Grow Cinnamon

Despite its popularity as a culinary ingredient and medicinal supplement, cinnamon is not commonly found in home gardens. Yet it is easy to grow and can thrive for years with minimal care. It needs acidic (4.5-5.5 pH), well-draining soil that is kept slightly dry. Since this evergreen is a native of the tropics, it prefers full sun to partial shade and likes temperatures 60°F (15°C) and above. For those wishing to grow cinnamon in colder climates it is best to plant in pots and bring indoors during the winter months. For USDA Zones 9-11 the plants should be covered in winter to protect from frost. With adequate pruning, plants can grow to about 3 feet in pots or up to 8 feet tall if planted in the ground.

Even though it is not difficult, patience is required for harvesting cinnamon. Experts recommend waiting 2 years and then cutting the entire tree back to a stump. New shoots will grow out of the stump in the third year and it is these young branches which are harvested. Individual branches are cut and the outer layer is removed. It is the yellowish-orange layer underneath which is the cinnamon. Strips are carefully peeled away with a sharp knife. The strips will curl up into the now familiar scroll shape as they dry. To get a thicker quill layer several pieces together.

### How to Make Cinnamon Powder

To maintain freshness, grind cinnamon in small batches. Break the sticks into smaller pieces before putting into a spice grinder. Pulverize until you have a fine powder. Store in an airtight jar and use as needed.

CHAPTER SIX

# *Garlic*

*(Allium sativum)*

*Garlic heads for sale at the market.*

**Garlic** has been called the *emperor* of culinary medicinal spices. It has been widely used and cherished since ancient times for its savory flavor and health promoting properties. Garlic is hot, pungent, oily and extremely aromatic. It is our most potent remedy to protect us from an overgrowth of pathogenic microbes, such as viruses, bacteria, fungus, mycotoxins, biofilms and related organisms and their microbiome altering by-products. Garlic has been the antibiotic of choice worldwide for millennia. Forty years ago, I saw the award-winning documentary *Garlic is as Good as Ten Mothers*. The film did a great job of presenting the history of garlic through the eyes of director Les Blank as he interviewed chefs, doctors, and garlic lovers, singing praises of the so-called "stinking rose."

In 1858, the famous scientist Louis Pasteur was the first to discover that garlic juice had anti-bacterial properties. Later research showed the sulfuric substance in garlic, called *allicin,* gave garlic its superpowers. A recent study found that daily garlic supplement reduced the number of colds by 63%. The remarkable benefit of eating garlic comes from its diverse biological activities: enhanced antioxidant defense, lowering of blood lipids, inhibition of blood aggregation, enhancement of cancer cell cycle arrest, apoptosis, inhibition of invasion and/or metastasis, and modulation of immune response. Being a "hot" spice, its kinder on your gut if you sauté it rather than eating it raw. With new viruses spreading globally, eating garlic on a daily basis is a flavorful way to build health, vitality and protection.

Eat garlic with parsley, basil, cilantro or other greens to neutralize the potent and, for some, noxious garlic smell. Garlic imparts a savory taste to bland vegetables, pasta, pilaf, eggs, seafood and meat. It is a primary ingredient in pesto, hummus, and guacamole. My allergy, liver detox and anti-plague remedy of choice is a half cup of minced garlic, mixed with an equal amount of parsley held in cup of raw apple cider vinegar for 2 weeks; then strained and taken by

*Preparing garlic heads for cooking.*

the teaspoon straight up or in water to ward off pathogens, toxins, mean people and evil spirits.

We recommend finding several ways to incorporate garlic in cooking and daily use to stay strong and immune competent. It is especially useful in winter months when viral infections escalate. There is no doubt that garlic is endowed with wonderful healing properties. Consuming garlic on a daily basis in homemade or purchased food preparations is a flavorful way to add health and longevity, be less reliant on antibiotic medicine to protect you from an overgrowth of microorganisms in your gut and oral cavities, such as bacteria, yeast, viruses and parasites. If you believe in real or psychic vampires, it is reputed to repel them as well. You can eat it with parsley or other green herbs to neutralize the characteristic garlic smell.

## Background and Uses

Garlic, *allium sativum,* is a member of the Lillaceae family, along with onions, chives, leeks and shallots. While its origins are in some dispute, it is believed to be a native of central and southern Asia or southwestern Siberia. It's one of the oldest known herbs, used for centuries as a medicine, for currency, to ward off evil, strengthen athletes and worshipped as a diety. Some of the earliest references to this medicinal plant were found in *Avesta,* a collection of Zoroastrian holy writings that was probably compiled during the sixth century BC (Dannesteter, 2003). Garlic has also played an important role as medicine for Sumerians and ancient Egyptians (Bayan, et al., 2014). There is some evidence that during the earliest Olympics in Greece, garlic was fed to the athletes to increase their stamina. Its intense and unique flavor and aroma make it a mainstay of cuisines around the world, a nearly indispensable ingredient in just about every form of Asian, European, African, Latin American and North American cooking.

## Plant Specifics

Today garlic is grown all over the world. It is grown underground, from a single clove, in the form of a bulb. Its long green shoots produce flower stalks called "scapes," which can be eaten. Covered in an inedible papery skin, the bulb, or head, is comprised of individual sections called cloves. These cloves are themselves enclosed in a paper like skin, and the pale yellowish flesh within is the part of the garlic that is used in cooking. Like its cousin the onion, garlic contains a sulfur-based enzyme, which is stored in tiny cells within its flesh.

*Allium sativum* can grow up to 3 feet (1 meter) in height. Its hardiness is USDA Zone 8. It produces hermaphrodite flowers. It is pollinated by bees, butterflies, moths, and other insects. There are two subspecies of *A. sativum,* ten major groups of varieties, and hundreds of varieties or cultivars. Garlic is easy to grow and can be grown year-round in mild climates. While sexual propagation of garlic is possible, nearly all of the garlic in cultivation is propagated asexually, by planting individual cloves in the ground. In colder climates, cloves are planted in the autumn, about six weeks before the soil freezes, and harvested in late spring or early summer. The cloves must be planted deep enough to prevent freezing and thawing which causes mold or white rot.

## Active Constituents

The presence of garlic compounds varies with the mode of preparation and extraction as follows:

- fresh bulbs main compounds are S-allyl-L-cysteine sulfoxide (alliin) and γ-glutamyl cysteine derivatives
- in steam distilled oils, sulfide family compounds are the main compounds
- powder from crushed and dried garlic contains *alliin* and *diallyl disulfide* (DADS)
- macerates (ground garlic) are enriched extractions with sulfide family compounds, dithiins, and (E-Z) ajoene compounds
- AGE (soaked, sliced, aged garlic extract in ethanol solution) contains *S-allyl-L-cysteine* (SAC) and *S-allyl mercaptocysteine* (SAMC)

## Garlic preparations and their chemical compounds

**Raw garlic:** The fluid that comes from pressing raw garlic or the homogenate has been the subject of the most intensive scientific study. Raw garlic homogenate is essentially the same as aqueous extract of garlic, which has been used in various scientific studies. *Allicin* (*allyl 2 propene-thiosulfinate* or *diallyl thiosulfinate*) is thought to be the principal bioactive compound present in aqueous garlic extract or raw garlic homogenate.

**Chopped garlic:** When fresh garlic is chopped or crushed, it triggers the alliinase enzyme to convert alliin into allicin, which is responsible for the aroma of fresh garlic. Other important sulfur containing compounds present in garlic homogenate are *allyl methyl thiosulfonate, 1-propenyl allyl thiosulfonate* and γ-*l glutamyl-S-alkyl-L-cysteine.* The adenosine concentration increases several-fold as the homogenate is incubated at room temperature. The enzyme alliinase responsible for converting alliin *(S-allyl cysteine sulphoxide)* to allicin is inactivated by heat.

**Water extract:** Thus, the water extract of heat-treated garlic contains mainly alliin.

**Garlic powder:** Since garlic powder is simply dehydrated, pulverized garlic cloves, the composition, especially alliinase activity of garlic powder is identical to those of fresh garlic. However, dehydration temperature should not exceed 140˚F (60°C), above which alliinase is inactivated .

**Aged garlic extract:** Another widely studied garlic preparation is *aged garlic extract* (AGE). Sliced raw garlic stored in 15-20% ethanol for 20 months is referred to as AGE. This whole process is supposed to cause considerable loss of allicin and increased activity of certain newer compounds, like *S-allylcysteine* (SAC), S-allylmercaptocysteine, allixin and selenium which are stable, highly bioavailable and significantly antioxidant [5]. Another recently identified antioxidant compound of AGE is N-alpha-(1-deoxy-D-fructos-1-yl)-L-arginine (Fru-Arg) which is not present in raw or heat-treated garlic. (Ryu K, Ide N, Matsuura H, Itakura Y., et al., 2001)

**Garlic oil:** In medical preparations, garlic oil is most commonly extracted using steam distillation. Steam-distilled garlic oil consists of the diallyl (57%), allyl methyl (37%) and dimethyl (6%) mono to hexa sulfides. A typical commercial preparation of garlic oil contains *diallyl disulfide* (DADS, 26%), *diallyl trisulfide* (DATS, 19%), *allyl methyl trisulfide* (15%), *allyl methyl disulfide* (13%), *diallyl tetrasulfide* (8%), *allyl methyl tetrasulfide* (6%), *dimethyl trisulfide* (3%), *penta sulfide* (4%) and *hexa sulfide* (1%). Oil-macerated garlic oil contains the *vinyl-dithiins* and *ajoenes*. Ether extracted garlic oil (essential oil) contains nine times as much of the *vinyl-dithiins* (5.7 mg/gm) and *allyl sulfides* (1.4 mg) (Ryu K, Ide N, Matsuura H, Itakura Y., et al., 2001)

## Traditional Medicine

Garlic has been used throughout history for the prevention and treatment of diseases. Ancient Chinese and Indian medicine recommended using garlic to aid respiration and digestion and to treat leprosy and parasitic infestation (Rivlrn, 1998). In medieval times, garlic was used as an antibiotic in the treatment of arthritis, toothaches, chronic cough, constipation, parasitic infestations, snake and insect bites, gynecologic diseases, as well as in infectious diseases.

## Uses in Modern Medicine

In recent years, there has been a resurgence of interest in using foods and food components in disease prevention. Garlic is one of the best researched herbal remedies. Clinically, it has been evaluated for lowering blood pressure, cholesterol, and glucose concentration, as well as for the prevention of arteriosclerosis and cancer. Epidemiologically, garlic consumption appears to reduce the risk of oral, stomach, esophageal, colon, and prostate cancers. In addition, garlic has been studied for properties including antibacterial, antithrombotic, antioxidant, immunomodulatory, and antidiabetic actions and modulation of drug metabolism. (Tsai, et al., 2012).

## Health Benefits of Garlic

Heart disease, stroke, infections and cancer are the leading causes of death in the western world. Garlic has been recognized as a preventative agent and treatment for many diseases, including atherosclerosis, hyperlipidemia, thrombosis, hypertension and diabetes. A scientific review of experimental and clinical studies of garlic benefits found that, overall, garlic consumption has significant cardioprotective effects in both animal and human studies. (Dr.Axe.com)

**Cancer:** Mechanisms underlying the anti-cancer actions of garlic:

- Induces apoptosis/arrests the cell cycle
- Blocks invasion/metastasis
- Suppresses cell proliferation
- Inhibits activation of carcinogen
- Enhances antioxidation
- Decreases histone deacetylase activity
- Interrupts tubulin polymerization
- Changes proteasome activity.

Based on the U.S. Food and Drug Administration's evidence-based review system for scientifically evaluating the risk of diverse types of cancer, 19 human studies revealed garlic's antitumorigenic potential in stomach, colon, rectal, breast, lung, and endometrial cancers (Kim, et al., 2009).

**High Blood Pressure:** An interesting phenomenon of garlic is that has been shown to help control high blood pressure. One study looked at the effect of aged garlic extract as an adjunct treatment for people already taking antihypertensive medication yet still having uncontrolled hypertension. Garlic showed itself to be highly effective once again (Dr.Axe.com).

**Helps prevents colds:** Garlic has been used extensively in the treatment of colds and other infections because of its antimicrobial, antiviral and antifungal properties.

## *Cancer: Select Clinical Data*

Below are selective clinical trials on the use of garlic for managing various types of cancer.

| DISEASE | DURATION | BENEFIT | DOSAGE |
|---|---|---|---|
| **Stomach Cancer** | **Human Trial 1991** | • The study examined the associations between allium vegetable consumption and stomach cancer in a large population-based case-control study in Shanghai. The study concluded that smoking makes one more susceptible to intestinal gastric cancer.<br>• A negative association was also noted between intake of garlic stalks (often vs. never) and risk of stomach cancer in Qingdao. Results confirm protective effects of allium vegetables (especially garlic and onions) against stomach cancer (Setiawan, et al., 2005). | • 750 cases diagnosed with stomach cancer and 750 age- and gender-matched controls and Qingdao 201 cases and 201 age- and gender-matched controls<br>• Controls were often, sometimes and never<br>• Garlic stalks<br>Never:0 kg/yr<br>Sometimes:0.1-1.5 kg/yr<br>Often: >0.5 kg/yr |
| **Lung Cancer** | **Human Trial 7 year** | • People who ate raw garlic at least twice a week during the 7 year study period had a 44% lower risk of developing lung cancer, according to a study conducted at the Jiangsu Provincial Center for Disease Control and Prevention in China.<br>• The study authors found protective association between intake of raw garlic and lung cancer has been observed with a dose-response pattern, suggesting that garlic may potentially serve as a chemo-preventive agent for lung cancer (Zi-Yi, et al., 2013) | • 1,424 lung cancer cases and 4,543 healthy controls<br>• Raw garlic taken<br>• Controls:<br>< twice weekly<br>> twice weekly<br>8.4g/week or<br>33.4g/week, respectively |
| **Colorectal Cancer** | **Human Trials 12 months** | • A double-blind, randomized clinical trial using high-dose aged garlic extract as the active treatment and low-dose aged garlic extract as the control was performed involving patients with colorectal adenomas or precancerous lesions of the large bowel.<br>• After 12 months of treatment, 37 patients (19 in the active and 18 in the control group) completed the study, the size and number of colon adenomas in the high-dose group being significantly lower (Tanaka, et al., 2006). | • High-dose aged garlic extract (2.4 ml/day) as the active treatment and low-dose aged garlic extract (0.16 ml/day) as the control<br>• 51 patients with colorectal adenomas/precancerous lesions of the large bowel |
| **Stomach and Colon Cancer** | **Human Trial** | • In persons who consume a high proportion of garlic, a decreased susceptibility to stomach and colon cancers has also been reported (Fleishauer, et al., 2006). | |

## Cancer: Select Clinical Data (continued)

| DISEASE | DURATION | BENEFIT | DOSAGE |
|---|---|---|---|
| **Brain Cancer** | **Cell Study** | • Organo-sulfur compounds found in garlic have been identified as effective in destroying the cells in glioblastomas, a type of deadly brain tumor.<br>• The study demonstrated efficacy in eradicating brain cancer cells, but *diallyl trisulfide* (DATS) proved to be the most effective. This research highlights the great promise of plant-originated compounds as natural medicine for controlling the malignant growth of human brain tumor cells. More studies are needed in animal models of brain tumors before application of this therapeutic strategy to brain tumor patients (Das, et al., 2007) | • Dose-dependent cytotoxic effects of the garlic compounds (DAS, DADS, and DATS) were tested in human glioblastoma T98G and U87MG cells<br>• Treatment of glioblastoma cells with garlic compounds triggered production of ROS that induced apoptosis with the phosphorylation of p38 MAPK and activation of the redox-sensitive JNK1 pathway.<br>• Pretreatment of cells with ascorbic acid attenuated ROS production, p38 MAPK phosphorylation, and JNK1 activation. Pretreatment with JNK1 inhibitor also significantly reduced cell death. |

## Other Inflammatory Diseases: Select Clinical Data

While garlic has demonstrated a wide variety of benefits for several conditions, below are clinical trial data for its benefits in the treatment of select inflammatory disease states.

| DISEASE | DURATION | BENEFIT | DOSAGE |
|---|---|---|---|
| **Cardiovascular** | | Effect of garlic supplementation on human cardiovascular disorders | |
| **Garlic Powder** | **Human Trial 12 months** | Lowered total cholesterol LDL-C and increased HDL-C (Sobenin. et al., 2010). | • 51 patients with CVD<br>• 300 mg/day<br>• Garlic powder |
| **Raw Garlic** | **Human Trial 42 days** | Lowered total cholesterol triglycerides, and increased HDL-C (Mahmoodi. et al., 2006). | • 30 hypercholesterolemic adults<br>• 5g/day<br>• Raw garlic |
| **Garlic Extract** | **Human Trial 4 months** | Lowered total cholesterol, LDL-C, triglycerides and increased HDL (Durak, et al., 2004). | • 23 hypercholesterolemic adults (13 with hypertension)<br>• 10g/day<br>• Garlic Extract |
| **Aged Garlic Extract** | **Human Trial 12 months** | Lowered total cholesterol, LDL-C, and homocysteine and increased HDL (Budoff, et al., 2009). | • 65 patients with intermediate CVD risk<br>• 250 mg/day co-administered with B vitamins (B12, B6, and folic acid) and L-arginine |
| **Garlic Oil** | **Human Trial 2 months** | Lowered systolic blood pressure, diastolic blood pressure, and oxLDL (Dhawan, et al., 2006). | • 20 hypertensive patients<br>• 250 mg/day<br>• Garlic oil |
| **Oil Macerated Garlic** | **Human trial 30 days** | Lowered total cholesterol, LDL-C, and triglycerides (Dudha, et al., 2008). | • 70 hypertensive adults, 1620 mg/day<br>• Oil macerated garlic |

## Other Inflammatory Diseases: Select Clinical Data (continued)

| DISEASE | DURATION | BENEFIT | DOSAGE |
|---|---|---|---|
| **Diabetes** | **Human Trial 24 weeks** | • The study evaluated the potential hypoglycemic effects of garlic in type-2 diabetic patients and hyperlipidemia.<br>• Group 1 showed significant reduction in fasting blood sugar at week 24 as compared to group 2. At the end of week 24, GR1 also showed considerable decrease in mean total cholesterol, triglycerides, while HDL cholesterol was significantly increased as compared to GR2. Combination of garlic with typical antidiabetic remedy has been shown to improve glycemic control in addition to antihyperlipidemic activity (Ashraf, et al., 2011). | • Type-2 diabetic patients (n=60) with fasting blood sugar level above 126 mg/dayl.<br>• Patients were divided randomly into 2 groups. Group 1 (n=30) was given tablet Garlic (KWAI) 300 mg thrice daily + Metformin 500 mg twice daily and<br>• Group 2 (n=30) was given Placebo + Metformin 500 mg twice daily respectively for 24 weeks. Serum lipids and fasting blood glucose were measured at week 0, 12 and week 24.<br>• Garlic tablet |
| **Osteoarthritis** | | • Garlic and onions. Women who consume a diet high in allium vegetables, such as garlic, onions and leeks, were found to have lower levels of hip osteoarthritis.<br>• Researchers at King's College London and the University of East Anglia have discovered that women who consume a diet high in allium vegetables, such as garlic, onions and leeks, have lower levels of hip osteoarthritis (Frances, et al., 2010). | |

## Summary of Clinical Findings

The underlying actions and clinical effects of garlic are that it is anti-inflammatory and cardio-protective, prevents and treats heart disease and other diseases such as diabetes, high blood pressure and osteoarthritis. It works by itself or in combination with conventional therapies. In human studies it has shown that it is beneficial alone or in combination in stomach, gastric, colon, colorectal, brain, and lung cancers to reduce the symptoms. It induces apoptosis, arrests the cell cycle, blocks invasion or metastasis, suppresses cell proliferation, inhibits activation of carcinogens and enhances antioxidation. While more clinical trials are needed to determine optimal dosing requirements for the various conditions, it is believed that using garlic as a culinary spice and a medicinal agent may change the course of several chronic diseases.

## Dosage Range

Doses of 250-10,000 mg of garlic per day have been used in human studies.

## Contraindications

Garlic is likely safe for most people when taken by mouth appropriately. Garlic has been used safely in research for 7 years. Consumed for hundreds of years, garlic is regarded as a safe food, however garlic may modulate drug-metabolizing enzyme activity and membrane transporter levels in the liver, lung, kidney, and intestinal tissues. This raises the possibility that garlic supplementation could cause interactions between food and drugs and change the therapeutic efficacy of any drugs administered (Tsai, et al., 2012)

## Toxicity

No significant toxicity has been reported following short- or long-term administration of garlic at standard doses.

## Supplementation

Commercially available garlic supplements fall into four categories: dehydrated garlic powder, garlic oil, garlic oil macerate, and aged garlic extract. The effective dosage of garlic has not been determined. Dosages generally recommended in the literature for adults are as follows.

Garlic powder is generated from garlic cloves that have been dehydrated and pulverized into powder. Due to deactivation of alliinase by heat during dehydration, the major active constituents of garlic powder are alliin and a small amount of oil-soluble sulfur compounds. To overcome the strong and irritant odor and the possible side effects of raw garlic and garlic oil, including growth retardation and destruction of gut microflora, an "aging" process has been applied to garlic. Aged garlic is prepared by soaking whole or sliced garlic cloves in alcohol or vinegar solution for 20 months, which removes the several irritant sulfur-containing compounds and also stabilizes some unstable compounds such as allicin. The water-soluble compounds SAC and SAMC are the most abundant sulfur containing components, and trace amounts of oil-soluble allyl sulfides exist in aged garlic. In contrast to odoriferous garlic oil and raw garlic, garlic powder and odorless aged garlic products are currently the most popular garlic supplements on the market.

## Other Inflammatory Diseases: Select Clinical Data

Below is a table of garlic preparations and amounts that can be used as a supplement.

| TYPE OF SUPPLEMENT | ADULT DOSAGE |
|---|---|
| **Raw Garlic** | 1-2 cloves of raw garlic per day |
| **Dehydrated garlic powder** | 300-mg dried garlic powder tablet (standardized to 1.3% alliin or 0.6% allicin yield) 2-3 times per day |
| **Aged Garlic Extract** | 7.2g per day |
| **Garlic Oil** | ½ teaspoon to 1 tablespoon per day or to oral tolerance |
| **Garlic Oil Macerate** | (1:2): 15 to 30 drops, 4 times per day |

## Kitchen Medicine

Although technically not a spice, garlic has been used for centuries to enhance the flavor of foods. It can be sautéed, baked, roasted, braised; added to soups, sauces, marinades, spice rubs, stir-frys; minced and used in vegetables and meat and fish preparations. Garlic is most commonly served heated because it mellows the hot and spicy flavor, and it is more pungent when eaten raw in cold foods such as salads, dips, spreads and savory beverages.

Slicing or crushing garlic ruptures the cells, releasing a pungent enzyme called allicin. To maximize health benefits it is recommended that you let your garlic sit at room temperature for 10-15 minutes to maximize the anti-bacterial, anti-fungal and cancer fighting properties. Unlike onions, which produce this enzyme in a form that allows it to become airborne, the compound in garlic is only transferred via direct contact. That's why onions irritate your eyes when you slice them, but garlic doesn't.

# Garlic Remedy

## Garlic For Health

*Sautéed garlic cloves are good for a cold or an upper respiratory infection. It is also a daily tonic and non-caffeinated digestive and metabolic stimulant.*

SERVES 1

### INGREDIENTS

1 teaspoon ghee (or unsalted butter)
2 cloves fresh garlic, peeled

### METHOD

1. Heat ghee in a small sauté pan.
2. Add the peeled garlic cloves whole, sauté for a few minutes and cover. The cloves should look buttery.
3. Once slightly cooled they can be chewed on.

# Garlic Salad

## Queen Quinoa Salad

*Quinoa salad is great as addition to summer salads. It can be placed into romaine lettuce cups and served as a side or main dish.*

SERVES 2

### INGREDIENTS

2 tablespoons extra-virgin olive oil
1 medium red onion, minced
2 large cloves garlic, minced
2 tablespoons ground cumin
1 teaspoon ground cayenne
1 teaspoon ground black pepper
½ cup carrots, julienned
1 cup kale, chopped
½ cup squash, chopped
½ cup zucchini, chopped
1 cup quinoa, cooked
½ cup parsley, minced
Sea salt

### DRESSING INGREDIENTS

1 teaspoon extra-virgin olive oil
1 teaspoon apple cider vinegar
½ teaspoon maple syrup

### SALAD INGREDIENTS

2 cups mixed greens
½ cup pecans
2 tablespoons shredded parmesan cheese

### METHOD

1. Heat olive oil to medium and sauté onions for a few minutes until translucent.
2. Stir in garlic and cook for a minute or less to prevent browning.
3. Add the cumin, cayenne, and pepper and heat until fragrant.
4. In order of hardness, add carrots, squash, kale and zucchini, cooking each for 2 minutes before adding the next vegetable.
5. Stir in the cooked quinoa, parsley and salt. Taste and adjust seasonings.
6. Remove from heat and allow to cool.
7. In a bowl, whisk the dressing ingredients, adding salad greens and pecans.
8. Arrange the salad greens on two plates and top with quinoa mixture.
9. Garnish with shredded parmesan cheese.

### Ode to Quinoa

A grain fed to Aztec warriors
to keep them strong
Full of protein and antioxidants
With complex, nutty flavor,
A complement to legumes,
nuts and seeds
Nicely paired with curry and
sambhar
An alternate to rice
Enjoy it yourself,
Feel the power
The mighty Aztecs once felt
Today

# Garlic Soups

## New Attitude Lentil Soup

*Lentil soup is great for the fall and winter seasons. Easy to make, it stores well, gaining flavor with each passing day.*

SERVES 4

### INGREDIENTS

1 cup brown lentils
4 cups filtered water, plus more for rinsing
1 tablespoon ghee (or unsalted butter)
1 medium red onion, diced small
2 large cloves garlic, minced fine
½ cup carrots, julienned into thin strips
½ cup celery, diced small
1 cup kale, chopped into bite-sized pieces
2 tablespoons ground cumin
1 teaspoon cayenne pepper
1 teaspoon black pepper
6 cups organic vegetable broth
Sea salt

### METHOD

1. Rinse lentils in filtered water, removing any pebbles or other debris.
2. Drain and place the lentils in a medium pot with 4 cups of filtered water. Bring to a boil and then reduce heat to low and simmer for 18-20 minutes, or until done. Lentils should appear whole and not too mushy. Strain under cold water to stop the cooking process and set aside.
3. In a large pot, melt the ghee on medium heat and add onions. Sauté for 5 minutes or until translucent.
4. Add garlic and sauté for a minute or less to prevent browning.
5. Add the cumin, cayenne, and pepper, then heat until fragrant.
6. One at a time, add carrots, celery and kale, cooking each for 2 minutes before adding the next vegetable.
7. Pour in the vegetable broth and bring to a boil before lowering heat to a simmer for 10 minutes.
8. Add cilantro and sea salt. Taste and adjust seasonings.
9. Stir in the cooked lentils and warm just until heated through.

## Garlic Soups (continued)

# Chili Gone Veg (no Carne)

*Here is an affordable dish that can feed a whole family on a meat-free Monday or any day.*

SERVES 6

### INGREDIENTS

- ¾ cup dry chickpeas (or 15 oz. can)
- ¾ cup dry red kidney beans (or 15 oz. can)
- ¾ cup dry black beans (or 15 oz. can)
- 2 tablespoons extra-virgin olive oil
- 1 yellow or white onion, diced small
- ¾ cup tempeh, crumbled
- 2-3 cloves garlic, minced fine
- 2 bay leaves
- 2 tablespoons chili powder
- 1 tablespoon ground cumin
- 1 tablespoon sea salt
- 1 tablespoon ground black pepper
- ½ cup celery, diced medium
- ½ cup green pepper, diced medium
- 2 jalapeños, seeded and diced small
- 1 cup kale, diced small
- 12 medium tomatoes, seeded and diced (or 28 oz. can)
- ½ cup tomato paste
- 6 cups vegetable stock
- ½ cup cilantro minced
- 1 avocado, diced for garnish (optional)

### METHOD

1. Soak beans in filtered water for at least 7 hours or overnight.
2. Drain and cook beans in filtered water for about an hour or until soft.
3. In a large stock pot, heat the olive oil and sauté onions on low heat until translucent.
4. Stir in tempeh and brown for a few minutes.
5. Add garlic with bay leaves, chili powder and cumin for about a minute or until fragrant.
6. Add celery, green peppers, kale and tomatoes and cook until all the vegetables are softened.
7. Stir in the tempeh and brown for a few minutes.
8. Stir tomato paste into vegetable stock until almost dissolved and then pour into pot.
9. Bring to a boil and lower heat to a simmer for 30 minutes until the tomatoes have broken down.
10. Stir in cilantro. Taste and adjust seasonings.
11. Remove bay leaves before serving.
12. Can be served over gluten-free grains like millet or quinoa. Garnish with avocado.

NOTE: *Soaking beans overnight removes the stachyose/raffinose, the gas producing ingredient.*

**SOURCE:** Modified from the "Vegetarian Chilly" recipe at http://www.allrecipes.com

# Garlic Dips

## Edamame Big Dipper

*A new version hummus using soy edamame instead of chickpeas.*

SERVES 4

**INGREDIENTS**

- 16 oz. shelled organic edamame (whole cooked soybeans — thawed, if frozen)
- ½ cup green onions
- ½ cup fresh cilantro
- ½ tablespoon fresh lime juice
- 2 cloves garlic
- 1 teaspoon sea salt or to taste
- ½ teaspoon black pepper
- 2 tablespoons extra-virgin olive oil

**METHOD**

1. Combine edamame, green onions, garlic, cilantro, three tablespoons of water, garlic, lime juice, sea salt and pepper in a food processor.
2. With the motor running on low, add olive oil through the feed tube and process until smooth. Stop and scrape down the sides, continue processing until you have a smooth consistency. Add additional oil or a little water if it is too thick.

NOTE: *Serve with vegetables (celery, carrots, radish, daikon, cucumber), rice crackers, or seaweed crackers for dipping.*

## A Chutney for All Seasons

*Garlic chutney is very flavorful, adding zest to grain, legume, seafood or meat dishes.*

SERVES 4

**INGREDIENTS**

- 2 teaspoons sesame oil
- 1 teaspoon mustard seeds
- 1 teaspoon urad dal (white lentils)
- ½ teaspoon fenugreek seeds
- 3-4 red chilies (whole or chopped)
- 1 pinch asafetida (optional)
- ½ cup peeled garlic cloves
- 1 small ball of tamarind (or about a teaspoon of paste)
- 1 teaspoon jaggery (use brown sugar if not available)
- ½ teaspoon sea salt or more to taste

**METHOD**

1. In a small pan, heat half the sesame oil and add mustard seeds. When they start to pop add urad dal, fenugreek, red chillies and asafetida, if using. Cook until spices take on a dark brown color. Remove from heat and place in a bowl to cool.
2. Using the same pan, heat the remaining oil, add garlic cloves and sauté on low heat, stirring until softened. Remove and add to the bowl.
3. Finally, lightly sauté the tamarind and salt, remove from pan and add to the bowl.
4. Once cooled, pour the contents of the bowl into a high speed blender (like a *Vitamix*) and add jaggery. Pulse until mixed well with some small pieces remaining.
5. Place chutney in a container with a lid and refrigerate until ready to serve.

**SOURCE:** Modified from *Pickles, Chutneys and Preserves* by Vasantha Moorthy.

# Garlic Entrees

## Baingan (Eggplant) Bharta

*Bharta is the Indian name for eggplant, slow cooked with an array of savory spices.*

SERVES 4

### INGREDIENTS

1 large eggplant
2-4 cloves garlic, halved

### BHARTA INGREDIENTS

2 teaspoons extra-virgin coconut oil
1 large onion, diced small
1-inch (2.5 cm) fresh ginger, minced
1-2 green (Indian bird's eye) chilies, diced small
3 cloves garlic, minced
1 teaspoon ground turmeric
1 teaspoon ground cumin
1 teaspoon ground coriander
1 pinch asafetida
½ teaspoon sea salt or more to taste
1 cup green peas, thawed if frozen
½ cup cilantro, minced

### METHOD

1. Preheat the oven to 375°F (190°C). Using a knife, make 6-8 slits in the eggplant and fill them with garlic halves.
2. Bake the eggplant whole for 30-45 minutes or until soft when pierced with a fork.
3. For a smokier flavor, sear over an open flame until all sides are blackened and eggplant is soft.
4. Set aside to cool. When cool enough to handle, peel the eggplant and mash in a bowl.
5. In a pan, heat the coconut oil over medium heat and sauté onions until soft.
6. Add ginger, chilies and minced garlic and cook for another minute.
7. Add the turmeric, cumin, coriander, asafetida and salt. Stir to combine. Lower heat and cover to meld flavors for a few minutes.
8. Remove cover and add mashed eggplant, peas and cilantro. Cook until heated through.
9. Taste and adjust seasonings.
10. Serve with bean recipe below.

## Rajma (Red Kidney Beans)

*This hearty dish comes from the Punjab, in India. It is popular in "Dhabas," Indian restaurants that serve homestyle food.*

SERVES 4

### INGREDIENTS

1½ cups dry rajma or red kidney beans (or 2 15 oz. cans)
Filtered water (if using dry beans)
2 tablespoons extra-virgin coconut oil
1 onion, diced small
1 teaspoon fresh ginger, grated
2 cloves garlic, minced fine
1 tablespoon turmeric powder
1 teaspoon cumin seeds
1 teaspoon ground coriander
1 teaspoon cayenne pepper
1 pinch asafetida
½ cup cilantro
Sea salt to taste

### METHOD

1. Soak the rajma for 7 hours or overnight. Drain and rinse the rajma and cook in a pressure cooker with fresh filtered water or on the stove until soft, about an hour. Drain and reserve about 1 cup of the cooking liquid. Cooking time will vary depending on the age or your beans.
2. Heat the coconut oil over medium heat, and sauté the onions for about 5 minutes.
3. Add ginger and garlic for a minute or less to prevent browning.
4. Add all the dried spices except salt for another minute or until fragrant.
5. Add the rajma (beans) with some of the cooking liquid and bring to a low simmer. Cover and simmer for 10 minutes.
6. Remove lid and add cilantro and salt. Taste and adjust seasonings.
7. Serve with brown rice and the "Baingan (Eggplant) Bharta" recipe above.

## *How to Grow Garlic*

This culinary staple is rarely propagated from seeds. Instead a few aromatic bulbs of garlic are saved from the harvest and replanted year after year.

### Time of Planting

Plant garlic in the fall, usually between September 15 and November 30, after the first light frost of the year. It thrives in northern, temperate and tropical climates. Varieties differ by region. In the tropical South Asian region, the garlic pods are smaller and more pungent whereas in the U.S., the garlic cloves are much larger but have a milder flavor.

### Spacing Requirements

Keep bulbs intact until right before planting. Break bulbs into individual cloves and plant the largest, healthiest looking cloves with the pointy side facing up, 6-8 inches (15-20 cm) apart. Cover with 2 inches (5 cm) of soil and a 6 inch (15 cm) layer of mulch.

### Time to Germination

Cloves may begin to sprout through the mulch in 4-8 weeks, depending on the variety and the weather conditions in your region. Do not be concerned. The plants can tolerate some frost or a light freeze and still survive the winter.

### Special Considerations

Garlic plants must be vernalized (overwintered) in order for their bulbs to develop. Do not remove mulch in the spring; it helps control weeds, preserves moisture and provides nutrients as it decomposes.

When garlic shoots begin to emerge in early spring, ensure even soil moisture by supplying 1-inch (2.5 cm) of water per week throughout the growing season. Scapes are the curly flower stems that often form as the garlic matures. Harvest them when they are 10 inches (25 cm) long. They are a delicious addition to your spring menus.

## *How to Grow Garlic (continued)*

### Common Pests and Diseases (and how to manage)

Garlic can suffer damage from nematodes, botrytis rot, and white rot. However, the biggest threat to garlic is weeds. Keep your garlic bed clean and make sure to plant garlic in well-fertilized, loose soil.

### Harvest (when and how)

Harvest after 3-4 leaves have died back and there are still 5 or 6 green leaves remaining on the plant — sometime in June or July depending on the year and your climate. Do not wait too long or the bulbs will begin to separate in the ground. Loosen the soil with a shovel or pitchfork and then dig the garlic carefully. Do not pull the stalk or it will break off from the bulb. Gently brush off most of the dirt. Tie plants in a bundle of 6-8 plants and hang in a shaded, dry, well-ventilated shed or garage. Leave plants hanging for 4-6 weeks so that bulbs can cure.

### Storing

After thoroughly drying, trim off the roots and cut the stalks off about 1½ inches (3.8 cm) from the bulb. Store in net bags. For optimum storage, hang in an area with 45-55% humidity and a temperature of 50-70°F (10-21°C). Hold back your nicest bulbs for replanting.

### Future Harvest Preparation

To regrow garlic, keep bulbs intact until no more than 1-2 days before replanting, then simply pull apart garlic bulbs and plant individual cloves as described above. Some garlic varieties will produce seeds if scapes are not removed from the plants, but these seeds will not be true to type.

*How to Grow Garlic (continued)*

### How to Make Garlic Powder

Make your own garlic powder by dehydrating and grinding garlic cloves.

**INGREDIENTS**

6 bulbs garlic

**METHOD**

1. Separate the cloves of garlic from the head. Peel off the papery skins and slice the cloves thin.
2. To dry garlic using a dehydrator: Spread out the sliced garlic in a single layer on dehydrator screens and dehydrate at 125°F (51°C) until the garlic is crispy and snaps when you break it, up to 12 hours. Rotate your screens half-way through to dry evenly.
3. To dry garlic in an oven: Spread the sliced garlic on a parchment lined baking sheet and dry in a preheated oven on the lowest setting, no higher than 140°F (60°C) for 1-2 hours until the garlic snaps when you break it.
4. Let the dehydrated garlic cool, then grind into a powder using a high-powered blender, spice grinder, or coffee grinder. Sift the powder to remove large pieces. They can be put back in the grinder to repeat the process.
5. Store the garlic powder in an airtight container in a dark, cool, and dry location.

NOTE: *6 large heads of garlic will make about ½ cup of garlic powder. Substitute ⅛ teaspoon of garlic powder for each clove called for in recipes.*

CHAPTER SEVEN

# Peppers

*(Capsaicin)*

**Peppers** have been used as a powerful flavor and medicine for thousands of years. *Capsaicin,* the active ingredient in cayenne pepper, is what fires up our mucous membranes and generates a rise in body temperature and even perspiration. Interestingly, peppers are eaten in warm tropical countries to induce sweating, which cools the head, skin and peripheral tissues. Peppers have been used traditionally as an anti-microbial agent to protect people lacking refrigeration from surface bacteria, mold and bugs on the food they eat. Peppers have been well studied in Ayurveda, Chinese Medicine, Latin American, and African systems to heal a multitude of health conditions, from treating surface wounds and acute bleeding to stimulating digestion, circulation and vital energy. Western naturopathic research reports this spice is a valuable adjunct in the treatment of pain, cardiovascular issues, diabetes, detoxification, arthritis, and cancer. Red and green chilies are vital components of fresh salsa, which goes so well with avocado, beans and Latin foods. Chili peppers should not be confused with the spice we get from peppercorns. Despite their similar names, peppercorns are not part of the capsaicin family. Instead they are the seeds of the *Piper nigrum* plant.

Cayenne pepper is the fruit of *Capsicum annuum* that has been dried and ground into a powder. In one of my first *Vitality*™ fasting retreats, over 35 years ago, I introduced the Master Cleanser, a fasting beverage wholly consisting of fresh squeezed lemon juice, maple syrup, cayenne pepper, and water. A faster was encouraged to drink 8 cups a day along with water and peppermint tea. Demonstrating the beverage, I got heavy-handed with the cayenne pepper in the recipe stating how terrific cayenne was as a cleanser and healer. Instead of adding ⅛-¼ teaspoon per cup, I added 1 teaspoon per cup, along with a teaspoon of maple syrup to balance the heat, and the juice from one lemon in one cup of water. When I drank this beverage, I experienced a dramatic flushing, sweating and racing heart. For the next 15 minutes, I was very uncomfortable, until finally it was absorbed and I felt fine, and even a bit euphoric to have worked through the shock to my system. Moral to the story, a little bit of fresh, potent cayenne pepper is plenty. As with adding any spice to your food, start with a small to moderate amount that your system can handle. We all have our own tolerance for concentrated herbs and spices.

*Chili peppers for sale at the market.*

*Coring sweet bell peppers for cooking.*

*Fresh cayenne, powdered cayenne, and fresh jalapenos*

## Background and Uses

*Capsaicin,* a member of the vanilloid and nightshade families, is the active ingredient in chili peppers that gives them their spicy heat. It is a type of *capsaicinoid* and a very powerful irritant, so using it for relief from pain and inflammation seems counterintuitive. (Leung, et al., 1996) However, there are a number of impressive health benefits to using this extract, so eating peppers and spicy foods is often encouraged for metabolic strength and to strengthen the immune system.

Chili is the Aztec name for cayenne pepper. The name "pepper" comes from the similarity of piquance (spiciness or heat) of the flavor to that of black pepper, *Piper nigrum,* although there is no botanical relationship with it or with Sichuan pepper. There is evidence Native Americans used peppers as food and medicine more than 9,000 years ago. Archeologists say Mexicans have been using them for some 7,000 years. Different varieties were cultivated in South America, where they are known as ajíes (singular "ají"), from the Quechua term for capsicum. Peppers only arrived in Europe in the 1400's and spread from there, mostly by the Portuguese, around the world. Today they have become a key ingredient in many cuisines as a spice and food, but the *capsicum* species is also used as a medicine and a lachrymatory (tear producing) agent.

The fruit (technically berries in the strict botanical sense) of *Capsicum* plants have a variety of names. The hottest varieties are commonly called chili peppers, or simply chilis. The large, mild forms are called bell peppers in North America, sweet peppers or simply peppers in the United Kingdom, Ireland and Malaysia, but typically called *capsicum* in New Zealand, (Bernstein, 1987) Australia, South Africa, Singapore, and India. Paprika refers to a powdered spice made of dried *capsicum* of several sorts, though in Hungary and some other countries it is the name of the fruit as well. Both whole and powdered chilis are common ingredients in dishes prepared throughout the world, and characteristic of several cuisine styles, including Mexican, Sichuan (Szechuan) Chinese, Korean, Cajun and Creole, along with most South Asian and derived (e.g. Jamaican) curries. India is the world's largest producer, consumer and exporter of dried chili peppers. It is one of the important commercial crops and a major constituent of the Indian diet. Chili peppers produce alkaloid compounds, *capsaicinoids,* responsible for the heat. Chili also contains carotenoids, phenols, foliates and oxidative products which show many biological activities in the human body. It is a good source of minerals like iron, magnesium and potassium, vitamins like A, B, C, E and P and dietary fibers.

## Plant Specifics

Capsaicin is an irritant for mammals, including humans, and produces a burning sensation in any tissue with which it comes into contact. It is believed that the compounds produced serve as deterrents to protect against certain mammals and fungi. (Lembeck, 1987) There are an estimated 50,000 pepper varieties. The plants grow between one and 3 feet (80 cm) high and have smooth pointed leaves. Star-shaped white flowers grow in the center of the leaves and then form different colored fruits.

## Active Constituents

Researchers have found a wide array of phytochemicals in capsicum including carotenoids, capsaicinoids and phenolic compounds such as the flavonoids quercetin and luteolin. The most commonly occurring capsaicinoids are *capsaicin* (69%), *dihydrocapsaicin* (22%), *nordihydrocapsaicin* (7%), *homocapsaicin* (1%), and *homodihydrocapsaicin* (1%). Capsaicin is found in adequate amounts in the placental tissue (which holds the seeds) and to a lesser extent in the seeds and pericarp portions of capsicum. Capsaicin is a highly volatile, hydrophobic, odorless, and colorless alkaloid. Structurally, capsaicin belongs to a group of chemicals known as vanilloids. The structure of capsaicin consists of a vanillyl (methylcatechol) head group (A-region) and an aliphatic tail (hydrophobic — C-region) linked by a central amide bond (B-region).

## Traditional Medicine

The terminology for the capsicum genus can be confusing because the names capsaicin, pepper, cayenne, paprika, chili, chile, chilli are all used interchangeably. Cayenne was introduced into several traditional medicine cultures across the globe, in Ayurveda, Chinese, Japanese, Korean, African, Latin American and Mayan cultures. In traditional Chinese medicine, cayenne is considered to have digestive stimulant action and is sometimes used to cause diaphoresis (Shih-Chen, et al., 1973). In China and Japan, the tincture is used as an ointment externally to treat muscle pain and frostbite (But, et al., 1997). In Ayurveda, the extracts of chili are used to alleviate the pain of arthritis, headaches, burns and neuralgia. It has the power to boost the immune system and lower cholesterol, effective in heart disorders. In traditional Chinese medicine, peppers that contain capsaicin are predictably categorized as hot and spicy. Like ginger and cinnamon, they are by nature therapeutically warming, promote circulation, and can help relieve pain. They are also used for thinning mucous secretions in some respiratory conditions, treatment of prostate and lung cancer, atherosclerosis, diminishing pain associated with rheumatoid arthritis and fibromyalgia, reducing insulin resistance in type-1 diabetes and the treatment of cluster headaches. It is also used to tonify spleen/stomach, aid digestion, warm the body, relieve diarrhea and vomiting. It's considered a blood cleanser because it promotes circulation of blood, opening channels and clearing obstructions. It also dissipates frostbite and pain due to colds and arthritis.

There is a considerable amount of lore dedicated to cayenne as a South and Central American herb of the Mayans and Aztecs. Considered a tonic for the heart, kidneys, lungs, pancreas, spleen and stomach. It is also said to increase fertility and delay senility. In particular, it is considered good at treating heart and circulatory problems. It is said to be a lifesaver in the event of a heart attack. A cup of cayenne tea (1 teaspoon of cayenne in a cup of hot water) will help calm the heart. Cayenne stimulates the flow of stomach secretions and saliva. It is also considered to improve the effectiveness of other herbs so used as an adjunct herb in formulas. Some recommend placing cayenne inside the nose to relieve hay fever, migraine headaches and sinus infections.

## Uses in Modern Medicine

Cayenne also has nutritional values, antimicrobial and pharmacological properties. It has many biochemical and pharmacological properties like antioxidants, anti-inflammatory, anti-allergenic and anti-carcinogenic. It is used in the pharmaceutical industry to alleviate ulcers, pain, inflammation, and hemorrhoids. The extracts are used to alleviate arthritis pain, headaches, burns and neuralgia. It can boost the immune system, lower cholesterol and is effective in treating heart disorders.

## Health Benefits of Peppers

### Pain and Muscle Spasms

In the official German Pharmacopeia cayenne is approved as a topical ointment for the relief of painful muscle spasms (Deutsches Arzneibuch, 1997). In the U.S., Pharmacopeia cayenne was used as a carminative, stimulant, and rubefacient (Leung, et al., 1996). Capsaicin, taken from capsicum, is recognized by the U,S. *Food and Drug Administration* (FDA) as a counter-irritant for use as a topical analgesic drug product (Palevitch, et al., 1995). For arthritis relief, capsaicin interferes with the pain of inflammatory joint disease when applied topically. It may block pain fibers by destroying substance P, which normally would mediate pain signals to the brain (Garrett, et al., 1997). Cayenne has been used to treat arthritis, rheumatism, neuralgia, lumbago, and chilblains.

### Herpes Zoster or Shingles Virus

Capsicum ointments containing 0.025% or 0.075% capsaicin, are used topically to treat shingles (herpes zoster). Many studies on topical preparations containing capsaicin have been documented. Human trials have investigated its use as a treatment for chronic post-herpetic neuralgia (Bernstein, et al., 1987).

### Gastric Ulcer

Capsaicin inhibits acid secretion, stimulates alkali and mucus secretion and particularly gastric mucosal blood flow which helps in prevention and healing of gastric ulcers. (Srinivasan, 2016) Despite the fact that too much can upset the stomach, because it is a "hot moving" herb, it is surprisingly helpful in the treatment of stomach ulcers.

### Weight Loss

Cayenne has been shown to encourage weight loss. Three main areas of potential benefit for weight management were found: increased energy expenditure increased lipid oxidation and reduced appetite.

(Whiting, 2012) Findings suggest that daily consumption of capsaicinoids may contribute to weight management through reductions in energy intake. Subsequently, there may be potential for capsaicinoids to be used as long-term, natural weight-loss aids. (Whiting, 2013) Capsaicin consumption 1 hour before low-intensity exercise is a valuable supplement for the treatment of individuals with hyperlipidemia and/or obesity because it improves fat burning. Capsinoid ingestion increases energy expenditure through the activation of brown adipose tissue in humans. (Leung., 2014). Certain promising effects have been observed in patients with various pro-inflammatory diseases such as: arthritis, cancer (brain, breast, colon, prostate, colorectal, pancreatic, melanoma) cardiovascular disease, diabetes, Crohn's disease, ulcerative colitis, irritable bowel syndrome, peptic ulcer, gastric ulcer, gastric inflammation, psoriasis, acute coronary syndrome, atherosclerosis, lupus, nephritis, renal conditions, vitiligo, AIDs, chronic arsenic exposure, alcohol intoxication and hepatic conditions (Gupta, et al., 2013).

### Metabolic Boosting

Capsaicin, the phytochemical responsible for the spiciness of peppers, has the potential to modulate metabolism via activation of *transient receptor potential vanilloid 1* (TRPV1) receptors, which are found not only on nociceptive sensory neurons but also in a range of other tissues. Clinically, ingestion of capsaicin or its less stable non-pungent analog capsiate-has been shown to boost metabolic rate modestly. (McCarty, 2017)

### Blood Sugar Balancing

Capsaicin-containing chili supplementation regularly improved postprandial hyperglycemia and hyperinsulinemia as well as fasting lipid metabolic disorders in women. (Yuang, et al., 2016)

### Cough Suppression

Capsaicin powder taken orally decreased cough sensitivity and cough symptoms. (Ternesten-Hasséus, et al., 2015)

### Eye Care

Cayenne makes a very good eye wash because it stimulates eye tissues and increases circulation. It can be made into an herbal tea and cooled. It may cause a slight burning sensation which will dissipate over time.

### Prevents Cancer

Cayenne pepper might help prevent cancer of the breast, prostate, liver, lungs, and skin. Again, this is related to the magic of capsaicin, which may induce cancer cells to kill themselves during the apoptosis process.

## *Cancer: Select Clinical Data*

Below is data that shows that the capsaicin in peppers has a therapeutic effect to manage cancer.

| DISEASE | DURATION | BENEFIT | DOSAGE |
|---|---|---|---|
| **Breast Cancer** | | • Decreased mitochondrial membrane potential, cell-cycle arrest, apoptosis data suggest significant chemo-preventative and anti-cancer potential for capsaicin (Chang, et al., 2011). | • MCF-7, BT-20, SKBR-3<br>• MDA-MB231, T47D<br>• BT-474, MCF10A |
| **Colon Cancer** | | • Cell cycle arrest, apoptosis, changes in cell morphology, DNA fragmentation [141-145] (Lu, et al., 2010). | • SW480, LoVo, HCT-116, CT-26<br>• HT-29, CoLo320, Colo205 |
| **Gastric Cancer** | | • Apoptosis, inhibition of cell proliferation (Lo, et al., 2005). | • Both 4g and 8g daily doses Gastric cancer AGS, SNU-668, HGC-27 |
| **Pancreatic Cancer** | | • Pancreatic cancer Apoptosis (Zang, et al., 2008). | • AsPC-1, BxPC-3, PANC-1 |
| **Prostate Cancer** | | • Apoptosis, dissipation of mitochondrial inner transmembrane potential (Mori, et al., 2006). | • Prostate cancer LNCaP, PC-3, DU-145 |

## *Other Inflammatory Diseases: Select Clinical Data*

Below are clinical data showing the use of capsaicin in the management of select inflammatory disease states.

| DISEASE | DURATION | BENEFIT | DOSAGE |
|---|---|---|---|
| **Arthritis** | **4 weeks** | • Pain relief was assessed using visual analog scales for pain and relief, a categorical pain scale. Most of the patients continued to receive concomitant arthritis medications.<br>• Significantly more relief of pain was reported by the capsaicin-treated patients than the placebo patients throughout the study; after 4 weeks of capsaicin treatment, RA and OA patients demonstrated mean reductions in pain of 57% and 33%, respectively.<br>• These reductions in pain were statistically significant compared with those reported with placebo.<br>• 80% of the capsaicin-treated patients experienced a reduction in pain after 2 weeks of treatment. Transient burning was felt at the sites of drug application by 23 of the 52 capsaicin-treated patients. It is concluded that capsaicin cream is a safe and effective treatment for arthritis (Deal, et al., 1991) | • Patients with *osteoarthritis* (OA) and 31 with *rheumatoid arthritis* (RA) received capsaicin (a substance P depletor) or placebo for 4 weeks.<br>• The patients were instructed to apply 0.025% capsaicin cream or its vehicle (placebo) to painful knees 4 times daily. |
| **Lower Back Pain** | **4 weeks** | • Low back mobility scores on Day 1 were better for the combination compared with all other treatments ($p < 0.044$); on Day 2-4, scores were better than for placebo and nicoboxil ($p < 0.003$).<br>• Patients assessed efficacy of the combination as greater than of the comparators ($p \leq 0.0129$). All treatments were tolerated well. No treatment-related serious adverse events were reported (Gaubitz, et al., 2016) | • This phase III randomized, double-blind, active- and placebo-controlled, multi-centre trial investigated efficacy, safety and tolerability of topical nicoboxil 2.5%/nonivamide 0.4% for treatment of acute non-specific low back pain [primary endpoint: *pain intensity* (PI) difference between pre-dose baseline and 8 hours after the first application]. |
| **Lower Back Pain** | **5 weeks** | • Low back mobility scores on Day 1 were better for the combination compared with all other treatments ($p < 0.044$); on Day 2-4, scores were better than for placebo and nicoboxil ($p < 0.003$).<br>• Patients assessed efficacy of the combination as greater than of the comparators ($p \leq 0.0129$). All treatments were tolerated well. No treatment-related serious adverse events were reported (Gaubitz, et al., 2016). | • This phase III randomized, double-blind, active- and placebo-controlled, multi-centre trial investigated efficacy, safety and tolerability of topical nicoboxil 2.5%/nonivamide 0.4% for treatment of acute non-specific low back pain [primary endpoint: *pain intensity* (PI) difference between pre-dose baseline and 8 h after the first application]. |

## *Other Inflammatory Diseases: Select Clinical Data (continued)*

| DISEASE | DURATION | BENEFIT | DOSAGE |
|---|---|---|---|
| **Cardio-vascular** | **4 weeks** | • After eating the chili-containing diet, the rate of oxidation (free radical damage to cholesterol and triglycerides) was significantly lower in both men and women than that seen after eating the bland diet.<br>• In addition, after eating the chili-spiced diet, women had a longer lag time before any damage to cholesterol was seen compared to the lag time seen after eating the bland diet. In men, the chili-diet also lowered resting heart rate and increased the amount of blood reaching the heart (Ahuj, et al., 2006). | • In a randomised cross-over study, 27 participants (thirteen men and fourteen women) ate "freshly chopped chili" blend (30g/day; 55% cayenne chili) and no chili (bland) diets, for 4 weeks each.<br>• Use of other spices, such as cinnamon, ginger, garlic and mustard, was restricted to minimum amounts. At the end of each dietary period serum samples were analysed for lipids, lipoproteins, TAS and Cu-induced lipoprotein oxidation. Lag time (before initiation of oxidation) and rate of oxidation (slope of propagation phase) were calculated. |
| **Diabetes** | **4 weeks** | • Significant increase in the regular consumption of chili may attenuate post-prandial hyperinsulinemia (Ahuja, et al., 2006). | • Metabolic effects of a chili-containing meal after the consumption of a bland diet and a chili-blend (30g/day; 55% cayenne chili) supplemented diet.<br>• Thirty-six subjects with a mean (+/-SD) age of 46 +/- 12 years and a body mass index (in kg/m2) of 26.3 +/- 4.6 participated in a randomized, crossover, intervention study with 2 dietary periods (chili and bland) of 4 weeks each. The postprandial effects of a *bland meal after a bland diet* (BAB), a *chili meal after a bland* diet (CAB), and a *chili meal after a chili-containing* diet (CAC) were evaluated. |
| **Neuro-pathic Pain** | **8 weeks** | • Neuropathic pain after spinal cord injury is common and often refractory to standard treatments and has demonstrated significant efficacy in human immunodeficiency virus-autonomic neuropathy. The patch defunctionalizes transient receptor potential vanilloid 1 receptors, impairing cutaneous nociceptors for a prolonged period (i.e., 8-12 weeks) with no systemic side effects.<br>• A retrospective review was conducted on the effects of the patch in 2 patients with spinal cord injury and neuropathic pain refractory. | • The capsaicin 8% patch is a FDA-approved treatment of neuropathic pain in postherpetic neuralgia to standard treatments. Two weeks after application, both patients reported complete pain relief. Average onset of relief of 4 days and average duration of relief of 197 days, requiring only 1-4 applications per year, paralleled findings reported in postherpetic neuralgia and human immunodeficiency virus-autonomic neuropathy trials. Upregulation of capsaicin-sensitive transient receptor potential vanilloid 1 receptors after spinal cord injury has been reported. The capsaicin 8% patch is a promising therapeutic agent for neuropathic pain in spinal cord injury. |
| **Psoriasis** | **6 weeks** | • Efficacy was based on a physician's global evaluation and a combined psoriasis severity score including scaling, thickness, erythema, and pruritus.<br>• Capsaicin-treated patients demonstrated significantly greater improvement in global evaluation after 4 weeks, as well as a significantly greater reduction in combined psoriasis severity scores.<br>• The most frequently reported side effect in both treatment groups was a transient burning sensation at application sites. (Ellis, et al., 1993. | • Patients applied capsaicin 0.025% cream (n = 98) or vehicle (n = 99) 4 times a day for 6 weeks in this double-blind study |

## Summary of Clinical Findings

Capsaicin is an antioxidant, anti-parasitic, anti-scorbutic, anti-scrofulous, anti-spasmodic, carminative, rubefacient, styptic, and vasodilator.

## Dosage Range

Dosage range of topical studied in clinical trials were cream: .025%; patch:8%

Other delivery routes studied were: 0-30g/day; 55% cayenne chili) and no chili (bland) diets.

## Contraindications

Nightshade sensitivity

## Toxicity

In rare cases, hypersensitivity reactions may occur (urticaria).

## Supplementation

Ointment or cream: Containing <0.05% capsaicinoids in an emulsion base, applied to affected areas. Tincture 1:10 (g/ml), 90% ethanol: applied locally or 1% in herbal formulation.

**WARNING:** Cayenne preparations may irritate the mucous membranes even in very low doses potentially causing painful burning sensations. Avoid direct contact with the eyes.

---

**SOURCE:** https://reference.medscape.com/drug/capzasin-p-zostrix-capsaicin-topical-999316

## Peppers (Capsaicin) Supplementation

Capsaicin is a powerful healing agent that can be used internally or externally. Start with small amounts to prevent an aggravation from excessive heat.

| TYPE OF SUPPLEMENT | ADULT DOSAGE |
| --- | --- |
| **Ointment or cream** | Containing <0.05% capsaicinoids in an emulsion base, applied to affected area. |
| **Tincture** | 1:10 (g/ml), 90% ethanol: applied locally or 1% in herbal formulation |

## Kitchen Medicine

Anyone can take advantage of the healing power of hot peppers by learning to cook with them. Once you find those that are to your taste, peppers can add tremendous flavor, and not just heat, to dishes. The next time you make healthy sautéed vegetables, add some chili peppers to turn up the spice volume. Add chili peppers to your favorite cornbread recipe to give it an extra kick. Add minced chili peppers to yogurt and use as a condiment or dip. Purée fresh chili peppers together with olive oil, garlic, coriander, peppermint, and caraway. If you would like, add your own favorite herbs and spices to this mixture to make your own version of *harissa,* a condiment popular in some Middle Eastern and North African countries. Keep a container of cayenne pepper on the table right next to the pepper mill, so you and your family can add a pinch of extra spice to any of your meals. Cayenne pepper and lemon juice make great compliments to cooked bitter greens such as collards, kale and mustard greens.

**WARNING:** Capsaicin can irritate or burn your eyes or hands. Chili oil can stick to the skin, so wash hands thoroughly after handling the peppers and be cautious about touching your face and eyes. Be aware that pepper dust from grinding dried peppers can irritate the throat and eyes. You can protect yourself by wearing a dust mask and goggles. Use gloves if you have any open cuts on your hands. If you find you can't take the heat, cool off with a glass of milk. A protein in milk called *casein* can help douse capsaicin's fire.

# Pepper Remedies

## Cayenne Salve

*This hot salve can be used topically on sore muscles and joints, bruises and on areas of nerve pain. When applied to lessen arthritic pain, it may take a week or two to see results. Stop if the target area becomes aggravated.*

YIELD: 4 OZ. (12 APPLICATIONS)

### INGREDIENTS

½ cup olive oil
2 tablespoons ground cayenne pepper
½ oz. beeswax

### METHOD

1. Combine the cayenne and olive oil in a double boiler or a small pan.
2. Heat the oil and cayenne until warm, turn off the heat, and let it sit (warmly) for about 20 minutes, then turn the heat on again.
3. Repeat this process for a couple of hours or up to 24 hours if desired.
4. Once the cayenne and olive oil have been infused, strain off the powder through a cheesecloth.
5. Reserve the infused oil in a measuring cup or small pitcher.
6. Heat the beeswax until it is melted. Pour into the infused oil and stir until the beeswax and oil are thoroughly combined.
7. Immediately pour this mixture into small jars or tins. Let it cool until solid. Cover and label it.

### CAUTION!

When cayenne comes in contact with your mucosal membranes or eyes, it will burn. Be sure to wash your hands thoroughly after touching cayenne or use gloves to apply the salve to the desired area. If you are using the cayenne salve as an herbal pain relief on your hands, consider applying it at night and then sleeping with gloves on.

**SOURCE:** Adapted from *Learning Herbs,* https://learningherbs.com/remedies-recipes/herbal-pain-relief

# Pepper Beverages

## Hot Spicy Wake Up Tea

*Cayenne tea aids blood flow to the brain and periphery. The combination of ginger, Tulsi, and turmeric make it a remarkable beverage. Reduce the amount of the pepper if the tea is too* caliente *for you.*

SERVES 1

### INGREDIENTS

8-12 oz. filtered water
1/4 teaspoon ground cayenne pepper
1/4 teaspoon Tulsi holy basil tea or powder (or substitute mint or green tea)
1/4 teaspoon ground ginger
1/4 teaspoon ground turmeric
1/4 teaspoon ground ashwagandha root (optional)
Juice of 1/2 lemon
1/2 teaspoon raw honey

### METHOD

1. Heat the water in a small pot, add cayenne, tea of your choice, ginger, turmeric and ashwagandha if using.
2. Stir the mixture until the cayenne has completely dissolved and cover to steep for up to 10 minutes.
3. Strain into a mug and add fresh lemon juice and raw honey.

NOTE: *This tea can also be made with just the cayenne pepper, adding lemon or raw honey to enhance the flavor.*

**CAUTION:** May cause a burning sensation at the back of the throat, but sipping slowly should help alleviate that burning and greatly increase your enjoyment of your tea.

## Paprika Spice Smoothie

*This is a great way to spice up your smoothie. Paprika is milder than cayenne pepper. Adjust the dose to your taste.*

SERVES 2

### INGREDIENTS

1 medium apple
4 oz. celery
4 oz. dandelion greens
1-inch (2.5 cm) fresh ginger
1-inch (2.5 cm) fresh turmeric
1 tablespoon flax seeds
1 scoop protein powder (optional)
6 oz. kefir
1 pinch paprika

### METHOD

1. Wash all of the ingredients. Peel the skin off of the ginger and turmeric.
2. Chop the apple, celery, dandelion greens, ginger and fresh turmeric.
3. In a blender, place a few ice cubes (optional) at the bottom, add all the ingredients and blend until smooth.

## Pepper Beverages (continued)

### Bangalore Buttermilk

*This is a traditional Ayurvedic inspiration.*

SERVES 2

**INGREDIENTS**

½ to 1 small Indian green chili (per taste and tolerance)
½ to 1-inch (1.27-2.5 cm) fresh ginger
½ small Indian green chili, seeded
1 cup buttermilk
1 sprig fresh curry leaves (or 1 teaspoon dried mint)
Sea salt to taste
Water as needed

**METHOD**

1. Chop chili and ginger.
2. Add all the ingredients into a blender and blend.
3. Pour into glasses and enjoy.

## Pepper Entrees

### India Rice n' Spice Pilaf

*Njavara is a brown rice native to the state of Kerala, India. Classic and modern Ayurvedic healers recommend it for people in a weakened or disease state.*

SERVES 2-4

**INGREDIENTS**

2 tablespoons extra-virgin coconut oil
½ teaspoon mustard seeds
2 tablespoons black sesame seeds
2 teaspoons cumin seeds
¼ teaspoon fenugreek seeds
2 cups tomatoes
½ teaspoon ground turmeric
½ teaspoon black pepper
½ teaspoon ground coriander
2 small red chilis, seeded and diced
½ teaspoon chili powder
Sea salt to taste
1 cup njavara rice, cooked (substitute wild rice or brown rice if not available)

**METHOD**

1. Melt the coconut oil in a medium pot and add the mustard seeds, stirring until they start to pop.
2. Add black sesame seeds, cumin, fenugreek and stir for another 30 seconds or until fragrant.
3. Add the tomatoes, turmeric, coriander, chilis and sea salt. Cook on medium-low for 5-10 minutes.
4. Fold in the rice. Taste and adjust seasonings before serving.

## Stuffed Poblano Peppers

*This healthy, heartwarming version of Mexican cuisine is vegetarian and gluten-free.*

SERVES 4

### INGREDIENTS

2 teaspoons olive oil
2 large poblano peppers
1 medium sweet potato, diced
½ red onion
¾ cup mushrooms, sliced
1 teaspoon cumin powder
1 cup soft goat cheese, cubed
2 tomatoes, sliced, or 1 cup cherry tomatoes, halved
1 avocado, cubed
1 tablespoon cilantro, roughly chopped
Salt and pepper
Lime or lemon juice

### METHOD

1. Turn broiler on high and drizzle each poblano with a teaspoon of oil.
2. Broil for 10-12 minutes or until poblanos begin to blacken and blister. Remove and set aside to cool.
3. Reduce the oven to 400°F (204°C) and roast the sweet potatoes on a parchment-lined baking sheet for 15-20 minutes.
4. While the vegetables are roasting, heat remaining oil in a small pan and sauté onions and mushrooms for a few minutes.
5. Add the tomatoes and cook for about 5 minutes. Add cumin and corn.
6. Once the poblanos are cool enough to touch, scrape the blackened skin off as best you can. Cut a slit half way through each from the top to bottom, being careful not to remove the stem. Using a paring knife, carefully remove the core, then use a spoon to scoop out remaining seeds. Sprinkle with salt and pepper.
7. Stuff each pepper with cooked sweet potatoes, cheese cubes and tomatoes. Return to oven for 10 minutes and serve warm.
8. Garnish with avocado, cilantro, a squeeze of lime or lemon juice. Serve with tomato sauce and enjoy!

NOTE: *For a vegan cheese substitute, blend 1 cup ground cashews with ¼ cup water.*

## Crema de Avocado

*This guacamole-like sauce is lovely topping for "Stuffed Poblano Peppers." Terrific creamy dressings for salads as well.*

YIELD: 1½ CUPS, 4 SERVINGS

### INGREDIENTS

1 ripe avocado, peeled and seed taken out
½ cup cilantro leaves
⅔ cup water
½ teaspoon salt
1 teaspoon coriander powder
⅓ cup lemon juice
2 garlic cloves, peeled
2 teaspoons maple syrup
Cracked pepper to taste

### METHOD

1. Put all the ingredients in a blender and blend until smooth.
2. Adjust thickness by adding water, 1 tablespoon at a time.
3. Adjust taste with more lemon, salt and pepper.

*Pepper Entrees (continued)*

# Sargent Pepper's Healthy Hearts Club Plan

*Quinoa is a seed that is rich in protein and fiber. This recipe is vegan and gluten-free.*

SERVES 2

### INGREDIENTS

2 large bell peppers
2 tablespoons olive oil, divided
¼ cup dry quinoa, rinsed
½ cup water or broth
½ medium onion, diced
½ cup mushrooms, chopped
2 cloves garlic, minced
½ tablespoon tomato paste
1½ teaspoons chili powder
½ teaspoon smoked paprika
¼ teaspoon cinnamon
¾ teaspoons cumin
½ teaspoon dried oregano
½ teaspoon sea salt
Fresh cracked pepper to taste
1 cup low sodium vegetable broth
2 cups kale or other leafy green, minced

### METHOD

1. Preheat the oven to 400°F (204°C).
2. Wash and cut each pepper in half. If the pepper has a stem, try to leave it intact. Just carefully cut it down the middle, leaving a piece on each half (this helps the pepper keep its shape). Remove membranes and seeds.
3. Using half of the oil, brush inside each pepper, and sprinkle with salt and pepper. Place cut-side up on a large rimmed baking sheet (lined with parchment paper) Roast until peppers are slightly tender, about 15 minutes. Remove from the oven and set aside.
4. While the peppers are cooking, start making the stuffing. In a medium pot, add the quinoa to ½ cup of low-boiling water or broth adding a pinch of salt. Cover and cook until the liquid is gone and quinoa is fluffy. This takes about 10-15 minutes. Remove from heat and fluff with a fork. Set aside.
5. Heat remaining oil in a large skillet, over medium heat. Add onion and sauté until translucent, about 3-5 minutes.
6. Add mushrooms and sauté until they are softened, about 4-6 minutes.
7. Add the garlic, tomato paste, and spices, cook for 1-2 minutes. Stir often.
8. Add the vegetable broth and greens; simmer for 2-4 minutes until liquid is absorbed.

9. Add cooked quinoa to the vegetable mix and remove from heat.
10. Divide mixture evenly among pepper halves, gently packing it down to fully fill them.
11. Place the peppers upright on a large rimmed baking sheet (lined with parchment paper). Bake until quinoa is lightly browned and crispy on top, about 10 minutes.

### TOPPING SUGGESTIONS

Add vegan sour cream, fresh-cut cilantro, squeeze of lime, hot sauce, salsa, avocado or diced red onion.

# Pepper Salad and Dressing

## Leaning Salad of Lentils

*An easy way to prepare a vegetable protein salad.*

SERVES 4

### INGREDIENTS

2 cups lentils or split green peas, cooked or sprouted
2 cups red cabbage, shredded
1 cup zucchini, spiraled or cubed
2 tablespoons fresh lemon juice
2 tablespoons extra-virgin olive oil
2 tablespoons raw honey
1 sprig curry leaves
1 pinch black pepper
Sea salt to taste

### METHOD

1. In a bowl combine the cooked or sprouted lentils, red cabbage, and zucchini.
2. For the dressing combine lemon juice, curry leaves, black pepper and sea salt.
3. Slowly whisk in olive oil until combined.
4. Add dressing to vegetables and toss.

## Paprika Vinaigrette

*Anti-bacterial and anti-inflammatory, adding turmeric and paprika to salad dressings or sauces provides a tangy flavor and bright orange color.*

SERVES 4

### INGREDIENTS

1 teaspoon ground turmeric
½ teaspoon ground paprika
¼ cup vinegar
1 tablespoon maple syrup
1-2 cloves garlic, minced
1 tablespoon dried green herbs (oregano, parsley)
1 tablespoon chia seeds
½ teaspoon salt
½ cup extra-virgin olive oil

### METHOD

1. Mix all the ingredients except olive oil in a blender. With the motor on low, slowly add the oil through the opening in the top. Cover and increase speed to blend until well combined.
2. Store in a glass container and refrigerate until ready to serve.

## How to Grow Peppers

Peppers are easy to grow as long as you give them enough sun, heat, and moisture.

Both sweet and hot peppers are native to Central and South America. Of all the domesticated pepper species, gardeners usually encounter two: *Capsicum annuum* and *Capsicum chinense*.

### When and How to Start Indoors

Peppers germinate and grow best when soil temperatures are above 75°F (24°C). In most regions of the country, peppers should be started indoors and then transplanted outdoors as the weather warms. Sow peppers indoors 6-8 weeks before transplanting. Plant seeds at a depth of ¼-inch (.63 cm) and make sure the soil remains warm throughout the germination period.

### Time to Germination

14-18 days

### When to Transplant

Move pepper seedlings outdoors 4-6 weeks after the last frost, being sure they are hardened off (gradually introduced to the direct sunlight, dry air, and cold nights).

### Spacing Requirements

Plant seedlings 12-24 inches (30-60 cm) apart in sunny, well draining soil.

### Special Considerations

Most sweet peppers mature in 60-90 days; hot peppers can take up to 150 days.

### Common Pests and Diseases

Peppers can be susceptible to diseases such as bacterial spot, anthracnose, blossom end rot, sunscald, and *pepper mild mottle virus* (PMMoV). Prevent disease by rotating crops regularly and not over-crowding plants.

### When and How to Harvest

Maturity in peppers is indicated by a color change in the fruit. Green peppers are harvested as immature fruits. Most varieties will ripen to yellow, orange, red, brown, or purple when they are fully ripe. Harvest with scissors or pruning shears.

### Eating

When stored at room temperature, peppers have a shelf life of 1-2 weeks. Preserved peppers, when pickled peppers are one of the most versatile culinary crops grown in the home garden. They can be eaten

## *How to Grow Peppers (continued)*

fresh, fried, roasted, stewed, stir fried, pickled, as well as puréed into soups, dips, and pestos. Peppers, especially thin fleshed varieties, can be braided into a decorative ristra, air dried, and then crushed to make pepper flakes, chili powder, or paprika.

### Storing

Pepper preserved in oil can last for many months. Dried peppers will keep almost indefinitely.

### How to Save Pepper Seeds

When saving seeds from peppers, remember that different species occasionally cross-pollinate so be sure to isolate varieties as recommended.

### Life Cycle

Pepper is an annual crop. It will complete its full life cycle — including germination, reproduction, and death — in one growing season.

### Recommended Isolation Distance

When saving seeds from peppers, separate varieties by 300-1,600 feet or hand pollinate several fruits using blossom bags.

### Recommended Population Sizes

A single pepper plant can produce viable seeds. However, to maintain a variety's diversity over time, save seeds from 5-20 pepper plants.

### Assessing Seed Maturity

Fruits are mature when they begin to soften. If frost threatens before the peppers mature, pull the entire plant and hang in a cool, dry location until they are mature.

### Harvesting

Harvest fruits up to 2 weeks past edible stage. Cut around the top of the pepper and use the stem as a handle to twist out the core. Use the tip of a knife to flick out the seeds; rinse and dry seeds. Be careful when processing the fruits of hot peppers as the oils and vapors of capsaicin can cause eye, skin, and respiratory irritation. Work in a well-ventilated area and take care to wear protective gloves and a respirator or dust mask to prevent irritation. Avoid touching your eyes or nose as you work. If you handle hot peppers bare-handed, immediately scrub hands with soap and warm water.

### Cleaning And Processing

Allow seeds to air-dry on newsprint, coffee filters, or screens for several days. When a test seed can be cleanly snapped in half, seeds are dry enough for storage.

### Storage And Viability

Store seeds in a cool, dry place for up to 3 years.

### How to Make Ground Pepper

When you are ready to use them, follow these directions:

1. Remove the tops and place peppers on a dehydration tray.
2. Dehydrate for 7-8 hours in a dehydrator or use the lowest possible setting in your oven.
3. Once complete, take the chilies including seeds and grind in a grinder, a little at a time.
4. Store in a glass jar away from sunlight.
5. Use gloves or wash your hands with soap and water after finishing.

CHAPTER EIGHT

# Oregano

*(Oreganum vulgare)*

**Oregano** is a powerful and versatile spice that has been used for thousands of years as a medicine and culinary herb. There are many varieties of oregano that grow well in backyard gardens and in kitchen window boxes. Like most herbs and spices, the aromatic oils of the plant are what give them their distinctive flavor, aroma and health benefits. Spices without smell or flavor are oxidized, dissipated, and of little value.

The essential oils and phenolic compounds in oregano have exhibited numerous health benefits for a wide variety of mental and physical ailments. I have found oregano to be a digestive tonic, liver/gallbladder bile mover and microbiome harmonizer. Oregano oil has been used as an anti-fungal agent. Taken as oregano oil caps, it will cause nausea or gastric distress if the dose is too high. I prefer to suggest oregano as a tea, in combination with ginger, Tulsi and turmeric as a milder way to bring its flavor and health properties to the body.

Oregano is also great in vegetable and bone broths, soups, stews and sauces, such as a mixed green pesto. It is a staple in Mediterranean and Latin cooking, friendly to all tomato-based dishes. Fresh oregano is more delicate than its dried counterpart.

Occasionally, I chew a few sprigs of oregano to clear my mind and sharpen my senses, or just sniff it and remember fun times and great eating in Tuscany, Italy and at Punta Serena retreat center near Manzanilla, Mexico.

*Bundles of fresh oregano at the market.*

*Cutting fresh oregano leaves for cooking.*

*Fresh oregano bundled for drying.*

## Background and Uses

Oregano, *Oreganum vulgare,* is a flowering member of the mint family *(Lamiaceae)*, native to Western and Southwestern Eurasia and the Mediterranean region. It was first used by the Greeks who considered it a gift from the goddess Aphrodite. The name is derived from the Greek words "oros" meaning mountain and "ganos" meaning joy, or "joy of the mountains" because it grows wild there. Oregano is a culinary and medicinal herb, used for the flavor of its leaves, which can be more potent when dried than fresh. It has an aromatic, warm, and slightly bitter taste, which can vary in intensity. Good-quality oregano may be strong enough almost to numb the tongue, but varieties adapted to colder climates may have a more muted flavor. Ancient Greeks used it as a medicine and then the Romans adopted it as a culinary herb. To this day it remains a staple of Italian-American cuisine.

## Plant Specifics

Oregano is related to the herb marjoram, and sometimes is referred to as wild marjoram. The herb has pinkish purple flowers and tiny olive-colored, spade-shaped leaves. It is a perennial in the Mediterranean but can be grown as an annual in colder climates, as it often does not survive the winter. Oregano is planted in early spring, the plants being spaced 12 inches (30 cm) apart in fairly dry soil, with full sun. Oregano prefers a hot, relatively dry climate, but does well in cooler climates with a soil pH of 6.0-8.0. It will grow from 8-32 inches (20-80 cm) tall.

Many subspecies and strains of oregano have been developed by humans over centuries for their unique flavors or other characteristics. Tastes range from spicy or astringent to more complicated and sweeter. Simple oregano sold in garden stores as *Oreganum vulgare* may have a bland taste and larger, less-dense leaves, and is not considered the best for culinary use, with a taste less remarkable and pungent. It can pollinate other more sophisticated strains, but the offspring are rarely better in quality.

The related species, *Oreganum onites* (Greece, Turkey) and *O. syriacum* (West Asia), have similar flavors. A closely related plant is marjoram from Turkey, which differs significantly in taste. Some varieties show a flavor intermediate between oregano and marjoram.

## Active Constituents

The oregano plant has tiny hair-like glands on its surface called trichomes. When the sun hits them they synthesize and produce essential oils and phenols to protect the plant from oxidation during periods of intense heat and sunlight. The main phenolic compounds present in oregano are flavonoids and phenolic acids which exhibit antioxidant, anti-inflammatory and anti-cancer properties. Essential oils in oregano have also exhibited these properties but are better known for their anti-microbial, anti-fungal and anti-viral properties. The main constituents of these essential oils are monoterpenoids and monoterpenes, with the primary ones being carvacrol and thymol ranging to over 80%. Some studies suggest that drying the plant, especially if using higher heat and longer drying times has a negative effect on these volatile oils. The compounds are found to be at their highest levels at the end of the growing season.

## Traditional Medicine

Oregano has been traditionally used in folk medicine to alleviate conditions such as asthma, bronchitis, coughs, diarrhea, indigestion, stomach ache, menstrual disorders, general infections, inflammation-related illnesses and diabetes (Gutiérrez E, et al., 2017).

## Uses in Modern Medicine

The potential health benefits of oregano can be attributed to its phytochemical content. *Flavonoids* (FA) and *phenolic acids* (PA) are among the most abundant and most studied phytochemicals in oregano species. Epidemiological, in vitro and in vivo, experiments have related long-term consumption of dietary FL and PA with a decreased risk of incidence of chronic diseases. The flavonoids and phenolic compounds from oregano have great potential to be anti-oxidant, anti-bacterial, anti-inflammatory, anti-cancer, and supportive of arthritis and atherosclerosis (Gutiérrez E, et al., 2017).

## *Health Benefits of Oregano*

### Anti-bacterial

The volatile oils in this spice have been shown to inhibit the growth of bacteria, including *Pseudomonas aeruginosa* and *Staphylococcus aureus*. In Mexico, researchers have compared oregano to tinidazol, a commonly used prescription drug to treat infection from the amoeba Giardia lamblia. These researchers found oregano to be more effective against Giardia than the commonly used prescription drug.

### Anti-inflammatory

Studies of oregano essential oil suggest it may have wound healing properties and is used in numerous skin care products.

### Antioxidant

Oregano contains numerous phytonutrients — including thymol and rosmarinic acid — that have also been shown to function as potent antioxidants that can prevent oxygen-based damage to cell structures throughout the body. In laboratory studies, oregano has demonstrated stronger antioxidant capacity than either of the two synthetic antioxidants commonly added to processed food — *butylated hydroxytoluene* (BHT) and *butylated bydroxyanisole* (BHA). Additionally, on a per gram fresh weight basis, oregano has demonstrated 42 times more antioxidant activity than apples, 30 times more than potatoes, 12 times more than oranges and 4 times more than blueberries.

Useful in upper respiratory infections according to the Lung Institute, carvacrol and rosmarinic acid are natural decongestants and antihistamines.

### Nutrient-Dense

The *World's Healthiest Foods* (whfoods.com) ranking system qualified oregano as a good source of fiber. Fiber works in the body to bind to bile salts and cancer-causing toxins in the colon and remove them from the body. This forces the body to break down cholesterol to make more bile salts. These are just some of the reasons that diets high in fiber have been shown to lower high cholesterol levels and reduce the risk of colon cancer. Oregano also emerged from our food ranking system as a bountiful source of many nutrients. It qualified within our system as an excellent source of vitamin K, a very good source of manganese, and a good source of iron and calcium (Bernhardt, 2016).

### Anti-cancer

Research published in the journal *PLOS ONE* in 2013 suggests that oregano exhibits anticancer activity. The scientists concluded that *Oreganum majorana* could help prevent and treat breast cancer by slowing or preventing its progression.

## *Cancer: Select Clinical Data*

Below are data from clinical trials documenting the healing power of oregano in cancer therapy..

| DISEASE | DURATION | BENEFIT | DOSAGE |
|---|---|---|---|
| **Breast Cancer** | **10 hours** | • Oreganum majorana exhibits anti-cancer activity by promoting cell cycle arrest and apoptosis of the metastatic MDA-MB-231 breast cancer cell line.<br>• Findings suggest *Oreganum majorana* as a promising chemo-preventive and therapeutic candidate that can modulate breast cancer growth and metastasis. (Dhaheri, et al., 2013). | • Human breast cancer cells MDA-MB-231 and MDA-MB-231-GFP were used |
| **Colon Cancer** | | • The main objective of this study was to evaluate the cytotoxic activity of *flavonoid-enriched extracts* (FEE) from the leaves of *wild* (WT), *in vitro* (IN), and *ex vitro* (EX) grown oregano plants in colon cancer cells HT-29 and the non-cancer cells CCD-18Co.<br>• Cell proliferation of HT-29 cells was reduced by 50% (García-Pérez, et al., 2011). | • Concentrations of 4.01, 1.32, and 4.84 mg of *gallic acid equivalents* (GAE)/L, respectively |
| **Brain Cancer** | | • Hesperetin isolated from *Oreganum majorana* has shown better antiproliferative activity than 5-fluorouracil against<br>• Rattus norvegicus brain glioma (C6) and HeLa cells (Erenler, et al., 2016). | • Brain glioma (C6) and HeLa cells |
| **Cervical Cancer** | | • Acetone extracts of selected plant species were evaluated for their in vitro cytotoxicity against noncancerous monkey cells.<br>• The plants studied were *Oreganum vulgare L.* (Oregano), *Rosmarinus officinalis L.* (Upright and ground cover rosemary), *Lavandula spica L.* (Lavender), *Laurus nobilis L.* (Bay leaf), *Thymus vulgaris L.* (Thyme), *Lavandula x intermedia L.* (Margaret Roberts Lavender), *Petroselinum crispum Mill.* (Curly leaved parsley), *Foeniculum vulgare Mill.* (Fennel), and *Capsicum annuum L.* (Kolda, et al., 2015). | • African green monkey kidney (Vero) cell line and an adenocarcinoma cervical cancer (HeLa) cell line. |
| **Liver/Breast/ Colorectal Cancer** | **48 hours** | • Thirteen edible plants from Southern Italy were evaluated for their in vitro antioxidant and anti-proliferative activity on 3 human cancer cell lines: breast cancer MCF-7, hepatic cancer HepG2 and colorectal cancer LoVo.<br>• 64% of inhibition against hepatic cancer cells were observed (HepG2) and LoVo. (Marrelii, et al., 2015). | • Breast cancer MCF-7, hepatic cancer HepG2 and colorectal cancer LoVo |

## Other Inflammatory Diseases: Select Clinical Data

While oregano has demonstrated a wide variety of benefits in the lab, it needs to be studied in human trials. Below are clinical trial data for its benefits in the treatment of select inflammatory disease states.

| DISEASE | DURATION | BENEFIT | DOSAGE |
|---|---|---|---|
| **Anti-microbial** | | • The main constituents of *O. dictamnus* essential oil identified by GCMS analysis were carvacrol oil and its main components were effective against *Staphylococcus aureus, Staphylococcus epidermidis, Escherichia coli, Listeria monocytogenes, Salmonella Enteritidis, Salmonella typhimurium, Saccharomyces cerevisiae,* and *Aspergillus niger* (Mitropolo, et al., 2014). | |
| **Anti-inflammatory** | | • These results suggest that carvacrol acts on different pharmacological targets, probably interfering in the release and/or synthesis of inflammatory mediators, such as the prostanoids, and thus favoring the healing process for gastric ulcers (Silva, et al., 2012). | • 50 mg/kg<br>• 100 mg/kg)<br>• Ruthenium red (3 mg/kg) |
| **Antiviral** | **15 minutes** | • This study provides novel findings on the antiviral properties of oregano oil and carvacrol against MNV and demonstrates the potential of carvacrol as a natural food and surface (fomite) sanitizer to control human norovirus. (Gilling, et al., 2014) | |

## Summary of Clinical Findings

The underlying actions and clinical effects of oregano are (1) anti-inflammatory, (2) anti-microbial, (3) anti-oxidant, and (4) anti-cancer properties. The majority of studies taking place in laboratory settings. Human trials need to be conducted to demonstrate health benefits and dosing.

## Dosage Range

In a small study, 200 mg/day emulsified *O. vulgare* oil was administered for 6 weeks

## Contraindications

Oregano can cause reactions to those allergic to plants in the Lamiaceae family. People on blood thinners and diabetic medications should consult their medical professionals before taking medicinal quantities.

## Toxicity

There is no clinical evidence to support specific therapeutic doses of oregano; however, due to its wide use in foods, it has been granted *Generally Recognized as Safe* (GRAS) status in the United States by the *Food and Drug Administration* (FDA).

## Supplementation

When taking oregano oil internally, it should always be diluted with water or mixed with coconut oil or olive oil. For fungal (athlete's foot) infection, apply the oil externally. To prevent negative skin reactions from oregano application, it's recommended that a small patch test be conducted first and always use a carrier oil. The dried herb oregano is typically fine for pregnant women, but generally speaking, it's not considered safe to use oregano oil in larger quantities during pregnancy. If side effects such as nausea, dizziness or an allergic reaction are ever experienced then stop using oregano oil right away and consider seeing a medical professional.

## *Supplementation: Oregano (Oregano vulgare)*

Oregano can be used effectively as a supplement, as well as a culinary spice. Forms and dosage are listed below.

| TYPE OF SUPPLEMENT | ADULT DOSAGE | CHILD/ADOLESCENT |
|---|---|---|
| **Dried** | 15g in tea with 250 ml of water | 7.5 grams |
| **Emulsified Oil** | 600 mg per twice daily | 100 mg per day |
| **Oil** | Dilute 3 drops twice daily up with carrier such as water, extra-virgin coconut/olive oil to up to 10 days only | Dilute 1.5 drops twice daily up with carrier such as water, extra-virgin coconut/olive oil to 10 days |

**SOURCE:** www.draxe.com/essential-oils/oregano-oil-benefits)

## *Kitchen Medicine*

Whether cooking with fresh or dried oregano, it is important to crush or chop the herbs to release their essential oils. Because of its bold, aromatic flavor it pairs well with bold tomato-based recipes like pizza and pasta but it is also used in marinades, vinaigrettes, stews and soups with meats, fish, vegetables, grains and beans. It also complements other strong flavors such as garlic, onions, basil, parsley, and thyme.

# Oregano Soup

## Minestra di Ceci (Chickpea Soup)

*Minestra di Ceci (chickpea soup) is a classic Italian comfort food, prepared with chickpeas as a primary protein ingredient.*

SERVES 4-6

**INGREDIENTS**

1½ cups dried chickpeas (or 2 15 oz. cans)
2 tablespoons extra-virgin olive oil
1 cup yellow onions, diced small
1 cup carrots, diced small
1 cup celery, diced small
8-10 cups vegetable stock
2 cups Swiss chard, roughly chopped
1 tablespoon fresh oregano, minced (or 1 teaspoon dried)
1 tablespoon fresh rosemary, minced (or 1 teaspoon dried)
1 tablespoon fresh parsley, minced (or 1 teaspoon dried)
1 teaspoon sea salt
½ teaspoon black pepper
Freshly grated parmesan cheese (optional)

**METHOD**

1. Rinse the dried chickpeas and soak in filtered water overnight or for at least 7 hours.
2. Strain the chickpeas, rinsing well and set aside.
3. In a large pot, heat the olive oil to medium, add the onions and sauté until translucent.
4. Add the carrots and celery and sauté for a few minutes to soften.
5. Stir in the garlic, tomatoes and tomato paste, breaking up the tomatoes with your spoon.
6. Add the strained chickpeas along with vegetable stock. Cover and simmer on low for 45 minutes.
7. Stir in the Swiss chard and oregano, rosemary and parsley.
8. Cook for another 10 minutes until chickpeas and Swiss chard are softened.
9. Add the sea salt and pepper. Taste and adjust seasonings.
10. Garnish with freshly grated parmesan.

NOTE: *You can substitute chickpeas for other beans or brown lentils*

**SOURCE:** https://en.wikipedia.org/wiki/List_of_Italian_soups

# Oregano Beverage

## Old and in the Way Tea

*Oregano has a peppery, slightly bitter taste and is valued more for its potential health benefits than its flavor. Traditionally, it has been used for health issues such as, sore throat, cough, nausea, digestive problems, irritable bowel syndrome, bloating and edema.*

SERVES 1

**INGREDIENTS**

1 cup of filtered water
2 tablespoons fresh oregano (or 2 teaspoons dried)
1 teaspoon honey (optional)

**METHOD**

1. Bring one cup of water to a boil.
2. Pour the boiling water over oregano (in a tea strainer if using dried).
3. Let the mixture steep for at least 4 minutes. Remove oregano.
4. Stir in with honey, if using.

# Oregano Sauces

## Oh My Goodness, Pesto

*Pesto is traditionally made from fresh basil. Here we combine oregano, parsley and basil with nuts and seeds.*

SERVES 4-6

**INGREDIENTS**

1 cup fresh oregano
1 cup fresh parsley
1 cup fresh basil
¾ cup parmesan cheese
½ cup almonds
½ cup pine nuts
½ cup walnuts
2-3 cloves garlic
¾ teaspoon sea salt
½ teaspoon black pepper
¾ cup extra-virgin olive oil

**METHOD**

1. Combine all the ingredients except oil in a high speed blender.
2. With the motor on the lowest setting, slowly pour the oil in from the top.
3. Turn the motor off to push the larger bits down toward the blade and blend again.
4. Add more oil (or water) if needed to achieve a smooth consistency.

NOTE: *Feel free to experiment with other nuts, seeds and greens. Serve with crackers, bread, pasta, in soups, sauces, with fish or meat.*

## Marinara Sauce

*Marinara is the name for traditional Italian tomato sauce. This tasty version can be made easily at home and added to perk up pasta, root vegetables, and main dishes.*

SERVES 4

**INGREDIENTS**

12 fresh Roma tomatoes
(or 28 oz. can whole tomatoes)
Bowl of ice cubes and water
(if using fresh tomatoes)
2 tablespoons extra-virgin olive oil
1 cup onions, diced small
2-4 cloves garlic, minced
4 tablespoons tomato paste stirred into
½ cup filtered water or broth
2 tablespoons fresh oregano
(or 2 teaspoons dried)
2 tablespoons fresh rosemary
(or 2 teaspoons dried)
2 tablespoons fresh parsley
(or 2 teaspoons dried)
2 tablespoons fresh basil (or 2 teaspoons dried)
1 teaspoon sea salt
½ teaspoon ground pepper

**METHOD**

1. If using fresh tomatoes, put a medium pot of water on the stove and bring to a boil. With a paring knife, cut an X at the bottom of each tomato, just deep enough to pierce the skin. When the water reaches a full boil, drop the tomatoes in and let them float around for a minute or two until you see the skins at the bottom of the tomato start to pull away.
2. Remove tomatoes with a slotted spoon and place in the bowl of ice water. When tomatoes are cool enough to handle peel off the skins and set aside. (Omit Steps 1 and 2 if using canned tomatoes.)
3. In a medium pot, heat the oil, add the onions and sauté until translucent.
4. Add the garlic and sauté for 30 seconds to a minute, taking care not to burn it.
5. Stir in tomato paste with liquid and peeled tomatoes, breaking them up with a spoon.
6. Add the parsley, oregano, rosemary, basil, salt and pepper.
7. Cover and simmer on low for 30 minutes, or until the tomatoes completely break down.
8. Taste and adjust seasonings.

# Oregano Entrees

## Pasta Fit for a Queen

*This delicious pasta dish can be served on its own or with a savory pesto or marinara sauce.*

SERVES 4

### INGREDIENTS

8 oz. quinoa pasta
3 tablespoons extra-virgin olive oil, divided
1 cup onion, diced small
2 cloves garlic, minced
½ cup, sliced
1 cup kale, chopped
½ cup cherry tomatoes, halved
½ teaspoon sea salt
¼ teaspoon black pepper
1 tablespoon, plus ½ teaspoon sea salt
2 tablespoons fresh parsley, minced
2 tablespoons fresh oregano, minced
Freshly grated parmesan cheese

### METHOD

1. Set a large pot of water on the stove and bring to a boil adding a tablespoon (or more) of sea salt. Once the water boils, add the pasta and cook according to package directions.
2. Drain pasta in a colander and set aside in a bowl. Stir in a tablespoon of olive oil to prevent sticking.
3. While the pasta cooks, heat the remaining oil in a skillet over medium heat, add the onion and sauté until translucent.
4. Stir in the mushrooms and lightly brown on all sides.
5. Add the kale and cherry tomatoes and heat until they begin to wilt.
6. Stir in half the fresh parsley and oregano along with the garlic, sea salt and black pepper and stir to combine. Taste and adjust seasonings.
7. Combine sauteéd vegetables with pasta, and either sauce if using.
8. Garnish with remaining fresh herbs and cheese.

## *Oregano Entrees (continued)*

# *Herbed Garlic Bread*

*Who doesn't love hot garlic bread? This one goes great with soups, salads or with a sandwich filling in between.*

SERVES 4-6

**INGREDIENTS**

½ cup flat leaf parsley, minced
½ teaspoon dried oregano
½ teaspoon dried thyme
2 medium cloves garlic, minced
¼ cup extra-virgin olive oil
½ teaspoon sea salt
¼ teaspoon black pepper
1 teaspoon fresh lemon juice
¼ teaspoon paprika
¼ teaspoon red pepper flakes (optional)
12-inch (30 cm) loaf multi-grain bread

**METHOD**

1. Whisk all the ingredients together: parsley, oregano, thyme, garlic, oil, salt, black pepper, lemon juice, paprika, red pepper.
2. Slice the multigrain loaf with a bread knife into ¾-inch (2 cm) slices.
3. Using a brush, apply the herb mixture on each slice.
4. Put loaf back together and wrap in parchment paper and then foil.
5. Preheat oven to 350°F (176°C). Place wrapped loaf in the oven for 10-12 minutes.
6. Serve warm.

**SOURCE:** Modified from https://www.marthastewart.com/326565/herbed-garlic-bread

# *Oven Joy Roasted Vegetables*

*Roasting root vegetables with oregano, rosemary, salt, garlic and olive oil is comfort food your family will love.*

SERVES 3-4

**INGREDIENTS**

3 red potatoes
3 purple potatoes
3 turnips
3 carrots
3 parsnips
1 sweet potato
3 golden beets
1 large onion, sliced
6-8 cloves garlic
2 tablespoons oregano fresh (or 1 teaspoon dried)
2 tablespoons rosemary fresh (or 1 teaspoon dried)
2 tablespoons parsley (or 1 teaspoon dried)
1 teaspoon black pepper
1 teaspoon paprika
½ teaspoon red pepper flakes
1 tablespoon sea salt
½ cup extra-virgin olive oil

**METHOD**

1. Preheat the oven to 425°F (218°C).
2. Using a vegetable brush, scrub the red and purple potatoes, turnips, carrots, parsnips and sweet potato but don't peel them. Cut into 1-inch (2.5 cm) cubes.
3. Peel and cube the beets.
4. Slice the onion into thick slices.
5. Peel the garlic, but keep it whole.
6. Place all of the vegetables in a roasting pan.
7. Add the oregano, rosemary, parsley, black pepper, paprika, red pepper flakes, sea salt and olive oil. Stir well to combine.
8. Bake for 45 minutes or until vegetables are soft and lightly browned.
9. Poke with a fork to check for doneness.

# *New Pizza on the Block*

*Ah, pizza! America's favorite Italian food. Make it at home with a gluten-free crust and delicious sauce and toppings.*

SERVES 3-4

## CRUST INGREDIENTS

1 cup warm water
1 1/2 teaspoons instant or rapid rise yeast
1 tablespoon honey
1 1/4 cups gluten-free flour
1/2 cup almond flour
1 tablespoon powdered psyllium husk
1 teaspoon baking powder
1 teaspoon salt
2 tablespoons extra-virgin olive oil

## TOPPINGS INGREDIENTS

1 tablespoon olive oil
1 teaspoon dried oregano
1 teaspoon dried parsley
1/2 cup marinara sauce
1 cup bell peppers, any color, sliced
1/2 cup mushrooms, sliced
1/2 cup spinach, chopped
1/2 cup grated parmesan cheese
1/2 cup shredded mozzarella cheese

## METHOD

1. Stir yeast and honey into warm water until combined. Allow to sit for 5 minutes until bubbly.
2. In a standard mixture, combine flours, psyllium husk, baking powder and salt. Turn mixer on low and slowly add yeast water and oil. Beat until sticky and incorporated 3-6 minutes.
3. Place dough in a lightly oiled bowl, cover with plastic wrap and place in a warm spot in your kitchen. Allow the dough to rise for about an hour (should have bubbles) and double in size.
4. Preheat oven to 300˚F (148˚C).
5. Spoon the wet dough on a parchment lined pan and shape into a large circle, about 12 inches (30 cm) round and 1/4-inch (.63 cm) thick. Place pizza into the oven for 45 minutes to dry a little, or until firm. Take out of oven.
6. Preheat the oven to 450˚F (232˚C).
7. Brush the crust with olive oil, ladle on marinara sauce with dried spices, and top with peppers, mushrooms, spinach and cheeses. Bake in 450˚F (232˚C) oven for 10-12 minutes until cheese melts and vegetables soften.

**SOURCE:** Crust recipe is modified from *America's Test Kitchen*: *The How Can it Be Gluten-free Cookbook*, 2014.

## Oregano Entrees (continued)

# We Gotta Fritatta

*Fritatta is a baked egg dish that can be made with vegetables, cheese and spices. Great for any meal of the day.*

SERVES 4

### INGREDIENTS

6 eggs
1 tablespoon extra-virgin olive oil
1 small shallot, minced
2 cloves garlic, minced
1 cup baby spinach
1 cup shredded mozzarella or other mild cheese
1 tablespoon fresh basil, minced (or 1 teaspoon dried)
1 tablespoon fresh oregano (or 1 teaspoon dried)
½ teaspoon sea salt
¼ teaspoon black pepper
1 tablespoon unsalted butter or ghee

### METHOD

1. Preheat the oven to broil.
2. Beat the eggs in a large bowl and set aside.
3. In rapid succession, heat the oil and sauté the shallots for 1 minute, garlic for 30 seconds and spinach, stirring until it wilts. Let the vegetables cool for a few minutes.
4. Add the cheese and all the spices to the whipped eggs. Add the vegetables when cool enough not to cook the eggs.
5. Melt butter in a medium sauté pan. When sizzling, pour in the egg mixture and allow to set, lifting the sides to let egg run underneath.
6. When eggs appear set on the bottom and sides, place the pan under the broiler for about 2 minutes, rotate and heat 2 minutes more. Eggs should appear fluffy and golden.
7. Slice into 4 wedges and serve with warm bread and salad.

# The Egg and I

*This savory herb and spice omelet is mouth watering. Aim to keep the eggs soft and light by cooking them watchfully on medium heat in a covered pan.*

SERVES 2

### INGREDIENTS

1 tablespoon extra-virgin olive oil
1 small onion, diced small
1 small tomato, seeded and diced
2 green chilies, diced small
2 tablespoons fresh cilantro, minced fine
1 tablespoon fresh oregano (or 1 teaspoon dried)
1 tablespoon unsalted butter
4 eggs
¼ teaspoon sea salt
½ teaspoon ground pepper
¼ cup goat cheese

### METHOD

1. Heat the oil in a pan, add onions and sauté until translucent.
2. Add tomatoes and chiles and cook for a few minutes until softened.
3. Stir in cilantro and oregano. Turn off heat and set aside.
4. Beat the eggs in a bowl with a little salt and pepper.
5. Melt the butter in an omelet pan. When sizzling, pour the eggs into the pan and lift the cooked sides to let all the egg run underneath.
6. Spread prepared filling across the center of the eggs and flip in the sides, or place filling on one side and flip in half.
7. Cover pan for another minute to make sure the eggs are cooked through.
8. Top with goat cheese if using.
9. Serve with toasted bread.

# Oregano Oil and Dressing

## Oregano-Infused Oil

*This oil can be used in your kitchen and medicine cabinet. You can put a few drops in your tea or use externally for cuts, bruises, fungal infections and pain.*

DOSAGE: 1-4 DROPS IN TEA OR TOPICALLY

**INGREDIENTS**

1 cup fresh oregano, leaves only
2 cups extra-virgin olive oil

**METHOD**

1. Make sure your oregano leaves are completely dry to prevent molding. Place them in a clean glass jar and crush them a bit with a pestle or muddler to release the oils.
2. Gently warm the olive oil (do not boil) and then pour over the fresh herbs.
3. Cover and leave in a warm place for two weeks (not in direct sunlight).
4. After two weeks, strain oil with a cheesecloth, squeezing out as much as you can.
5. Store in a glass jar in a dark, cool place.

## Oregano Vinaigrette

*This recipe will make a simple salad sing with flavor. You can try it with a different vinegar if you wish.*

SERVES 4

**INGREDIENTS**

1 tablespoon fresh oregano (or 1 teaspoon dried)
1 tablespoon fresh basil (or 1 teaspoon dried)
1 tablespoon fresh thyme (or 1 teaspoon dried)
¼ cup balsamic vinegar
1 tablespoon maple syrup
1 garlic clove, crushed
¼ teaspoon red pepper flakes
½ teaspoon sea salt, or more to taste
¼ teaspoon black pepper
½ cup extra-virgin olive oil

**METHOD**

1. If using fresh herbs, mince them.
2. Whisk together vinegar and maple syrup until combined.
3. Add garlic, red pepper flakes, sea salt, ground pepper and herbs.
4. Slowly add olive oil and continue whisking until emulsified.
5. Taste and adjust seasonings.
6. Chill until ready to use.

## *How to Grow Oregano*

*Oreganum vulgare* is a hardy perennial herb that can be grown from seeds, cuttings or small plants. As a native of the Mediterranean region it enjoys full sun and well-drained soil. The plant grows in the garden or in containers, growing as high as 80 cm or 2.5 feet. It has small olive-colored leaves and lilac, pink, or purple flowers. Seeds can be sown indoors 6 weeks before the last frost, or plant outdoors 12 inches (30 cm) apart after all danger of frost has passed. Oregano prefers a soil pH range between 6.0 and 8.0. Water regularly but allow soil to dry between waterings to prevent mold and disease. It is susceptible to whitefly, spider mites, and powdery mildew. Oregano flavor is at its peak when flowers appear. Continuous picking of leaves during growth prevents flowering and provides greater volume for harvest.

Oregano should be harvested in the morning, after the dew has dried when the essential oils in herbs are highest in concentration. Use scissors or garden shears to remove stems from the plant. Cut back to just above a growth node or set of leaves. This will allow the plant to branch from the cut area and continue growing. Rinse and shake off the excess moisture before drying oregano.

## *How to Grow Oregano (continued)*

### How to Preserve Your Oregano

There are a couple ways to dry your harvested oregano. Picking individual leaves off stems is time consuming but offers a faster drying time. It's easier to dry the entire stem and then crumble off the crisp leaves.

The herbs can be bundled from the stems and hung in a dark, dry spot. You can place a perforated paper bag around the herbs to catch the leaves as they fall. A dehydrator also works well or place them on mesh screens or trays for several days in a warm room. Turning the stems regularly provides even exposure and speeds the drying process. Do not dry in direct sunlight.

Once the leaves are dry and the stems are stiff, hold the stem at the bottom and pull straight up. The leaves will fall off easily. Dried oregano can be stored in a dark, dry location. Use glass bottles or airtight plastic containers. Light and air will degrade the flavor of the herb. Use within 6 months for the best flavor and quality. When ready to use, crumble the leaves with your hand or use a mortar and pestle to release the flavor and oils.

CHAPTER NINE

# Saffron

*(Crocus sativus L.)*

*Harvesting the red threads of the saffron crocus.*

**Saffron** is sublime. I know of no spice that has the aroma and mystique of saffron. It is the most expensive spice in the world, derived from the flower of *Crocus sativus*, commonly known as the saffron crocus. Its gorgeous orange red threads are gathered by hand and dried to use as a coloring and flavoring agent. It originated in Greece, where it was and still is revered for its medicinal properties. People take saffron to enhance libido, elevate mood and improve memory. Whether this is a placebo effect or consequence of a physiological enhancement, we cannot be certain. The bright shimmering colors signal that numerous carotenoids are present in the delicate saffron threads. This makes it a powerful antioxidant and mucous membrane lubricant. The specific carotene pigments in saffron may have an anti-depressant benefit; protect brain cells against progressive damage, cool inflammation and aid in weight management.

Saffron has been used in the traditional cuisine and medicine of Ayurveda, and in Perso-Arabic systems, to heal a multitude of health conditions. Beware of fake saffron. It lacks the intoxicating smell and taste of real saffron. While it is pricey, a few strands a day can be added to tea, soups, and stews. I will use a few saffron threads to finish a fruit salad, along with fresh basil. Recently, I purchased a small vial of saffron from a fellow traveler. I could tell by the smell that it was the real deal. I kept it in my pocket for a timely aroma blast or thread munch to experience its indescribable essence. Months later, I still have the small vial as I use it sparingly, making it a great value, not a great expense.

*Saffron threads for cooking*

## Background and Uses

Saffron *(Crocus sativus)* lives up to its exotic and elusive reputation because it is difficult to harvest, very expensive and highly prized throughout history. It is grown from a crocus sativus bulb which usually produces only a single purple flower in autumn. Three fragile red threads, or stigma, are painstakingly plucked by hand from the center of the flower and then carefully dried so as not to break them. It takes at least 70,000 such flowers to create a pound of saffron. That makes this labor intensive herb the most expensive spice in the world, sometimes referred to as "red gold" as it has rivaled the price of precious metals throughout history. For centuries it has been valued as a dye, a paint, a culinary spice, a mood enhancer and was even used for self-tanning. Legend has it that Cleopatra, Alexander the Great and even Henry the VIII all used saffron to enhance their looks.

Although there are competing claims for its origin, the crocus sativus flower is recorded in Asia Minor and Greece as far back as the 10th century. Today it is still grown mostly along a wide swath of land from the eastern Mediterranean to Central Asia with Iran producing the majority of saffron sold around the world. The spice is rich in antioxidants and may offer many health benefits. It is considered a required ingredient in certain culinary dishes like paella and bouillabaisse and often used in risottos and curries.

## Plant Specifics

*Saffron crocus corms* or bulbs are usually planted in early spring or early fall in USDA Zones 6-10 with temperatures averaging from -20°F (-28°C) to 40°F (4°C). High or low temperatures do not affect the plant growth, however a long duration of extremely low temperatures or extremely humid environments will inhibit growth of this plant. Crocus corms can be planted in full to partial sun and well-draining soil. Flowers bloom in late fall and should be harvested in the morning after any dew has dried. The floral aroma is described as honey or hay-like with hints of vanilla. It takes about 165 flowers to grow a gram of saffron. The crimson threads taste slightly pungent and astringent. They are water soluble and impart a rich golden-yellow hue to dishes and textiles.

Physiologically, *C. sativus* has lilac to mauve-colored petals. The bright red stigma can grow as long as 1 inch (2.5 cm). Flowering usually lasts about 3 weeks, and the only way to harvest the crop is by hand picking, which is time-consuming. To produce 2.2 pounds (1 kg) of saffron spice, about 138 pounds (63 kg) of flowers are needed. It takes 2-3 hours of labor to harvest the stigmas from 1,000 flowers, or about 370-470 hours to produce 2.2 pounds (1 kg) of dried saffron.

## Active Constituents

Saffron is composed of water, nitrogenous matter, sugars, soluble extracts, volatile oil, and fibers. Saffron is rich in vitamins riboflavin and thiamine (Rechinger, 1975). The pungent, almost bitter taste of saffron originates from its *picrocrocin* (β-D-glucoside of hydroxysafranal). The cleavage of carotenoid zeaxanthin will produce picrocrocin and crocin as well as safranal. It is a glycoside resulting from the cracking of acid and alkali into a glucose molecule and an aglycon. This aglycon easily undergoes hydrolysis and turns into volatile safranal. The increase in temperature while drying converts the picrocrocin into safranal. Zeaxanthin, reddish in color, is one of the carotenoids found naturally in retina.

The fresh stigma has no smell because the picrocrocin has not hydrolyzed. The sharp smell of saffron develops during the drying and storage stage. The drying can cause enzymatic or thermal dissociation. The maximum UV absorption of safranal is 330 nm.

Its aroma profile depends on its geographical origin, as the producing countries use different post harvesting methods; the difference lies primarily in the method of dehydration. It is important to identify the origin and mechanism by which the volatile compounds are generated (Blumenthal M, Abdullaev, et. al., 2004). Crocin gives color to saffron; it is a *crocetin gentiobiose ester* (C20H2404) with a beta shaped glycosidic bond. It is able to undergo hydrolysis by breaking the beta shaped glycosidic bond. Crocin is a unique water-soluble carotenoid in nature. It is a water-soluble crocetin that can dissolve in water easily and produce an orange-red solution, with maximum UV absorption of 440 nm, the highest and most easily detachable among the constituents. The identification of crocetin esters is done by using a liquid chromatography-electrospray ionization-mass spectrometry method.

The chemical composition of saffron is determined by HPLC with diode array detection using aqueous extract as per ISO 3632. The quality of saffron *(crocetin esters, picrocrocin, and safranal)* can be determined using this method as suggested in ISO 3632 (Brown, et al., 2004). No qualitative differences in relation to the flavonoid fraction were observed when saffron samples from different geographical origins were analyzed. This could be due to the poor genetic variability between cultivars. Difference in flavonoid profile was noted due to post harvesting methods, and the highest flavonoid was reported for Spanish saffron (Sarris J, 2007).

## Traditional Medicine

Saffron has been used in folk medicine and Ayurvedic health system as a sedative, expectorant, anti-asthma, emmenagogue, and adaptogenic agent. Saffron was used in various opioid preparations for pain relief in the 16th to 19th centuries (Schmidt, et al., 2007). Saffron has been used in traditional medicine for treating several diseases including depression, cardiovascular disease, menstruation disorders, asthma, insomnia, digestive ailments and others.

## Uses in Modern Medicine

With regard to their medicinal usage, many scientific articles have been published documenting antioxidant properties and treatment of cancer and cardiovascular disease. Reviews on these matters also have been given throughout the literature (Rechinger, K, 1975; Blumenthal, M, 1998). The antioxidant property is a major contributor that helps to prevent or reduce diseases.

Saffron has been studied in the treatment of *diabetes mellitus* (DM), *Alzheimer's disease* (AD), *cardiovascular disease,* (CVD), erectile dysfunction and for its anti-tumor, anti-cancer, antidepressant and anti-bacterial effects. Besides the above-mentioned uses, studies showed improvement of ethanol-impaired memory of mice, effects on learning behavior and neuronal cell death and management of psoriasis. (Abdullaev, 2004; Abe, 2000; Brown, et al., 2004).

## Health Benefits of Saffron

- Clinical trials conducted evaluating the efficacy of saffron in mild-to-moderate depression found that saffron was more effective than placebo and at least equivalent to therapeutic doses of imipramine and fluoxetine. No significant differences were found in adverse effects in any of the studies (Sarris, 2007; Thachil, 2007).
- As a dietary supplement, saffron extracts may prevent retinal damage in rats and have a role in the treatment of ischemic retinopathy and age-related macular degeneration (Maccarone, et al., 2008].
- Anti-nociceptive and anti-inflammatory activities were reported from stigmas and petals of saffron (Hosseinzadeh, et al., 2002).
- Literature review showed a decrease in cholesterol and triglyceride levels and a reduction in vascular damage were observed when hyper-lipidemic rabbits were treated with crocetin. Hypoxia at the vascular wall was also reduced. (Gainer, et al., 1975).
- In addition, an antioxidant effect was observed in human platelets together with the inhibition of lipid peroxidation. (Chatterjee, et al., 2005).
- There is a report that reviewed the potential role of saffron extracts in cancer therapy (Abdullaev, et al., 2004). Saffron appears to be a selective cytotoxic plant but its mechanism is not clearly determined.

## Cancer: Select Clinical Data

Saffron has demonstrated cancer fighting ability. Below are the data from selected pre-clinical trials.

| DISEASE | DURATION | BENEFIT | DOSAGE |
|---|---|---|---|
| **Breast Cancer** | | Proliferation<br>• This study also suggested that crocetin can be used as chemopreventive agent in breast cancer (Chryssanthi et al. 2007). | MCF-7, MDA-MB-231 |
| **Cervical Cancer** | | Apoptosis<br>• This indicated the binding activity of crocetin at molecular level suggesting it's cancer preventive effect (Tavakkol-Afshari, et al., 1992). | HeLa Cells |
| **Colorectal Cancer** | | Proliferation<br>• Crocin (obtained from *Crocus sativus*) significantly inhibited the growth of colorectal cancer cells and it has been suggested as a viable agent for the treatment of colorectal cancer (Aung, et al., 2007). | HCT-116, SW-480, and HT-29 |
| **Leukemia** | | Cytotoxity and proliferation<br>• Crocetin demonstrated significant cytotoxicity and inhibited proliferation (Tarantilis, et al., 1994). | HL60 |
| **Liver Cancer** | | Lipid peroxidation<br>• Another in vivo study reported that crocetin has antitumor activity in a lung cancer animal model by scavenging free radicals and increasing the activity of drug metabolizing enzymes (Magesh, et al., 2006). | Wistar rat (AFB1) C3H1OT1/2 cells |
| **Lung Cancer** | | Lipid peroxidation, GST, catalases, superoxide dismutase<br>• Another in vivo study reported that crocetin has antitumor activity in a lung cancer animal model by scavenging free radicals and increasing the activity of drug metabolizing enzymes (Magesh, et al., 2006). | Swiss albino mice (B[*a*]P) |

## Other Inflammatory Diseases: Select Clinical Data

Below are clinical data for saffron's value in managing select inflammatory disease states.

| DISEASE | DURATION | BENEFIT | DOSAGE |
|---|---|---|---|
| **Alzheimer's** | **Human Trial 16 weeks** | • The psychometric measures, which included AD *assessment scale-cognitive subscale* (ADAS-cog), and clinical dementia rating scale-sums of boxes, were performed to monitor the global cognitive and clinical profiles of the patients (Akhondzadeh, et al., 2010). | • Forty-six patients with probable AD were screened for a 16-week, double-blind study of parallel groups of patients with mild to moderate AD.<br>• Patients were randomly assigned to receive capsule saffron 30 mg/day (15 mg twice per day) (Group A) or capsule placebo (two capsules per day) for a 16-week study. |
| **Antioxidant** | **Human Trial 6 weeks** | • *Lipoprotein oxidation susceptibility* (LOS) was estimated initially and after 3 and 6 weeks.<br>• There was a constant decrease in LOS during this period. The significant fall in LOS indicates the potential of Saffron as an antioxidant (Verma, et al., 1998). | • 50 mg of Saffron dissolved in 100 ml of milk was administered twice a day to 20 human subjects. |

## *Other Inflammatory Diseases: Select Clinical Data (continued)*

| DISEASE | DURATION | BENEFIT | DOSAGE |
|---|---|---|---|
| **Antiinflam-matory** | **Mice Study** | • Aqueous and ethanolic maceration extracts of Crocus sativus L. stigma and petals.<br>• They concluded that aqueous and ethanolic extracts of saffron stigma and petal have an antinociceptive effect, as well as acute and/or chronic anti-inflammatory activity (Hossein, et al., 2002). | • The maximum non-fatal doses of stigma aqueous and ethanolic extracts were 0.8g/kg and 2g/kg (i.p.), respectively.<br>• The maximum non-fatal doses of petal aqueous and ethanolic extracts were 3.6g/kg and 8g/kg (i.p.), respectively.<br>• LD50 values of the petal aqueous and ethanolic extracts were 6.67g/kg, i.p. (4.95, 8.99) and 9.99g/kg, i.p. (8, 13, 12, 28), respectively. |
| **Blood Pressure** | **Human Trial 1 week** | • Saffron (Crocus sativus) stigma tablets were evaluated for short-term safety and tolerability in healthy adult volunteers<br>• Saffron with higher dose (400 mg) decreased standing systolic blood pressure and mean arterial pressures significantly. (Modaghegh, et al., 2008). | • The study was a double-blind, placebo-controlled design consisting of a 1 week treatment of saffron tablets. Volunteers were divided into 3 groups of 10 each (5 males and 5 females).<br>• Group I received placebo; groups 2 and 3 received 200 and 400mg saffron tablets, respectively, for 7 days |
| **Diabetes II** | | • Saffron significantly reduced the fasting blood glucose and HbA1c levels but significantly increased the blood insulin levels without any significant effects on the blood SGOT, SGPT and creatinine levels in the diabetic rats compared with the control diabetic rats.<br>• The results suggest that saffron may have anti-hyperglycemic and blood insulin level elevating effects without hepatic and renal toxicities in the alloxan — diabetic rats. Further, crocin, crocetin and safranal may be involved in these effects of saffron (Kianbakht, et al., 2011). | • Saffron methanolic extract (80 and 240 mg/kg), crocin (50 and 150 mg/kg) and safranal (0.25 and 0.5 ml/kg) |
| **Erectile Dysfunc-tion** | **Human Trial 4 weeks** | • Saffron resulted in significantly greater improvement in erectile function and intercourse satisfaction domains than the placebo group.<br>• Saffron is a tolerable and efficacious treatment for fluoxetine-related erectile dysfunction (Modabbernia, et al., 2012). | • Randomized double-blind placebo-controlled study.<br>• 36 married male patients with major depressive disorder whose depressive symptoms had been stabilized on fluoxetine and had subjective complaints of sexual impairment entered the study.<br>• The patients were randomly assigned to saffron (15 mg twice per day) or placebo for 4 weeks. The International Index of Erectile Function scale was used to assess sexual function at baseline on weeks 2 and 4. |
| **Depression** | **Human Trial 6 weeks** | • A randomized trial compared the efficacy of saffron with imipramine in the treatment of mild-to-moderate depression.<br>• The result showed that saffron at this dose was found to be effective comparable to imipramine in the treatment of mild-to-moderate depression (Akhondzadeh, et al., 2004). 25] | • 30 patients were assigned to receive capsule saffron (30 mg/day) three times<br>• In this double-blind, single-center trial, patients were randomly assigned to receive capsule of saffron 30 mg/day (TDS) (Group 1) and capsule of imipramine 100 mg/day (TDS) (Group 2) for a 6-week study. |
| **Blood Pressure** | **Rat Study** | • Saffron reduced blood pressure from 133.5±3.9 to 117±2.1 mmHg in rats. This reduction was postulated to be due to the effect of the extracts on the heart itself, total peripheral resistance or both (Fatehi, et al., 2003). | • Aqueous (500 mg/kg) and ethanolic extracts of C. sativus petals reduced blood pressure in a dose-dependent manner in rats. Administration of the aqueous extract of saffron petals (500 mg/kg) |

## Summary of Clinical Findings

Saffron and its derivatives particularly from crocetin have demonstrated significant anticancer activity in breast, lung, pancreatic and leukemic cells. The above table summarizes the anticancer effects of crocetin against several cancer types and also presents the underlying mechanisms of action.

Saffron has been used traditionally and now in modern medicine, the studies above are showcasing its benefits, antioxidant, anti-inflammatory, and anti-cancer properties. It has demonstrated use for the heart, endocrine, mental and sexual health. Clearly more clinical research is needed to determine dosing needs for understanding safety and efficacy of saffron and its health constituents.

## Dosage Range

Saffron dosage included in the human trials listed above were in the range of 30-500 mg per day. Saffron is generally not toxic when ingested in culinary amounts, but a lethal dose at 20g and an abortifacient dose at 10g have been indicated in the literature (Schmidt, et al., 2007). A relatively limited number of studies have examined the toxicity of saffron. According to in vivo studies, saffron has very low toxicity for doses of up to 1.5g per day, while toxic effects have been documented for daily doses ≥5g, with a lethal dose of approximately 20g.

## Contraindications

Having been granted *Generally Recognized as Safe* (GRAS) status in the United States by the *Food and Drug Administration* (FDA), saffron is well tolerated by most people.

In a short-term study, there were no major adverse events and no changes in the studied haematological, biochemical, hormonal, and urinary parameters, except for decreasing amylase levels, mixed white blood cells, and partial thromboplastin time after one month.

## Toxicity

No significant toxicity has been reported following short or long-term administration of saffron extracts at standard doses.

## Supplementation

Dried powder is safe to take daily. Please ask your health care provider if saffron supplement is appropriate for you.

| TYPE OF SUPPLEMENT | ADULT DOSAGE |
|---|---|
| **Dried powder** | 1.5g/day |
| **Tincture** | (1:2): 15-30 drops, 4 times per day |

## Kitchen Medicine

Saffron is a seductive mistress in the kitchen, luring you in with her delicate and vibrant crimson threads and sweet, grassy aroma. When added to a dish, her flavor transforms to savory and astringent imparting a beautiful yellow-orange hues into foods. Her potent health benefits must be teased out by soaking saffron threads in alcohol, acidic or warm liquid for a minimum of 20 minutes. This is a process called blooming. Be aware saffron's flavor continues to expand and mature over 24 hours, so a little goes a long way. As a general rule, it is recommended that you use no more than 3 threads per person or serving.

Saffron is widely used in Persian, Indian, European, and Arab cuisines. Confectioneries and liquors also often include saffron. It is used in dishes ranging from the jeweled rice and khoresh of Iran, the Milanese risotto of Italy, the paella of Spain, the bouillabaisse of France, to the biryani with vegetables and meats in South Asia. Saffron has also been used as a fabric dye, particularly in China and India, and in perfumery. It is used for religious purposes in India.

Saffron has been used in European cuisine since antiquity to color and flavor foods. In addition, it is one of the important and traditional ingredients in Swedish saffron cake, called Saffranskaka. Some dairy products also include saffron for flavor and color. Ancient Romans believed that saffron had the ability to prevent hangovers when used for steeping their wine. It also has sedative, antispasmodic, expectorant, as well as aphrodisiac properties.

# Saffron Entrees

## French Bouillabasse

*Bouillabaisse is a classic Mediterranean fisherman's stew made with fresh local fish and shellfish in a sublime sauce of orange peel, saffron, and fennel.*

SERVES 8

### INGREDIENTS

½ pound shrimp
6 cups water
1 bay leaf
12 whole black peppercorns
Peel from 1 orange
3 tablespoons extra-virgin olive oil
2 small fennel bulbs, thinly sliced, fronds reserved
½ teaspoon kosher salt
1 small onion, diced
1 leek, white part only, thinly sliced
4 cloves garlic, minced
4 tomatoes, skins and seeds removed, diced
1 cup dry white wine
1 teaspoon fresh thyme
1 teaspoon fresh marjoram
½ teaspoon saffron threads
½ teaspoon ground cayenne pepper
½ pound sockeye salmon, skin removed, cut into 1-inch (2.5 cm) wide strips
½ pound cod, cut into 1-inch (2.5 cm) wide strips
½ pound Manila clams
½ pound bay mussels

### METHOD

1. Peel the shrimp, reserving the shrimp shells. Bring the water to a simmer and add the shrimp shells, bay leaf, peppercorns, and orange peel to the pot and simmer gently for 15 minutes.
2. In a heavy-bottomed soup pot, add the onion, leek, fennel bulb and a pinch of salt. Slowly sweat them over low heat until tender but not browned (about 20 minutes).
3. Add the garlic, sauté one more minute until garlic is tender, but not browned.
4. Add the tomatoes and the wine. Turn up the heat until the wine begins to boil. Reduced heat and cook until wine is reduced by about half.
5. Strain the shrimp and orange stock into the pot. Add the thyme, marjoram, saffron, and cayenne and simmer for 10 minutes.
6. Add the fish first. About two minutes later add the mussels and clams. About two minutes later add the shrimp. Simmer until the shrimp is just cooked through. About two more minutes.
7. Remove from heat and serve immediately, garnishing each plate with some reserved fennel fronds.

**SOURCE:** http://www.slowburningpassion.com/how-to-make-a-classic-french-bouillabaisse/

## *Saffron Entrees (continued)*

# *Crown Jewel Pilaf*

*The aroma of this dish is out of this world.*

SERVES 4-6

### INGREDIENTS

1½ cups long grain brown basmati rice
1 tablespoon salt, divided
1 large orange, preferably organic
½ cup whole dried barberries or dried cranberries
½ teaspoon saffron, loosely-packed (about ¼ gram)
¼ cup orange blossom water, divided
2 tablespoons oil, butter or ghee, divided
¼ cup raw almonds, sliced
¼ cup raw pistachios, chopped
¼ cup golden or green raisins
¼ cup maple syrup, divided
1-2 large carrots, peeled and cut into 2-inch (5 cm) long matchsticks
4-inch (10 cm) whole cinnamon stick
1 teaspoon freshly ground cardamom

### METHOD

1. Wash the rice in a large container of water, swishing it around with your hand then straining off the water and repeating until the water runs clear. Cover again with water, add ½ tablespoon of salt and soak between two and 24 hours. Strain again through a fine-mesh sieve and set aside.
2. Set a small pot of water to boil. Use a vegetable peeler to take thick strips of rind off the oranges, including a little of the white pith. Slice these strips crosswise into very small slivers. When the water is boiling, drop the slivers into the water and cook for one minute. Drain and rinse with cold water. Set aside. (This cuts the bitterness of the orange rind.)
3. Clean the barberries by removing any stems or debris. Place them in a sieve set inside a bowl. Cover with cold water and soak for 20 minutes. Pull the sieve from the bowl and rinse under cold water to flush out any remaining sand. Set aside. (If using cranberries, skip this step.)
4. With a mortar and pestle, crush the saffron threads until a powder forms. Stir in 3 tablespoons orange blossom water and set aside (reserving last tablespoon).
5. Heat oil in a large skillet over medium heat. Add the almonds and the pistachios, and sauté for about a minute. Add the raisins to the pan and toss with the nuts. Empty the mixture into a bowl and set aside.
6. In the same skillet, heat remaining tablespoon of oil with half the saffron orange blossom water mixture and half the maple syrup over medium heat. Add the carrots and orange peel and sauté for two minutes. Add the remaining maple syrup and saffron orange blossom water mixture, the cinnamon stick and the cardamom and sauté for one minute. Add 1 cup water, bring to a boil over high heat, then lower to medium heat and cook for about 10 minutes, or until the carrots lightly caramelize and the liquid has reduced to a syrup. Remove the carrots and orange peel, reserving the syrup, and set aside.
7. In a large heavy-bottomed pot with a lid, bring five cups of water to a boil. Add the remaining ½ tablespoon salt and rice to the pot with the remaining tablespoon of plain orange blossom water. Boil briskly until the rice has risen to the surface and when bitten into, a grain of rice feels soft, 6-10 minutes. Strain the rice into a large fine-mesh sieve, rinse with cold water and turn it out into a bowl.
8. Gently mix the reserved carrot/orange syrup into the par-boiled rice. Take a large spoonful of rice at a time and gently spread it over the bottom of the pot. Give the pot a shake to even out the base. Add more spoonfuls of rice, one at a time, gradually shaping it into a pyramid. (This shape leaves room for the rice to expand and enlarge.)
9. Wrap the lid of the pot with a clean dish towel and cover firmly to prevent steam from escaping. Cook 40-45 minutes over low heat.
10. To serve, arrange on a serving platter layers of rice, then the caramelized carrot mixture (discarding the cinnamon stick). Top with the barberry/nut mixture.

**SOURCE:** https://www.thekitchn.com/recipe-iranian-jeweled-rice-recipes-from-the-kitchn-194680

# *Indian Spice Lentil Burgers with Saffron Yogurt Sauce*

*This recipe is a flavorful alternative to meat, nut or grain burgers. Wonderful with saffron yogurt sauce topping.*

SERVES 6

## INGREDIENTS

½ cup dried green lentils
½ pound red potatoes, peeled and cubed
¾ teaspoon salt
½ cup carrots, finely chopped
½ cauliflower, finely chopped
½ cup petite green peas, frozen
5 teaspoons olive oil, divided
½ cup yellow onion, finely chopped
½ teaspoon ground cumin
½ teaspoon fresh ginger root, peeled and minced
¼ teaspoon mustard seed
⅛ teaspoon ground red pepper
1 garlic clove, minced
1 tablespoon fresh cilantro, minced
¼ cup non-gluten flour
1 large egg, whisked
½ cup dry gluten-free bread crumbs
1 cup whole milk yogurt
1 pinch saffron
1 pinch turmeric for color
Salt to taste

## METHOD

1. Combine yogurt, saffron and turmeric and salt to taste, then refrigerate.
2. Combine lentils and potatoes in medium saucepan. Cover with water. Bring to boil, then reduce heat. Simmer 20 minutes, or until tender. Drain well. Add salt and mash. Set aside.
3. Steam carrot, cauliflower and peas for 3 minutes, or until tender. Set aside.
4. Heat 1 teaspoon oil in a large non-stick skillet over medium heat until hot. Add onion; saute 2 minutes. Add cumin, ginger, mustard seeds, red pepper and garlic; saute 1 minute. Stir in cilantro. Add onion mixture, carrot mixture and non-gluten flour to the lentil-potato mixture. Add egg. Mix thoroughly.
5. Divide mixture into 6 equal portions shaped into 4-inch (10 cm) patties. Dredge patties in breadcrumbs.
6. Heat 2 teaspoons oil in skillet over medium heat until hot. Lay 3 patties gently in pan. Cooking 2-3 minutes each side until browned. Keep warm until ready to serve. Top with saffron yogurt sauce.

**SOURCE:** Recipe adapted from *Cooking Light,* May 1997.

## *Saffron Entrees (continued)*

# *Spanish Paella*

*Paella is staple seafood stew from Spain. featuring saffron is its signature ingredient. The color, flavor and composition is dazzling and often, unforgettable.*

SERVES 8

### INGREDIENTS

3 pounds chicken
Sea salt
15 large shrimp (feel free to add clams, calamari, prawns or mussels)
8 cups chicken stock
1 teaspoon saffron threads
Extra-virgin olive oil
3 cups bomba or calasparra rice (arborio rice works as a substitute)
1 large onion, diced
1 large bell pepper, diced
3 garlic cloves, minced
4 plum tomatoes, diced
2 oz. (½ can) tomato paste
10-15 flat green beans
½ tablespoon paprika
½ cup fresh parsley, more for garnish
2-3 tablespoons fresh thyme
2 lemons, quartered

### METHOD

1. It's best to have all of your ingredients prepared before you start cooking.
2. Cut the chicken into 10 pieces (reserve backbone for stock) lightly salt and pepper.
3. Peel shrimp, leaving only the tail and lightly salt and pepper.
4. Make chicken stock from scratch (time permitting), adding a bit of rosemary and thyme. If you're using prepared stock, heat it up with those herbs and then remove them before starting.
5. Keep stock warm, stir in the saffron threads breaking them up to release the oils. Stir to dissolve and darken stock a bit. This will take about 20-30 minutes.
6. Coat the bottom of your paella pan or skillet with olive oil.
7. Brown the chicken for 2-3 minutes on each side without stirring. Remove from pan and set aside while you cook your vegetables.
8. Sauté onion and bell pepper until they're softened. Add garlic, plum tomatoes and flat green beans, stir to combine.
9. Push the vegetables to one side of the pan and on the other add the tomato paste. Stirring to carmelize, flipping and spreading it until it begins to loosen (1-2 minutes over high heat).
10. Mix all of the vegetables and meat together with the caramelized tomato paste. Add the paprika, parsley and thyme.
11. Add rice, mixing together and stirring 1-1½ minutes. When the rice is slightly translucent add enough chicken stock to cover the whole mixture. If it's been kept warm, it will begin to boil almost immediately. Reduce heat to keep it at a low simmer.
12. Stir several times in the first 5-10 minutes, adding broth as necessary to keep the rice fully covered. Once you have added all the stock, turn down to low and let it cook another 10-20 minutes. Don't worry about rice burning to the bottom, this caramelization (called socarrat) is a tasty delicacy.
13. When you have about 8 minutes left, lay shrimp on top, turning over after 2-4 minutes to cook the other side.
14. When the rice on top is al dente, take paella off of heat and cover. You must let it sit for 15-20 minutes. Take the lid off prematurely and end up with a crunchy mess. Patience is the key.
15. Once you're sure it's ready, uncover, serve garnished with lemon wedges and parsley.

**SOURCE:** https://www.masaffron.com/recipes/2018/3/16/spanish-paella-with-saffron

# *Saffron Biryani*

*Safforn is native to Kashmir, India. Our basic recipe is vegetarian, with brown rice used for a higher nutrition content. Seafood or poultry can be added if so desired.*

SERVES 4-6

## INGREDIENTS

2 cups brown basmati rice
4 cups filtered water or broth
½ teaspoon saffron threads
2 tablespoons extra-virgin olive oil
1 tablespoon ghee
½ teaspoon asafetida
½ teaspoon cumin seeds
1½ teaspoon chili powder
½ teaspoon ground turmeric
6 cloves garlic, minced
2.5 cm or 1-inch (2.5 cm) slice ginger, minced
2 green chilies, chopped fine
1 cup onion, minced
3-4 medium tomatoes, seeded and diced
½ cup cauliflower florets
½ cup green beans, sliced into bite-sized pieces
½ cup red bell pepper, diced medium
½ teaspoon sea salt, or more to taste
1 cup peas, thawed if frozen

## METHOD

1. Wash the rice and soak for 3-4 hours or up to overnight. Strain before using.
2. Bring filtered water or broth to a low simmer. Stir in saffron threads, turn off heat and set aside.
3. In a heavy-bottom pot over low heat, melt the ghee and extra-virgin olive oil. Add the asafetida, cumin, chili powder and turmeric. Stir until fragrant and then add the garlic, ginger and chilies for another minute or two.
4. Stir in the onions and sauté until golden. Add tomatoes and continue to cook until they start to break down.
5. One at a time, add the cauliflower, green beans and bell peppers and heat for two minutes before adding the next vegetable.
6. Stir in the strained rice, salt and warm saffron water or broth and bring just up to a boil. Reduce heat to medium-low and cook half covered for about 40 minutes.
7. Add peas when rice is nearly cooked, cover the pot and cook for another 5 minutes.

NOTE: *This can be served with raita.*

**SOURCE:** Shiela Moorthy

## *Saffron Entrees (continued)*

# *Khoresh-e Ghormeh Sabzi*

*In this traditional herb stew the meat is replaced with mushrooms and mushroom stock for a heartier flavor.*

SERVES 6

### INGREDIENTS

- 1 cup dried red kidney beans, soaked overnight
- 1 quart mushroom stock or broth
- ½ teaspoon saffron threads
- 4 tablespoons extra-virgin olive oil, divided
- 4 bunches parsley, chopped small
- 1 bunch cilantro, chopped small
- 1 onion, finely chopped
- 4 scallions, sliced thinly (green stems only, reserving whites for garnish or another use)
- 1½ pounds mixed mushrooms, your choice, sliced or cut into 1-inch (2.5 cm) chunks
- 1 tablespoon turmeric
- 1 tablespoon dried fenugreek (or 1 bunch fresh fenugreek)
- 1 teaspoon ground pepper
- 1 bunch spinach, roughly chopped
- 1 cup Swiss chard, roughly chopped
- 4 dried black limes (limoo amani) punctured several times with a fork, or ¼ cup lemon or lime juice
- Salt to taste

### METHOD

1. You can make your own stock by pouring boiling water over dried mushrooms to soak for at least 20 minutes.
2. Strain broth through a cheesecloth or fine sieve. After straining, rinse any remaining grime off the rehydrated mushrooms and add to the pot.
3. In a saucepan, heat the mushroom stock to a low simmer. Stir in saffron threads and remove from heat. Allow to bloom for at least 20 minutes.
4. In a large skillet, heat half the oil over medium heat and cook fresh herbs for about 15-20 minutes, stirring occasionally. They should give off a dark green oil when pressed with a spoon. They are ready when they seem dry and emit a strong, savory aroma. Set aside.

5. In a large pot, sauté the onions in remaining oil for about 10 minutes, until golden brown.
6. Stir in mushrooms and cook for about 10 minutes, flipping to achieve golden color all over.
7. Add the turmeric, fenugreek and pepper to the onions and sauté for a few more minutes.
8. Strain and rinse the beans and add to the pot with cooked herbs, greens and black limes or juice.
9. Pour in saffron mushroom stock, and enough water to cover everything. Bring up to a boil, and then cover and simmer on low to medium heat for about 2 hours.
10. Add salt last so as not to toughen the beans, start with 1 teaspoon. Taste and adjust seasonings.
11. This is usually served over Persian rice.

**SOURCE:** https://www.196flavors.com/iran-ghormeh-sabzi/

# Saffron Dessert

## Carrot Payasam

*This is a dessert that resembles a loose pudding or sweet soup.*

SERVES 4

**INGREDIENTS**

5-6 strands saffron
4-5 green cardamom seeds
1 tablespoon rice (white or brown)
8-10 almonds
1 cup grated carrots
½ liter milk
¼ cup jaggery sugar (or brown sugar)
1 teaspoon raisins or other dried fruits to taste

**METHOD**

1. Warm ¼ cup milk and stir in saffron. Set aside.
2. Remove the dark seeds from the green cardamom pods.
3. Soak the rice, almonds and cardamom seeds in water for 20 minutes.
4. Strain rice mixture, place into a small spice grinder and process until it becomes a paste.
5. Parboil the carrots with a little milk.
6. When carrots are bright and starting to soften, add the rice paste and sugar and cook for 5 more minutes.
7. Add the soaked saffron and remove from heat.
8. Pour the carrot mixture into a blender and process until smooth.
9. Add more milk until you reach your desired consistency.
10. Place in a bowl, garnish with dried fruits, and serve.

**SOURCE:** Pramila Murthy

# Saffron Beverage

## Evening Saffron Milk

*Adding saffron to Golden Milk gives it a more vibrant color and may support a better nights sleep.*

SERVES 1

**INGREDIENTS**

1 cup organic coconut milk (or A2 milk)
1 cinnamon stick
1 teaspoon ground turmeric
¼ teaspoon ground black pepper
10-12 small strands of saffron
½ teaspoon cinnamon powder to sprinkle
1 pinch grated nutmeg

**METHOD**

1. Heat nut milk (or A2 milk) in a pan with the cinnamon stick.
2. Stir in turmeric, pepper and saffron strands.
3. Reduce heat to lowest setting. Cover and allow saffron to bloom for 20 minutes.
4. Pour the warmed golden milk into a mug.
5. Garnish with cinnamon powder and enjoy as a bedtime drink.
6. Sprinkle nutmeg on top before serving.

## How to Grow Saffron

Despite its exotic reputation, saffron is remarkably easy to grow in most home gardens. Remember however, you need to grow a lot of flowers to get a little saffron. About 50-60 flowers will yield a tablespoon of this precious herb.

Saffron is grown from the saffron crocus bulb known as a corm, and has to be planted 6 weeks before the first fall frost. It flowers in fall and not spring like most crocus bulbs. The spice comes in the form of three red stigmas (threads) in the center of this crocus flower. It is rare for a saffron crocus corm to produce more than one flower. They can be planted directly in the ground in USDA Zones 6-10. Otherwise plant corms indoors in the fall and bring them outdoors the following spring.

Bulbs can be purchased from a reputable online nursery or a local gardening store. Once purchased, plant them as soon as possible because they don't store well. They probably will not bloom the year you plant them. Instead, roots will take hold the first autumn and perhaps some foliage if warm enough. That will die back and you'll see buds the following spring and flowers in late summer or early fall.

Plant your corms in a sunny location, pointy side up. Space them 2-3 inches (5-7.5 cm) apart and 3-4 inches (7.5-10 cm) deep. Saffron crocus plants need well draining soil. If planted in swampy or poor draining soil, corms will rot. Other than needing good soil and sun, saffron crocus are not picky. After your bulbs are planted, water them well and then do very little. They will be hardy down to -15°F (-26°C). You can fertilize them once a year, though they grow fine without being fertilized. Only water them if the rainfall in your area falls below 1.5 inches (3.81 cm) per week.

## How to Grow Saffron (continued)

### Harvesting and Using Saffron

The best time to harvest the stigmas is mid-morning on a sunny day when the flowers have fully opened and are dry. You can either pick the flowers and then carefully pluck the stigmas from the center or pull the stigmas out of the flowers in the garden. Gently dry the threads in a warm place to preserve them. You can dehydrate at a maximum temperature of 50°F (10°C). Once dry, store in a dark, closed container away from sunlight.

After harvest, the leaves will yellow and dry up. At that point remove your foliage and allow the bulbs to rest over winter. The bulbs will be dormant and therefore no watering is required. It is recommended that you remove the corms every four to five years to separate the mother corms from the cormlets. Store in a dark and dry place over winter and replant in a different spot for best yield.

### How to Make Saffron Powder

Saffron will keep fresh for six months or more in its threadlike form. To make a powder gently heat the threads, being careful not to burn. Cool and then grind them in a small spice grinder or use a mortar and pestle. Ground saffron can be added directly to a recipe but the preferred method is soaking (blooming) in liquid first.

**SOURCE:** https://www.whiteflowerfarm.com/how-to-harvest-saffron-crocus
https://www.gardeningknowhow.com/edible/herbs/saffron/growing-saffron-crocus.htm

CHAPTER TEN

# *Salt*

## *(Sodium Chloride)*

**Salt** is like no other spice, partly because it's actually a mineral, and also a seasoning we quite literally cannot live without. Our bodies cannot store adequate amounts of salt, so we need to consume it daily to survive. Fortunately for us, that is not difficult since salt minimizes bitterness, balances sweetness, enhances aromas and heightens the experience of eating. It is at the very foundation of flavor, food, health and life of animals, vegetables, and minerals. Many take it for granted, but not the chef, not the nutrition consultant, nor a student or aficionado of geology, culture or civilization. Salt's bad reputation is from the glut of commercial salt poured as a hidden ingredient into packaged, processed and prepared foods. It is a flavor enhancer, over-used to compensate for the staleness of devitalized food. Natural salt is gray, pink, or even black in color. Salt is a tonic for digestion, metabolism, the brain, central nervous system and the cardiovascular system. It is an essential ingredient for wellness and longevity.

As the ocean and salt flats have been polluted, the purity of salt may be compromised. Enjoy several varieties of global salts and salty condiments such as sea vegetables, fermented foods and miso. Try a pinch of salt in lemon water at mid-afternoon when you are drowsy instead of a sweet and a caffeinated drink to boost your energy. Combine salt with any of the spices discussed in our book to prepare a more flavorful and nourishing food, beverage or self-healing remedy.

I have included a favorite poem by the renowned Chilean poet, Pablo Neruda on the next page.

*Salt comes in many colors and textures.*

*Homemade garlic, dill salt pickles*

## Ode to Salt

This salt
In the salt cellar
I once saw in the salt mines.
I know
You won't
Believe me,
But
It sings,
Salt sings, the skin
Of the salt mines
Sings
With a mouth smothered
By the earth.
I shivered in those solitudes
When I heard
The voice of
The salt
In the desert.
Near Antofagasta
The nitrous
Pampa
Resounds:
A broken
Voice,
A mournful
Song.
In its caves
The salt moans, mountain
Of buried light,
Translucent cathedral,
Crystal of the sea, oblivion
Of the waves.
And then on every table
In the world,
Salt,
We see your piquant
Powder
Sprinkling
Vital light
Upon
Our food. Preserver
Of the ancient
Holds of ships,
Discoverer
On
The high seas,
Earliest
Sailor
Of the unknown, shifting
Byways of the foam.
Dust of the sea, in you
The tongue receives a kiss
From ocean night:
Taste imparts to every seasoned
Dish your ocean essence;
The smallest,
Miniature
Wave from the saltcellar
Reveals to us
More than domestic whiteness;
In it, we taste infinitude.

**SOURCE:** *Elementary Odes* by Pablo Neruda (1961) A Cypress Book.

## Background and Uses

Salt has been used as a natural flavoring for thousands of years, and it's so vital to our existence that a portion of our tongues is even designated to taste saltiness. However, in recent years, salt has come under fire and has been characterized as an unhealthy substance that we should cut out of our diets in favor of heart health. The *Centers for Disease Control* (CDC) reports a whopping 70% of the sodium in American diets comes from processed, packaged and restaurant foods. Cooking from scratch with fresh, whole, unprocessed ingredients is key to reducing sodium intake. Unless you have been told specifically by your doctor to follow a low-salt diet, the average person eating home cooked food need not worry about their sodium intake. When you add salt is also important. A small amount of salt added to food during the cooking process will be better absorbed and distributed throughout the dish, than a larger amount sprinkled on food at the table.

It's also important to keep in mind that not all salt is created equal and there is definitely a difference between unrefined, mineral-rich varieties like sea salt versus table salt that has been heavily processed and stripped of all of its natural nutrients.

## Plant Specifics

All types of salt — including table salt — originate from a sea or a salty body of water, but not all salts currently on the market actually come from the oceans in existence today. What does that mean? Salts that are not sea salt are often derived from underground salt deposits left behind by seawater at some point.

Sea salt is a type of salt produced from the evaporation of current seawater. The evaporation is accomplished by either open-air solar evaporation or by a quicker vacuum evaporation process. Some of the pricier sea salts available today often come from the slower sun-fueled evaporation method. When you eat a sea salt that has experienced very little processing, you have a salt that contains health-promoting trace minerals. It also has natural flavors and colors that make it a lot tastier and more interesting to use for cooking as well as in homemade beauty products.

## Active Constituents

Sea salt can be either unrefined or refined, although unrefined sea salt is generally recommended to maximize its potential health benefits. Refined sea salt, on the other hand, is washed to strip it of its trace minerals and often contains harmful food additives.

The different types of salt are:

- table salt
- kosher salt
- sea salt
- Himalayan pink salt
- Celtic sea salt
- kala namak (Indian black salt)
- flake salt
- Hawai'ian black salt
- Hawai'ian red salt
- smoked salt
- pickling salt
- Fleur de sel

Table salt is usually refined, additives are used to prevent caking, and iodized. We should be getting iodine from natural foods and not from refined salt with other unhealthy additives. Any other non-refined salt can be used. Better sources of iodine include seaweed, dairy, cod, tuna, shrimp and eggs.

## Traditional Medicine

*Sendha namak,* or rock salt, has long been used in Ayurvedic medicine to boost skin health and treat coughs, colds, and stomach conditions. Rock salts offer trace minerals in the purest form of salt — unprocessed and raw, devoid of environmental pollutants and chemical components. It contains 84 out of the 92 trace elements required by the body including potassium, iron, calcium, zinc, magnesium, copper and so on.

## Uses in Modern Medicine

The body uses sodium to maintain fluid levels. A balance of fluid and sodium is necessary for the health of the heart, liver, and kidneys. It regulates blood fluids and prevents low blood pressure. Low sodium levels can result if there is too much fluid in the body, for example, because of fluid retention. Diuretics are given in this case, to reduce fluid retention. Other causes of low sodium in the body include Addison's disease, a blockage in the small intestine, diarrhea and vomiting, an underactive thyroid and heart failure. If sodium levels fall in the blood, this affects brain activity. A person will feel sluggish and lethargic. They may experience muscle twitches, followed by seizures, a loss of consciousness, coma, and even death. If sodium levels fall quickly, the onset of symptoms should be treated as a medical emergency. In older people, symptoms can be severe. One study found that when rats were deprived of sodium, they kept away from activities that they normally enjoyed. The researchers suggested, therefore, that sodium could act as an antidepressant.

## Health Benefits of Salt

### Rich in Trace Minerals

High-quality sea salts typically contain upwards of 60 trace minerals and for specific types like Himalayan sea salt, that number is said to be closer to 84. Either way, sea salts are a great source of micronutrients.

### Prevents Dehydration and Balances Fluids

By consuming sea salt in moderation each day, you also ensure that you are maintaining sufficient sodium levels, which helps balance your sodium-potassium ratios. Sodium and potassium are two electrolytes that work together to ensure that there is proper fluid balance in your cells as well as your blood plasma and extracellular fluid (Perez, et al., 2014).

### Loaded with Electrolytes

Electrolytes have so many important functions — from regulating your heartbeat to allowing your muscles to contract so that you can move. Sea salt in moderation can help in avoiding an electrolyte imbalance, which can cause all kinds of serious negative symptoms, including some that are potentially deadly. (Balci, et al., 2013).

### Promotes Brain, Muscle and Nervous System Function

Without this communication system working as it should, the brain, muscles and nervous systems are especially inclined to suffer. Both too much and too little sodium cause cellular malfunction. So as much as you hear about making sure you don't get too much salt in your diet, it's also absolutely just as important to make sure we get enough (Giuliani, et al., 2014).

### Supports Digestive Health

Not getting enough salt in your diet can also negatively impact your digestive health. In fact, a lack of salt in the diet can lead to a reduction of *hydrochloric acid* (HCL) in your stomach. If you have low stomach acid, it can seriously throw your digestive system out of whack, contributing to issues like heartburn, stomach pain, vomiting and constipation. Consuming the right amount of sea salt can help your body produce proper amounts of HCL since sea salt provides chloride, one of the building blocks of stomach acid (Fatima, et al., 2019).

### Promotes Nutrient Absorption

Having enough stomach acid also helps our bodies to absorb vitamins and minerals like calcium, zinc, iron, folate and vitamin B12. For this reason, consuming high-quality sea salt regularly can help your body absorb more nutrients from the foods that you eat. This is great news since it's not only what you eat, but how your body processes what you eat that gives your body the essential nutrients it needs on a daily basis.

## Summary of Clinical Findings

Selected studies showcased above suggest that salt is an important ingredient that enables our bodies to maintain electrolyte balance, heart health, blood pressure management, brain and digestive health. Not using salt on a daily basis can have a negative health impact.

## Dosage Range

The Dietary Guidelines for Americans recommends limiting sodium to less than 2,300 mg a day or about 1 teaspoon.

## Contraindications

Excess sodium intake has been linked to health problems, such as osteoporosis, kidney disease, and heart disease.

## Kitchen Medicine

It seems like no coincidence that salt plays a crucial role in our health, and our palates often crave it. While salt has its own distinct taste, it also enhances the flavor of other ingredients. Carbohydrates like pasta and bread would not be nearly as enjoyable without salt. It is used as a tenderizer in brines and marinades by opening up the tissues. It also preserves meats, vegetables, dairy and fish by preventing the growth of bacteria. It serves as a binder in sausages and cured meats, giving them a smooth texture and preserving their color. Salt boosts the strength of gluten in dough and the color of bread crusts and slows the growth of yeast and mold. It promotes fermentation of cheeses and vegetables, intensifying their flavor and even consistency.

## Fermenting and Pickling

Fermenting and pickling are methods of food preservation that alter the taste, texture and digestibility of a food as a result of soaking or crushing it to capture bacteria and lactic acid in the environment. The most basic pickle is a vegetable that has been preserved in a brine (salt or salty water) and allowed to age and transform. Quick commercial pickles are made by soaking cucumbers in a solution of vinegar or lemon juice without salt. They are not fermented. Fermented salt pickles are a staple of European and American cuisine as their sour salty taste is a nice contrast to sandwich meats, cheese and delicatessen foods.

Sauerkraut, a naturally fermented food of great benefit, is cultured by packing cabbage with salt and letting it ferment. Traditional dill pickles are made by fermenting cucumbers in salty water. Kimchi can be made with a variety of vegetables and spices such as cabbage, radish, garlic, anchovy and chile, plus the essential ingredient of salt. It is a staple of Asian cuisine and complement for grilled or barbequed meat and fish.

Miso and traditionally fermented Shoyu or tamari are fermented soybean products. They are used as a salt substitute on Japanese, Chinese and Asian fusion cooking. They bring the complex flavor of unami (richness) to soups, stir fry, and grilled marinades, that especially when combined with ginger, garlic or chili add a flavorful complexity to foods and act as a digestive tonic as well.

## Sea Vegetables

Sea vegetables are large, edible algae that can be harvested and eaten in soups, salads or as in wraps, either as nori, wherein the seaweed provides the wrapper, or in the filling of a tortilla filled with vegetables, sprouts and a protein spread such as hummus, cashew butter, feta or goat cheese.

Sea vegetables or seaweed, is one of the most nutrient dense foods on the planet, rich in salt, minerals and trace elements not found in land animals or plants. Very low in calories, it's a wonderful snack food to naturally boost one's metabolism. Enjoy eating seaweed such as hiziki, dulse or arame broken up into pieces with almonds in a snack mix. The salty, pungent flavor is a nice contrast to the sweet and oily taste of nuts.

## Neti Pot Salt Rinse to Clean the Sinuses

A neti pot is a do-it-yourself treatment for nasal congestion. A neti pot, which looks like a teapot, flushes mucus from your nose. Using a saline solution with the device instead of just water helps decrease irritation. It is a staple of Ayurvedic healing practices. To use the device, pour a measured saline solution into one nostril at a time. The solution will flow through your nasal cavity and come out of your other nostril. According to a 2009 study titled *Saline Nasal Irrigation for Upper Respiratory Conditions,* rinsing with saline solution can help manage numerous conditions, Rabago and Zgierska, 2009.

Saline solution may:

- cleanse your nasal cavity
- remove inflammation-causing elements
- improve the ability of your respiratory system to self-clean

## *Neti Pot Benefit and Use*

A neti pot is a clay vessel filled with saline solution for nasal irrigation to alleviate congestion. It may take an application or two to become comfortable with the procedure. If your nostrils sting during or after use, stop and dilute your saline solution by 50%. Your body will let you know when you need to use a neti pot, and when you have used it enough.

### NETI POT SOLUTION

Follow these steps to create your saline solution:

1. Add 1 teaspoon of kosher, Celtic or Himalayan salt to a 16 ounce glass of lukewarm water.
2. Add ½ teaspoon of baking soda to the glass.
3. Stir the solution.

### STEPS

1. Add the saline solution to a clean, dry neti pot
2. Bend over the sink and look straight down at the sink basin.
3. Turn your head at a 45° angle.
4. Gently press the spout of the neti pot into the nostril closest to the ceiling.
5. Breathe through your mouth during this step.
6. Tip the neti pot so the saline solution reaches your nostril.
7. Let it drain in one nostril and out the other.
8. Breathe through both nostrils to clear out your nose. Use a tissue to absorb remaining saline and mucus that drips from your nose.
9. Repeat the steps above to use the neti pot on your other nostril.
10. If you are comfortable with the process, you can irrigate both sides again, or stop when you feel you are done.

### SAFETY TIPS

1. Use distilled, filtered water, or tap water boiled for 4 minutes and cooled to room temperature.
2. Wash the neti pot with hot soap and water after each use. Air dry.
3. Discontinue use of your neti pot if it stings your nostrils or causes ear pain.
4. If using it with a young child, reduce the salt by 50% or more.
5. Never force it on anyone who isn't comfortable with the procedure.

**SOURCE:** *How to Use a Neti Pot* https://www.healthline.com/health/how-to-use-a-neti-pot

# *Salt Beverages*

Sea salt can be used to flavor curries, stir-fries, rice pilafs, grains such as millet and quinoa, in meat, tofu, smoothies, and soups. In warm weather cultures, salt may be added to fruit to enhance its flavor and protect one from dehydration. To get a wide range of trace elements without chemicals or additives use only unrefined sea or land salt rather than commercial iodized table salt.

## *Salty Lassi*

*This is a cooling drink for a hot summer night.*

SERVES 1

**INGREDIENTS**

6 oz. kefir or buttermilk
2 oz. filtered water
1 pinch ground black pepper
1 pinch dried mint
Sea salt to taste
Ice cubes (optional)

**METHOD**

1. Place all the ingredients in a blender and process until smooth.
2. Pour into a glass and enjoy.

## *Miso Chi Booster*

*Tired of yet another sweet smoothie? Try this delicious warm beverage.* Vital Scoop™ *is a green food nutrient powder formulated by Dr. Bauman.*

SERVES 4

**INGREDIENTS**

3 cups hot water
2 tablespoons white miso
1½ tablespoons nutritional yeast
1 teaspoon dulse flakes
1 scoop *Vital Scoop™* (or other green protein powder)
2 tablespoons toasted sesame seeds
¾ cup cashews, soaked for about 30 minutes
Granulated garlic, sprinkled to taste
Chili powder, sprinkled to taste

**METHOD**

1. Bring water to boil and remove from heat. Allow to cool for 5 minutes.
2. Add 2 tablespoons of miso and stir until dissolved.
3. In a blender add miso broth, nutritional yeast, dulse flakes, *Vital Scoop™*, toasted sesame seeds and cashews and process until smooth.
4. Serve with a sprinkle of granulated garlic and/or chili powder.

**SOURCE:** Bauman and Marx, *Flavors of Health Cookbook,* (2012)

# *Salt Breakfast*

## *Corn and Methi Roti*

*My wife Chris and I (Dr. B) were blessed to visit SM's mother in Bangalore, India. We loved learning preparing authentic homestyle Indian with her. The corn and methi roti, served with garlic chutney, and buffalo yogurt will be a treasure we will never forget.*

SERVES 4

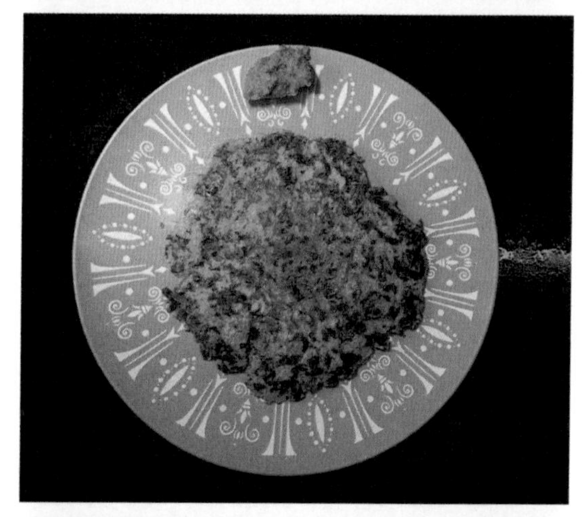

**INGREDIENTS**

4 tablespoons extra-virgin olive oil, divided
½ teaspoon cumin seeds
½ teaspoon ajwain (carom) seeds
2 cups corn flour
1 cup fresh fenugreek leaves, washed and chopped small (spinach or chard if methi not available)
½ teaspoon red chili powder
½ teaspoon ground coriander
Sea salt to taste
Water to mix the dough

**METHOD**

1. In a sauté pan, heat 1 tablespoon of oil briefly, add the cumin and ajwain seeds letting them pop at low heat.
2. Combine flour with fenugreek, red chili powder, coriander and a little salt in a large mixing bowl. Stir to combine and add toasted seeds.
3. Slowly add warm water a little at a time, stirring and combining.
4. Once the dough can be shaped into a ball, brush with a tablespoon of oil to prevent drying.
5. With your hands make 1-inch (2.5 cm) balls with the dough and place it on a chakla (a wooden cylindrical platform). Using a belan (rolling pin), roll out the dough in a round shape about 6-8 inches (15-20 cm) in diameter. (You can also use a cutting board or your kitchen countertop and traditional rolling pin).
6. Heat a non-stick pan or skillet and brush it with oil.
7. Lay the flattened roti in the pan and cook until golden brown on each side.
8. Repeat with the remaining roti, adding more oil as needed.
9. You can serve it with butter, chutney and jam.

NOTE: *Indian chakla and belan are available online. An Indian grocery store may also carry them.*

## Scottish Steel Cut Oats

*This is my (SM) daily breakfast. I have a small slow porcelain cooker. As soon I wake up, I plug it in and in 45-60 minutes I am ready to eat and smile.*

SERVES 1

### INGREDIENTS

½ cup filtered water
1 pinch sea salt
¼ cup steel cut oats
¼ cup almond milk (optional)
1 teaspoon almonds, slivered
1 pinch cinnamon powder to sprinkle
A splash of maple syrup (optional)
1 teaspoon raisins
Berries in season, amount to taste

### METHOD

1. Bring water and salt to a boil and stir in oats.
2. Lower heat and stir occasionally until oats absorb most of the water, about 20 minutes.
3. Add the almond milk in the last 10 minutes. Turn off heat and cover.
4. Allow to sit 5 minutes undisturbed to finish steaming.
5. Serve warm, add maple syrup, almond slivers, raisins, or berries (in season).

NOTE: *You can also make overnight oats by putting all the ingredients except the fruit and nuts into a jar and refrigerate. Oats will be ready in the morning, just add your favorite toppings.*

# Salt Sauce and Salad

## Mama P's Chutney

*This can be served with the "Corn and Methi Roti" recipe on page 170.*

SERVES 4

### INGREDIENTS

2 tablespoons extra-virgin olive oil
6-8 garlic cloves
1 tablespoon urad dal (black lentils)
2-3 dried red chiles (or 1 teaspoon dried chili flakes)
1 tablespoon dried or fresh coconut
1 teaspoon jaggery (Indian sugar)
1 teaspoon tamarind paste
Sea salt to taste

### METHOD

1. Heat oil in a sauté pan and add garlic. Stir until golden on all sides.
2. Add urad dal, chiles, coconut and sugar and continue stirring until toasted and fragrant.
3. Remove from heat and stir in the tamarind.
4. Place ingredients in a small spice grinder and process to your desired consistency.
5. Chill until ready to serve.

## *Salt Sauce and Salad (continued)*

## *Carrot Seaweed Salad*

*Sea vegetables are an excellent source of mineral rich salt. Carrots and seaweed make a perfect match in this salad.*

SERVES 2

**INGREDIENTS**

- ½ cup arame seaweed
- 1 teaspoon apple cider vinegar
- ½ teaspoon honey
- 1 cup carrots, grated
- ¼ teaspoon fresh dill, chopped

**METHOD**

1. Soak the seaweed for 30 minutes in a small bowl.
2. While it is soaking, whisk apple cider vinegar and honey together in a medium bowl.
3. Add carrots, dill and seaweed and toss to combine.
4. Taste and adjust seasonings.

# *Salt Remedy*

## *Sea Salt Body Scrub*

*This is a great exfoliant for dry skin.*

SERVES 1

**INGREDIENTS**

- ½ cup sea salt
- ½ cup brown sugar
- 1 tablespoon coconut oil
- 3-5 drops lemon essential oil
- 3-5 drops lavender essential oil
- 1 teaspoon raw honey

**METHOD**

1. Mix all ingredients and place in a jar.
2. Use a little at a time, and rinse with warm water.

# Salt Entree

## Salt-Bake Red Snapper

*This fish is tender and moist, with a flavor hard to beat using other cooking methods. The salt crust insulates the fish, steaming it in its own juices and sealing in flavor, while the fish's crispy outer skin prevents the salt from penetrating its flesh.*

SERVES 2-4

### INGREDIENTS

1 pound whole red snapper or branzino, scaled, gutted, fins and gills removed, rinsed and dried off
3 cups kosher salt
6 large egg whites
Fennel tops and fronds
3¼-inch (8.25 cm) lemon slices
2 fennel bulbs, sliced lengthwise in half
1 tablespoon olive oil
1 lemon, cut in half
Extra-virgin olive oil
Red pepper vinaigrette or other flavored vinaigrette
Picked fennel fronds or dill for garnish

### METHOD

1. Preheat oven to 350°F (176°C).
2. Brush fennel bulbs with olive oil, then lightly salt. Turn heat up under a medium skillet over medium-high heat until hot. Lay fennel bulbs in pan, turning until begins to become limp, brown and caramelize. Set aside.
3. In a large mixing bowl, begin combining the kosher salt and a few egg whites at a time. Mix until the combination has the feel of wet sand. To ensure correct consistency, grab a handful of mixture, squeeze it, then let go. If it sticks to your hand, incorporate more egg white.
4. Overlap, or "shingle," lemon slices, sliced fennel, and fennel tops, into the fish's cavity until full. Pack the gratin dish or oval roaster with a ½-inch (1.27 cm) thick layer of the salt-egg white mixture. Place fish on the bed of salt-egg white mixture. Begin packing more salt mixture on top of fish until completely covered. Press down on the mixture until it firmly seals the fish inside. Transfer to the oven.

*(recipe continued on page 174)*

## *Salt Entree (continued)*

# *Salt-Bake Red Snapper (continued)*

5. Bake for 20 minutes. Remove from the oven when a meat thermometer inserted through the crust into the thickest part of the fish registers 125°F (51°C).
6. Let it rest for 5-10 minutes after taking it out of oven, but not longer. Use a serrated knife to slice around the circumference of the crust, carefully avoiding cutting into the fish. Lift the salt crust off. Transfer the fish onto two layers of paper towels on the cutting board. Dust off any residual salt from the fish and cutting board.
7. Working gently, use the serrated knife to score the skin around the head and down the spine of the fish. Carefully peel the skin off the fish starting at head. Lift the top fish fillet off the vertebrae and set on serving plate. Remove the back bone and then lift the bottom fillet up in the same manner. Using tweezers, carefully pull out the rib bones.
8. Squeeze lemon juice and a drizzle of extra-virgin olive oil over the fish. Drizzle red pepper vinaigrette around the fish. Place a few caramelized fennel wedges atop the fillet, and garnish with freshly picked fennel fronds. Serve immediately for maximum flavor and enjoyment.

**SOURCE:** Recipe by Chef Thomas Keller, Master Class recipe, 2019.

# Salt Dessert

## Sea Salt Dark Chocolate Coconut Bars

*As a youth, Mounds was my favorite candy. This healthy chocolate coconut confection, sweetened with maple syrup, has it beat, hands down.*

SERVES 16 1-INCH (2.5 CM) SQUARES

### INGREDIENTS

2 cups unsweetened shredded coconut
2 tablespoons maple syrup
3 tablespoons coconut oil
1 medjool date, pitted
1 teaspoon vanilla extract
2 cups dark chocolate chips*
2 teaspoons flaky sea salt

### METHOD

1. Combine coconut, maple syrup, coconut oil, and vanilla extract in food processor. Blend until well combined into a thick, grainy paste.
2. Line a loaf pan with parchment paper, and press down coconut mixture into the pan in an even layer.
3. Refrigerate for 20-30 minutes.
4. Melt chocolate chips.
5. Remove coconut layer from fridge, and pour melted chocolate over it. Spread into an even layer, and sprinkle with sea salt.
6. Place back in the fridge for another 30 minutes, or until chocolate has completely hardened.
7. Cut into 16 1-inch (2.5 cm) squares.

NOTES: *If you wish to have sugar-free choclolate chips, you can use the stevia-sweetened Lily chocolate chips. Store in an airtight container in the fridge or freezer.*

**SOURCE:** Recipe modified from Alex Aldeborgh, MS, RDN of Daisybeet.com

## How to Make Sea Salt

*You can harvest seawater to make your own sea salt. Wherever you choose to do so, it is important to use the cleanest source possible, staying away from urban areas. Avoid water in close proximity to sewage, chemical plants, pharmaceutical plants or other similar areas to prevent contamination.*

### How to Harvest Sea Salt

1. Gather seawater in a one gallon jug.
2. Store a few days and remove any floaters.
3. Heat the sea water in a large pot, on low heat ensuring the water is below boiling point, until the water is reduced. This could take a few hours or longer if you are harvesting more water. When the level is down to 1-inch (2.5 cm) and you have a salty slurry, remove from heat.
4. Place the slurry on baking sheets. Let them dry out to remove the last bit of moisture.
5. To speed up the process you can put place pans in the oven on a low setting to dry.
6. For optimum natural taste, let the slurry dry in a cloth bag for a few days.
7. Now it is ready for grinding. Grind in a spice grinder to desired coarseness.
8. One gallon of seawater will yield about ½-1 cup of sea salt.

# Glossary

*To assist you in learning about and cooking with spices and ingredients that may be unfamiliar to you, we are including this list of terms with brief definitions to broaden your knowledge and use of these nourishing and flavorful ingredients.*

**A2 milk** is a variety of cows' milk that contains a β-casein protein known as type A2. Historically the U.S. Jersey cows were producing more A2 than A1 protein, however a mutation occurred and the cows started producing more A1 protein. The A1 protein form of casein can be more difficult to digest. A2 milk protein producers showed clinical trials to support their claim that A2 is easier to digest than A1 milk.

**Ajwain** is referred to as a seed, but is actually the fruit of the ajwain herb. It is also known as ajwain caraway, bishop's weed or carom. The herb is commonly used in Indian cuisine where the "seeds" and the leaves are used. The seeds are greenish brown in color and look similar to cumin or caraway, but the flavor is closer to thyme. They are rich in fiber, minerals, vitamins and antioxidants and have been shown to have anti-bacterial, anti-fungal and anti-inflammatory properties. Available in specialty markets and online.

**Arame**, or sea oak, is a species of kelp indigenous to the Pacific ocean and popular in Japanese cuisine. It has a mild, delicate flavor and texture. It is commonly sold dried and is reconstituted by soaking in warm water. Arame is rich in iodine, calcium and potassium. It is available in health food stores and markets, or online.

**Arborio rice** is a starchy short-grain rice originally from the town of Arborio in northern Italy. It is primarily used to make risotto because it releases its starches during cooking providing a creamy texture. It is available in most markets or online.

**Asafetida** comes from the gum resin of a perennial fennel plant called *ferula asafoetida*. The resin is ground into a powder and most often used in Indian and Iranian cooking. Its pungent scent is tamed when cooked, and its taste is described as a pleasant onion or leek flavor. Studies suggest it may be useful for digestion and in treating pain, respiratory and reproductive issues and mood disorders. Available in specialty markets and online.

**Biryani** is a Persian-inspired rice dish from the Mughal dynasty in India. Mughal cooking, called "dum" is a slow cooking method. Biryani is typically rice combined with meats, nuts, dried fruits and potatoes. The meat or a vegetable protein is marinated with spices such as ginger, cloves, pepper and cinnamon and combined with rice. It is cooked very slowly to release a complex, pleasant aroma and exquisite flavor.

**Bomba rice** is a short-grain variety of rice, primarily cultivated in eastern Spain. It is commonly used in paella because it can absorb three times its volume in liquid without becoming sticky. It is also called Valencia rice. Available in specialty markets and online.

**Bouillabaisse** is a hearty stew first made by fishermen in the French port city of Marseilles from the fish scraps that couldn't be sold to restaurants or markets. It typically features fish and seafood with tomatoes and potatoes in a spice mix that includes garlic and saffron imparting a beautiful aroma, flavor and color.

**Channa** is the Indian name for chickpeas. Different types are known as gram or Bengal gram, garbanzo or garbanzo bean, Egyptian pea, chana, and chole. Chickpea seeds are high in protein, vitamins, minerals and fiber. Chickpeas prepared with a blend of Indian spices is a staple of traditional vegetarian Indian cuisine.

**Chia seeds** are tiny oval seeds from the plant *Salvia hispanica* which is part of the mint family. They come in black or white and are rich in protein, fatty acids, minerals, antioxidants and soluble fiber. Black seeds tend to have a higher protein content and white seeds are higher in Omega 3 fatty acids.

**Consommé** is a clear soup made from a stock that has been reduced and clarified. Egg whites are then added to remove fat and sediment. It is a time-consuming process that yields a clean and deeply flavored soup.

**Curry leaves** are small shiny leaves grown on the curry leaf tree, native to India. They are not related to curry powder which is a blend of other spices, herbs and seeds. They impart a pungent citrus flavor and aroma to food. They are high in antioxidants, fiber, calcium vitamins and minerals. You can find them fresh or dried at specialty markets and online.

**Dried barberries** are deep red and tart berries grown on a shrub or bush in Europe, North Africa, the Middle East and Central Asia. Organic barberries have been used medicinally for centuries to treat digestive issues, skin conditions and infections. The fruit, stem and root bark contain *berberine* which is anti-bacterial and anti-inflammatory. Available in specialty markets and online.

**Dried black limes** are small limes that have been blanched in salt brine and then dried in the sun or dehydrated. They are used whole or ground in dishes from Iran, Iraq and Northern India. Dried limes are used to add flavor to soups, stews and rice dishes. They are sour, with a citrus and smoky flavor. In their powdered form they can be rubbed on meats, sprinkled on grains or added to beverages or tea. Available at specialty stores and online.

**Edamame** are young, green soybeans usually sold in their pods fresh or frozen. They are different from mature soy beans which are tan or beige, similar to tofu or tempeh. Edamame pods are boiled or steamed and may be served with salt or other condiments. This low calorie snack is high in protein and rich in vitamins and minerals.

**Fenugreek** is a fragrant herb, native to southeastern Europe and western Asia, but now cultivated worldwide. Its seeds and leaves are used in Indian cuisine imparting a slightly sweet and nutty flavor. The seeds are brown in color and taste bitter. Dry roasting them brings out a sweet, slightly maple flavor. Methi is the Hindi word for the fresh fenugreek leaves. It is great for the digestive track. Dried methi can be substituted for fresh. Available fresh and dried from specialty stores and online.

**Garam masala** is a dry roasted powdered blend of spices that play an integral role in Indian cuisine. It originated in Northern India, with its colder climate to provide warmth to the cuisine of that region. There is no one masala recipe, but a typical garam masala includes cumin, coriander, cloves, cinnamon, nutmeg, cardamom and black pepper. Blends vary by region and recipes are passed down through families.

**Ghee** is a clear form of butter with the milk solids and water removed. It is different from traditional clarified butter because the milk solids are cooked longer and allowed to brown giving it a nuttier flavor. It can be made by slowly simmering unsalted butter in a pan, straining off surface milk solids. It is ready when the butter turns light gold and remaining solids turn brown and sink to the bottom of the pan. The mixture can then be strained through a cheesecloth and the liquid ghee saved in a sealed glass jar. Ghee is widely sold in natural food stores and available online.

**Gluten-free flour** is wheat-free flour. Varieties include almond, buckwheat, teff, sorghum, amaranth, rice, oat, millet, tapioca, garbanzo and arrowroot flours. They all behave differently and cannot be used interchangeably. Gluten-free flour blends, such as *Bob's Red Mill*, are the best substitute for wheat flour. Nut and seed flours can be made by grinding nuts or seeds at home or purchased as a ground meal. Both flours and meals are best refrigerated to prevent oxidation by heat and light.

**Golden milk** is a beverage traditionally made with cow's milk, turmeric, ginger and black pepper. Nut or coconut milk can be used instead. Its anti-inflammatory, antioxidant and digestive properties are reported to improve sleep.

**Gremolata** adds a burst of flavor to meat, fish and pasta dishes when added as a condiment or garnish and is commonly used in Mediterranean cuisine. It usually consists of freshly chopped parsley, lemon zest and garlic, although mint, basil or cilantro can be substituted for the parsley as well.

**Jaggery** is an unprocessed unrefined sugar made from cane juice and sometimes date palm sap. It has a caramel brown-sugar like flavor. Its color can vary from golden to dark brown in color. 70% of all jaggery comes from India where a lighter colored jaggery is preferred. Jaggery is slightly healthier than refined sugar because of its molasses content, but should still be used in moderation.

**Kashaya** is a term that comes from Ayurveda and refers to a drink to support cold, sore throat and flu symptoms. The drink can often include tulsi holy basil, black peppercorns, coriander, cumin, ginger, ajwain seeds and honey.

**Kasuri methi** is the name used in India for dried fenugreek leaves. The taste is compared to celery and fennel with a slightly bitter bite. Methi is a very popular herb in Indian, Persian and North African cuisines. Available in specialty stores and online.

**Kombu** is a sea kelp popular in Japanese cuisine. It can be used in soups, stocks and to flavor rice and bean dishes. It adds a rich "umami" and slightly salty flavor when infused into foods. Kombu is sold dried in large slices, pickled in vinegar or dried and shredded. It is one of three main ingredients in Dashi (Japanese fish stock). Kombu is a great source of iodine, vitamins, minerals, Omega 3s and amino acids.

**Mace**, the spice, should not be confused with the popular pepper spray with the same name. The spice comes from the red lacy coating (or aril) covering the nutmeg seed. It is removed from the seed and broken into pieces called blades. Mace has a strong aromatic flavor described as a cross between nutmeg, cardamom and cinnamon with a hint of citrus and pepper.

**Masala** is the generic name for a blend of spices used in Indian cuisine. It can be made from any number of spices either dried or ground into a paste. Some common North Indian blends include cumin, coriander, cayenne, black peppercorns, clove and cardamom.

**Masala chai** is black tea with spices such as ginger, cinnamon, cloves and milk. The typical preparation method is to simmer all the ingredients in water and milk and sweeten at the end.

**Methi roti** is a pan grilled flatbread made with fresh fenugreek (methi) leaves and flour.

**Moong dal** refers to split mung beans. When opened they appear as tiny yellow or green split peas. They cook faster and do not need to be soaked in advance. They are packed with protein and fiber and are low in fat, thus are considered beneficial for weight loss.

**Njavara rice** is a red rice grown in India used in Ayurvedic medicine. It is reported to support the immune system, and aid in the management of diabetes, rheumatoid arthritis and osteoporosis. Available in specialty markets and online.

**Paella** is a popular dish in Spanish cuisine, originally from Valencia. It is made with bomba rice and usually includes saffron, chicken, seafood, chorizo sausage and peas cooked and served in a large shallow "paella" pan.

**Palak** is the Indian name for spinach. A popular vegetarian dish called palak paneer consists of cubed paneer cheese in a thick sauce made from puréed spinach and seasoned with ginger, garlic, garam masala, and other spices.

**Paneer** is a homemade fresh cheese made by curdling milk with an acid like lemon juice or vinegar. One can make the paneer at home from whole milk. It is also available in Indian grocery stores and many natural food markets.

**Poblano pepper** is a mild flavored chili pepper from Puebla, Mexico. Deep green when fresh, the peppers turn dark red and become hotter as they ripen. Stuffed fresh and roasted they are popular in Latin American dishes such as "Chiles Rellenos Poblano." If allowed to dry in the sun the peppers turn reddish brown and are called ancho chilis or chile ancho. Dried and ground into a spice, they impart a sweet, hot and smoky flavor to dishes like "Mole Poblano."

**Rajma** is a popular vegetarian curry made with red kidney beans in a thick tomato-based sauce with a blend of whole Indian spices. It is usually served with rice.

**Rapid rise yeast** or quick rise yeast is dry yeast that doesn't need to be "proofed" or hydrated before adding to flour. It only requires one rise of the dough before baking. It may include ascorbic acid which is used as a dough conditioner.

**Red gram/dal**, also known as red gram or tur are small, round or oval legumes. In English, they are commonly known as pigeon peas and they are widely consumed in Asia, Africa, and Latin America. They are a great source of fiber and potassium.

**Tamarind** is a tropical fruit native to Africa, but it also grows in India, Pakistan, Southeast Asia and the West Indies. The fruit grows in bean-like pods filled with seeds surrounded by a fibrous pulp. Once ripe, the pulp can be extracted and made into a tart paste. Tamarind is popular in Indian chutneys and curries, to tenderize meats, as a sauce in Thai cuisine, in beverages and desserts in Latin America. Available in specialty markets and online.

**Tandoori masala** is a mixture of spices blended for use when cooking with a tandoor, or clay oven, in traditional Indian cooking. The typical spices include garam masala, garlic, ginger, onion, and cayenne pepper. The spices are traditionally ground together with a mortar and pestle. Tandoori masala is combined with yogurt to make Tandoori chicken and roasted in a clay pot at high heat. When prepared in this fashion, the chicken has a pink-colored exterior and a savory flavor.

**Thai chili paste** is a spicy chili sauce typical of Thai cuisine. Ingredients typically include fresh or dry chilies, garlic, shallots, lime juice, fish or shrimp paste. Traditionally, the ingredients are pounded together using a mortar and pestle, with either salt or fish sauce added to taste. Blended Thai chili paste can be purchased at a Thai or natural food market or online.

**Urad dal** is a lentil that is also called black gram. Urad dal is a high protein black lentil which comes in three categories: whole urad, split urad with skin and split urad without the skin. Available in specialty markets and online.

**Wakame** is a super nutritious seaweed harvested in thin green strands and often used in seaweed salad and miso soup. A hallmark of Japanese cuisine, it has a subtle, sweet flavor and sturdy texture. It can be used dried or fresh and like other sea vegetables is high in iodine, Omega 3s and minerals.

# Shopping Guide for Spices and Special Ingredients

When looking to purchase spices, aim to buy whole leaf, root or seeds that you can grind yourself in your own kitchen. These will be the freshest and most flavorful. If you purchase bulk spices from a natural grocery from open containers, smell the spice to see if it has a pungent aroma. Spices that you purchase online, whether whole spices, powders, or tinctures, are sold in sealed containers. Start by buying one or two ounces of an unknown product to see if you like it. If it is excellent quality as you determine from the smell, taste and effect, you can purchase more for your pantry.

Many of the spices in our book come from India. Look for an Indian market locally and get to know the owner or buyer. Ask him or her if their bulk or packages are fresh. When did they arrive? How long have they been on the shelves? Below is a list of online shopping sites for spices, herbs and special ingredients that you may not be able to find in your natural, ethnic, or gourmet food market.

## Indian and International Spices

- https://www.thespicehouse.com/collections/india?
- https://www.myspicesage.com/spices-seasonings
- https://indiangrocery.com/Cooking-Essentials/Spice-Mixes
- https://www.myspicer.com
- https://www.savoryspiceshop.com
- https://www.penzeys.com
- https://www.spicejungle.com
- https://www.thrive.com
- https://www.amazon.com

## Ayurvedic Spices and Products

- https://ayurvedamegastore.com
- https://indianonlinespices.com
- https://wholesale.khanapakana.com
- https://www.ayurvedicherbsdirect.com
- https://www.banyanbotanicals.com/shop/category/bulk-herbs-spices-formulas
- https://www.pureindianfoods.com/spice-blends-s/62.htm

## Herb and Spice Tinctures and Supplements

- https://www.gaiaherbs.com
- https://www.innateresponse.com
- https://www.douglaslabs.com
- https://www.prairieherbfarms.com
- https://www.mountainroseherbs.com
- https://www.starwestbotanicals.com
- https://www.dragonherbarium.com
- https://www.herbco.com
- https://www.livingearthherbs.com
- https://www.amazon.com

# References and Recommended Websites


## INTRODUCTION

Bauman, E., and Marx, L. (2012). *Flavors of Health Cookbook.* Bauman College Press

Duke, JA., Editor. (2002). *CRC Handbook of Medicinal Spices.* Routledge Publishing. CRC Press

Go, A., Mozaffarian, D., Roger, VL., Benjamin, EJ., Berry, JD., & Blaha, MJ., et al. (2014 update). Heart disease and stroke statistics. *Circulation [Online],* 128. doi:10.1161/01.cir.0000441139.02102.80

Hasani-Ranjbar, S., Jouyandeh, Z., & Abdollahi, M. (2013). A systematic review of anti-obesity medicinal plants — An update. *J Diabetes Metab Disord,* [Online], 12(1):28. doi:10.1186/2251-6581-12-28

Hossain, M. (2011). Fish as source of n-3 *polyunsaturated fatty acids* (PUFAs): Which one is better-farmed or wild?. *Advance J Food Sci Technol,* 3(6): 455-66

Kumar, VR., Inamdar MN., Nayeemunnisa., & Viswanatha GL.(2011). Protective effect of lemongrass oil against dexamethasone induced hyperlipidemia in rats: possible role of decreased lecithin cholesterol acetyl transferase activity. *Asian Pac J Trop Med,* (8):658-60 doi: 10.1016/S1995-7645(11)60167-3

Mozaffarian, D., Lemaitre RN., King IB., Song X., Huang H., & Sacks FM. et al. (2013). Plasma phospholipid long-chain ω-3 fatty acids and total and cause-specific mortality in older adults: A cohort study. *Ann Intern Med [Online],* 158(7): 515-525

Nichols, P., Glencross, B., Petrie, JR., & Singh, SP. (2014). Readily available sources of long-chain omega-3 oils: Is farmed Australian seafood a better source of the good oil than wild-caught seafood? *Nutrients [Online],* 6(3), 1063-79

Free-range eggs contain more vitamin D according to Mother Earth News Study. (2009). *Organic Consumers Association* (OCA), Retrieved from http://www.organicconsumers.org/articles/article_17169.cfm

Sahib, A. (2016 Feb 21). Anti-diabetic and antioxidant effect of cinnamon in poorly controlled type-2 diabetic Iraqi patients: A randomized, placebo-controlled clinical trial. *J Intercult Ethnopharmaco,* 5(2):108-13. doi: 10.5455/jice.20160217044511. eCollection

Urpi-Sarda, M., Casas, R., Chiva-Blanch, G., Romero-Mamani, ES., & Valderas-Martínez P. et al. (2012, Jun). Virgin olive oil and nuts as key foods of the Mediterranean diet effects on inflammatory biomarkers related to atherosclerosis [Abstract]. *Pharmacol Res,* 65(6): 577-83. Available from: doi:10.1016/j.

## CHAPTER ONE: TURMERIC

Aggarwal, B., Takada, Y., & Oommen, OV. (2006). From traditional Ayurvedic medicine to modern medicine: Identification of therapeutic targets for suppression of inflammation and cancer. *Expert Opin Ther Targets,*10, 87-118 [PubMed]

Aggarwal, B. (2004). From chemoprevention to chemotherapy: Common targets and common goals. *Expert Opin Investig Drugs,* 3:1327-38 [PubMed]

Ali, N., Yeap, SK., Abu, N., Lim, KL., Ky, H., Pauzi, AZM, & Akhtar, MN. (2017 Feb 21). Synthetic curcumin derivative DK possessed G2/M arrest and induced apoptosis through accumulation of intracellular ROS in MCF-7 breast cancer cells. *Cancer Cell Int.,* 17:30. doi: 10.1186/s12935-017-0400-3.

Alschuler, Lise. (2018). Turmeric (Curcuma longa) *An Overview of the Research and Clinical Indications. NANP* (Whitepaper)

Anand, P., Kunnumakkara, AB., Newman, RA., & Aggarwal, BB. (2007). Bioavailability of curcumin: problems and promises. *Mol Pharm,* 4(6):807-818. doi: 10.1021/mp700113r

Araujo, C. and Leon, LL. (2001). Biological activities of Curcuma longa L. *Mem Inst Oswaldo Cruz,* 96:723-8.

Bayet, R., Kwiatkowski, F., Leheurteur, M., Gachon, F., Planchat, E., Abrial C, & Chollet, P. (2010 Jan 21) Phase I dose escalation trial of docetaxel plus curcumin in patients with advanced and metastatic breast cancer. *MCancer Biol Ther.* 9(1):8-14

Belcaro, G., Cesarone, MR., Dugall, M., Pellegrini, L., Ledda, A., Grossi, MG., & Togni, S. (2010 December). Appendino efficacy and safety of Meriva®, a curcumin-phosphatidylcholine complex, during extended administration in osteoarthritis patients. *Altern Med Rev*

Bundy, R., Walker, A., F, Middleton, RW., & Booth, J. (2004). Turmeric extract may improve irritable bowel syndrome symptomology in otherwise healthy adults: A pilot study. *J Altern Complement Med.*;10:1015-8. [PubMed]

Disilvestro, RA., Joseph, E., Zhao, S., & Joshua, B. (2012;11(1). Diverse effects of a low dose supplement of lipidated curcumin in healthy middle aged people. *Nutr J.* :79. doi: 10.1186/1475-2891-11-79.[PMC free article] [PubMed] [Cross Ref]

Golombick, T., Diamond, TH., Manoharan, A., & Ramakrishna, R. (2012 May). Monoclonal gammopathy of undetermined significance, smoldering multiple myeloma, and curcumin: a randomized, double-blind placebo-controlled cross-over 4g study and an open-label 8g extension study. *Am J Hematol.;* 87(5): 455-60. doi: 10.1002/ajh.23159. Epub

Gupta, S., Patchva, S., & Aggarwal, B. (2013 Jan; 15(1)). Therapeutic Roles of Curcumin: Lessons Learned from Clinical Trials. *AAPS J.* 195-218. PMCID: PMC3535097

Hallman, K., Aleck, K., Dwyer, B., Lloyd, Quigley, Meghan, Sitto Nada., Siebert, AE., & Dinda. (2017) The effects of turmeric (curcumin) on tumor suppressor protein (p53) and estrogen receptor (ERα) in breast cancer cells *Breast Cancer (Dove Med Press)*. 9:153-161. doi: 10.2147/BCTT.S125783. eCollection

He, ZY., Shi, CB., Wen, H., Li, FL., Wang BL., & Wang. (2011 Mar) Upregulation of p53 expression in patients with colorectal cancer by administration of curcumin. Format; 29(3):208-13. doi: 10.3109/07357907.2010.550592. *Cancer Invest*

Ide, H., Tokiwa, S., Sakamaki, K., Nishio, K., Isotani, S., & Muto, S. (2010). Combined inhibitory effects of soy isoflavones and curcumin on the production of prostate-specific antigen. *Prostate.* ;70(10):1127-1133. doi: 10.1002/pros.21147. [PubMed] [Cross Ref

Kanai, M., Yoshimura, K., Asada, M., Imaizumi, A., Suzuki, C., Matsumoto, S., & Aggarwal, BB. (Jul 2011). A phase I/II study of gemcitabine-based chemotherapy plus curcumin for patients with gemcitabine-resistant pancreatic cancer. *Cancer ChemotherPharmacol.;* 68(1): 157-64. doi: 10.1007/s00280-010-1470-2. Epub 2010 Sep 22.

Khosropanah, MH., Dinarvand, A., Nezhadhosseini, A., Haghighi, A., Hashemi, S., Nirouzad, F., & Dehghani H. (2016 Winter); Analysis of the antiproliferative effects of curcumin and nanocurcumin in MDA-MB231 as a Breast Cancer Cell Line. *Iran J Pharm Res* 15(1):231-9.

Kuttan, R., Sudheeran, PC., & Joseph, CD.(1987 Feb 28); Turmeric and curcumin as topical agents in cancer therapy. 73(1):29-31. *Tumori.*

Marcus, and Craze, R., (2000) *The Herb and Spice Companion*; p. 83. Quantum Publishing.

Polasa, K., Raghuram, TC., Krishna, TP., & Krishnaswamy, K. (2000). Effect of turmeric on urinary mutagens in Mills S, Bone K. *Principles and Practice of Phytotherapy.* Toronto, ON: Churchill Livingstone

Prucksunand, C., Indrasukhsri, B., Leethochawalit, M., & Hungspreugs, K. Southeast Asian J Trop Med Public Health. (2001 Mar). Phase II clinical trial on effect of the long turmeric (Curcuma longa Linn) on healing of peptic ulcer. *Southeast Asian J Trop Med Public Health Mar* 2001; 32(1): 208-15.

Quispe-Soto, ET., and Calaf, GM. (2016 Dec) 49(6): Effect of curcumin and paclitaxel on breast carcinogenesis. *Int J Oncol.* 49(6): 2569-77 doi: 10.3892/

Ruby, AJ., Kuttan, G., Babu, KD., Rajasekharan, KN., & Kuttan R. (1995). Anti-tumour and antioxidant activity of natural curcuminoids. *Cancer Lett* ;94:79-83. [PubMed]

Ryan, JL., Heckler, CE., Ling, M., Katz, A., & Williams, JP., (2013 Jul ). Curcumin for radiation dermatitis: a randomized, double-blind, placebo-controlled clinical trial of thirty breast cancer patients. *Radiat Res*;180(1): 34-43. doi: 10.1667/RR3255.1. Epub 2013 Jun 7. Pentland, AP, Morrow, GR.

Saab, MB., Estephan, E., Bec, N., Larroque, M., Aulombard, R., Cloitre, T., & Gergely, CJ. (2011 Aug;4) (Multi-microscopic study of curcumin effect on fixed non-malignant and cancerous mammalian epithelial cells. *Biophotonics.* 7-8):533-43. doi: 10.1002jbio.201000119. Epub

Selvam, R., Subramanian, L., Gayathri, R., & Angayarkanni (1995) The anti-oxidant activity of turmeric (Curcuma longa) *J Ethnopharmacol.* ;47:59-67. [PubMed]

Shoba, G., Joy, D., Joseph, T., Majeed, M., Rajendran, R., & Srinivas, PS. (1998). Influence of piperine on the pharmacokinetics of curcumin in animals and human volunteers. *Planta Med.* 64(4):353-356. doi: 10.1055/s-2006-957450. [PubMed] [Cross Ref]

Subhashini, CPS. and Singh, R. (2016 May-Jun) Ovalbumin-induced allergic inflammation lead to structural alterations in mouse model and protective effects of intranasal curcumin: A comparative study. *Allergol Immunopathol* (Madr).; 44(3):246-56. doi: 10.1016/j.aller.2016.01.001. Epub 2016 Apr 1.

Sugawara, J., Akazawa, N., Miyaki, A., Choi, Y., Tanabe, Y., Imai, T., & Maeda, S. (2012 Jun) Effect of endurance exercise training and curcumin intake on central arterial hemodynamics in postmenopausal women: pilot study. *Am J Hypertens.* ;25(6):651-6. doi: 10.1038/ajh.24. Epub

Usharani, P., Mateen, AA., Naidu, MU., Raju, YS., & Chandra, N. ( 2008). Effect of NCB-02, atorvastatin and placebo on endothelial function, oxidative stress and inflammatory markers in patients with type-2 diabetes mellitus: a randomized, parallel-group, placebo-controlled, 8-week study. *Drugs R D.* 2008;9(4):243-50.

Winston, D. (2016) Herbal Therapeutics: Specific Indications for Herbs & Herbal Formulas (10th Edition) pp.58. *Herbalist & Alchemist,* Washington, NJ 07882

Wu, S., and Xiao, D. (Dec 2016) Effect of curcumin on nasal symptoms and airflow in patients with perennial allergic rhinitis. *Ann Allergy Asthma Immunol.;* 117(6): 697-702. e1 doi: 10.1016/j.anai.2016.09.427. Epub 2016 Oct 24.

Yallapu, MM., Nagesh, PK., Jaggi, M., & Chauhan, SC. (Nov 2015) Therapeutic Applications of Curcumin Nanoformulations. *AAPS J.;* 17(6): 1341-56. doi: 10.1208/s12248-015-9811-z. Epub 2015 Sep 3.

## CHAPTER ONE: RECOMMENDED WEBSITES

*Spice Board of India*: http://www.indianspices.com/spices-development/properties/medicinal-other-values-spices

Bauman College: http://www.baumancollege.org

Bernhardt, Ed (2008), *Medicinal Plants of Costa Rica*, pp. 106-107 www.zonatropical.net

http://www.whfoods.com; http://www.medindia.net/patients/lifestyleandwellness/fenugreek.htm

Winston, David, (2014) *Herbal Therapeutics*, p. 156. http://www.herbaltherapeutics.net

How to grow turmeric: dailyhealthpost.com/how-to-grow-turmeric-indoors-it-is-far-better-than-buying-it

http://www.whfoods.com

## CHAPTER TWO: BASIL

Amrani, S., Harnafi, H., Bouanani, Nel, H., Aziz, M., Caid, HS., Manfredini, S., & Bravo, E. (2006 Dec). Hypolipidaemic activity of aqueous ocimum basilicum extract in acute hyperlipidaemia induced by triton WR-1339 in rats and its antioxidant property. *Phytother Res,* 20(12):1040-5

Bhattacharyya, D., Sur, TK., Jana, U., & Debnath, PK. (2008 Sep). Controlled programmed trial of ocimum sanctum leaf on generalized anxiety disorders. *Nepal Med Coll J,* 10(3):176-9

Cohen, MM. (2014 Oct-Dec). Ocimum sanctum: Tulsi — a herb for all reasons. *J Ayurveda Integr Med,* 5(4):251-9. doi: 10.4103/0975-9476.146554

Dhandayuthapani, S., Azad, H., & Rathinavelu, A. (2015 Jul). Apoptosis induction by ocimum sanctum extract in LNCaP Prostate Cancer Cells. 18(7). *Med Food, J* 776-85. doi: 10.1089/jmf.2014.0008. Epub 2015 Feb 18

Goel, RK., Sairam, K., Dorababu, M., Prabha, T., & Rao, ChV. (2005 Aug). Effect of standardized extract of Ocimum sanctum Linn. on gastric mucosal offensive and defensive factors. *Indian J Exp Biol.* 715-21;43(8)

Kelm, MA., Nair, MG., Strasburg, GM., & DeWitt, DL. (2000 Mar). Antioxidant and cyclooxygenase inhibitory phenolic compounds from Ocimum sanctum Linn. *Phytomedicine,* 7(1):7-13

Magesh, V., Lee, JC., Ahn, KS., Lee HJ., Lee, HJ., Lee, EO., & Kim, SH. (2009 Oct;23(10) Ocimum sanctum induces apoptosis in A549 lung cancer cells and suppresses the in vivo growth of Lewis lung carcinoma cells. *Phytother Res,* :1385-91. doi: 10.1002/ptr.2784

Manaharan, T., Thirugnanasampandan, R., Jayakumar, R., Kanthimathi, MS., Ramya, G., & Ramnath, MG. (2016 May12(Suppl 3). Purified essential oil from ocimum sanctum linn. triggers the apoptotic mechanism in human breast cancer cells. *Pharmacogn,* S327-31; doi: 10.4103/0973-1296.185738

Matiz, G., Osorio, MR., Camacho, F., Atencia, M., & Herazo, J. (2012 Jan-Mar). Effectiveness of antimicrobial formulations for acne based on orange (Citrus sinensis) and sweet basil (Ocimum basilicum L) essential oils] *Biomedica* ;32(1):125-33. doi: 10.1590/S0120-41572012000100014

Mondal, S., Varma, S., Bamola, VD., Naik, SN., Mirdha, BR., Padhi, MM., & Mahapatra SC. (2011 Jul 14. Epub 2011 May 17). Double-blinded randomized controlled trial for immunomodulatory effects of tulsi (ocimum sanctum linn.) leaf extract on healthy volunteers, 136(3):452-6. doi: 10.1016/j.jep.2011.05.012

Phasomkusolsil, S. and Soonwera, M., (2010 Jul) (4.Insect repellent activity of medicinal plant oils against aedes aegypti (linn.), anopheles minimus (Theobald) and Culex quinquefasciatus assay based on protection time and biting rate. *Southeast Asian J Trop Med Public Health,* 831-40;41

Rai, V., Iyer, U., & Mani, U. V. (1997). Effect of tulsi (ocimum sanctum) leaf powder supplementation on blood sugar levels, serum lipids and tissue lipids in diabetic rats. *Plant Foods Hum Nutr,* 50(1):9-16.

Rastogi, S., Shukla, Y., Paul, BN., Chowdhuri, DK, & Khanna, SK. (2007 Nov 1; Epub 2007 Jun 22). Protective effect of ocimum sanctum on 3-methylcholanthrene 7,12-dimethylbenz(a)anthracene and aflatoxin B1 induced skin tumorigenesis in mice. *Das. M.Toxicol Appl Pharmacol,* 224(3):228-40

Saxena, RC., Singh, R., Kumar, P., Negi, MP., Saxena, VS., & Geetharani P., et al. (2012). Efficacy of an extract of ocimum tenuiflorum (OciBest) in the management of general stress: a double-blind, placebo-controlled study. *Evid Based Complement Alternat Med,* 894509. [PMC free article

Sen, P., Maiti, P. C., Puri, S., Ray, A., Audulov, NA, & Valdman, AV. (1992). Mechanism of anti-stress activity of ocimum sanctum linn, eugenol and tinospora malabarica in experimental animals. *Indian J Exp.Biol,* 30(7):592-596

Shimizu, T., Torres, MP., Chakraborty, S., Souchek, JJ., Rachagani, S., Kaur ,S & Batra, SK. (2013 Aug 19, Epub 2013 Mar 21). Holy Basil leaf extract decreases tumorigenicity and metastasis of aggressive human pancreatic cancer cells in vitro and in vivo: potential role in therapy. *Cancer Lett,* 336(2):270-80. doi: 10.1016/j.canlet.2013.03.017

Shivpuje, P., Ammanangi, R., Bhat, K., & Katti., S. (2015 Sep 1). Effect of Ocimum sanctum on oral cancer cell line: an in vitro dtudy. *J. Contemp Dent Pract,* 16(9):709-14

Yates, B., (2019). Basil (Ocimum sanctum) An Overview of the Research and Clinical Indications. *Gai Herbs Professional solutions (whitepaper)*

## CHAPTER TWO: RECOMMENDED WEBSITES

*Spice Board of India*: http://www.indianspices.com/spices-development/properties/medicinal-other-values-spices

https://www.britannica.com/plant/basil

http://www.whfoods.com

https://www.mdidea.com/products/proper/proper086research.html

http://en.wikipedia.org/wiki/Ocimum_tenuiflorum; http://www.chopra.com

https://www.youtube.com/watch?v=UOV53h6Vpfs

https://www.organicfacts.net/health-benefits/herbs-and-spices/health-benefits-of-holy-basil-tulsi.html#Treats_Asthma

https://en.wikipedia.org/wiki/Tulsi_in_Hinduism

https://en.wikipedia.org/wiki/Thai_basil

http://balconygardenweb.com/how-to-grow-tulsi-plant-care-and-growing-holy-basil

https://www.naturalnewsblogs.com/holy-basil-cancer-treatment/ (Dr. Adem Gunes, 2016)

https://thetruthaboutcancer.com/holy-basil-benefits/ (Dr. David Jockers, 2017)

## CHAPTER THREE: ASHWAGANDHA

Abbas, A., Mahdi., Kamla Kant, S., Mohammad, KA., Singh. R., Satya Narain, S., Vishwajeet Singh, Deepansh, & Dalela, E. Based Complement Alternat Med. (2011; 2011 Jun 18). Withania somnifera improves semen quality in stress-related male fertility. *Evid. Based Complement Alternat Med.* Published online doi: 10.1093/ecam/nep138 PMCID: PMC3136684 PMID: 19789214 576962

Abbas, SS. and Singh, N. (2006). Anti-stress agents herbs of Indian origin — herbal drugs, a twenty first century perspective. *Delhi: Institute of Nuclear Medicine and Allied Sciences, Defence Research and Development Organization* (DRDO), *Govt. of India;* pp. 578-591 [Ref list]

Andallu, B., & Radhika, B. (2000 Jun). Hypoglycemic, diuretic and hypocholesterolemic effect of winter cherry (Withania somnifera, Dunal) root. Indian J Exp Biol;38(6):607-9

Atta-ur-Rahman, Samina-Abbas, Dur-e-Shahwar, Jamal, SA., Choudhary, MI., & Abbas, S. (1991). New withanolides from withania spp. *Journal of Natural Products* 56: 1000-1006

Bhandari, CR. (1970). *Ashwagandha (Withania somnifera) Vanaushadhi Chandroday An encyclopedia of Indian herbs) Vol. 1.* Varanasi, India: CS series of Varanasi Vidyavilas Press; pp. 96-97. [Ref list]

Chandrasekhar, K., Kapoor, J., & Anishetty., K;. (2012 Jul-Sep). A prospective, randomized double-blind, placebo-controlled study of safety and efficacy of a high-concentration full-spectrum extract of ashwagandha root in reducing stress and anxiety in adults. *Indian J Psychol MedZ;* 34(3): 255-262. doi: 10.4103/0253-7176.106022PMCID: PMC3573577 PMID: 23439798

Choi, BY. and Kim, BW. (2015). Withaferin-a Inhibits colon cancer cell growth by blocking STAT3 transcriptional activity. *J Cancer Prev.* ;20:185-192. [PMC free article] [PubMed]

Dongre, Swati., Langade, Deepak., & Bhattacharyya, S. (2015). Efficacy and safety of ashwagandha (withania somnifera) root extract in improving sexual function in women: a pilot study. *Hindawi Publishing Corporation BioMed Research International Volume,* Article ID 284154, 9 pages http://dx.doi.org/10.1155/2015/284154

Ghosal, S., Srivastava, RS., Bhattacharya, SK., Upadhyay, SN., Jaiswal, AK., & Chattopadhyay, U. (1989). Immunomodulatory and CNS effects of sitoindosides IX and X, two new glycowithanolides form withania somnifera. *Phytother. Res.*, 2:201-206

Gupta, RC., Bansal, SS., Aqil, F., Jeyabalan, J., Cao, P., Kausar, H., Vadhanam, MV. Controlled-release systemic delivery — a new concept in cancer chemoprevention. *Carcinogenesis.* 2012;33:1608-1615. [PMC free article] [PubMed]

Kalsi, R., Singh, N., & Gupta, GP. (1987). Effects of stress and anti-stress drugs on *succinate dehydrogenase enzyme* (SDH) in rat brain (A possible role of SDH in stress adaptation phenomenon) physiology of human performance, defence *Institute of physiology and allied sciences, defence research and development organization* (DRDO), *Govt. of India,* Delhi, 114-117

Khazal, KLF., Samuel, T., Hill, D, and Grubs CJ. ; (2013 Apr); 33(4): 1519-1523. PMCID: PMC3675906 NIHMSID: NIHMS475189 PMID: 23564793 Effect of an Extract of Withania somnifera Root on Estrogen Receptor-positive Mammary Carcinomas *Anti Cancer Res.*

Kritikar, KR. and Basu, BD. (1935). *Withania somnifera, Indian medicinal plants.* 2nd Edition. IIIrd. Lalit Mohan Basu, Allahabad; pp. 1774-1776. [Ref list]

Misra, B. *Ashwagandha — Bhavprakash Nigantu (Indian Materia Medica) Varanasi:* Chaukhambha Bharti Academy; 2004. pp. 393-394. [Ref list]

Munagala, R., Kausar, H., Munjal, C., & Gupta, RC. (2011 Nov; Epub 2011 Aug 22). Withaferin A induces p53-dependent apoptosis by repression of HPV oncogenes and upregulation of tumor suppressor proteins in human cervical cancer cells *Carcinogenesis*; 32(11):1697-705. doi: 10.1093/carcin/bgr192

Namasivayam, AR., (1999 Jan). Antistressor effect of Withania somnifera. *J Ethnopharmacol*; 64(1):91-3. [PubMed] [Ref list]

Prakash, J., Yadav, SK., Chouhan, S., & Singh, SP. Neurochem Res. 2013 May;38(5):972-80. doi: 10.1007/s11064-013-1005-4. Epub 2013 Feb 22.Neuroprotective role of Withania somnifera root extract in maneb-paraquat induced mouse model of parkinsonism

Raut, AA., Rege, NN., Tadvi, FM., Solanki, PV. (2012). Exploratory study to evaluate tolerability, safety, and activity of ashwagandha (withania somnifera) in healthy volunteers. *J Ayurveda Integr Med;* 3:111-4. Source of Support: Indian Council for Medical Research (ICMR)

Samadi, AK., Mukerji, R., Shah, A., Timmermann, BN., & Cohen, MS. (2017 Aug 22). A novel RET inhibitor with potent efficacy against medullary thyroid cancer in vivo. *Surgery.* 2010;148:1228-1236. [PMC free article] [PubMed]

Sharma, AK., Basu, I., & Singh, S. (2018 Mar; 2017. Epub). Efficacy and safety of a ashwagandha root extract in subclinical hypothyroid patients: a double-blind, randomized placebo-controlled trial. *J Altern Complement Med,* 0183. (3):243-248. doi: 2410.1089/ac

Sharma, GS. (1938). *Ashwagandharishta — rastantra sar evam sidhyaprayog sangrah, Krishna-Gopal Ayurveda Bhawan (Dharmarth Trust), Nagpur* 743-744.

Sharma, PV. (1999). Ashwagandha, dravyaguna vijana, *Chaukhambha Viashwabharti, Varanasi,* 763-765

Shenoy, Shweta., Chaskar, Udesh., Sandhu, Jaspal, S., & Paadhi, MM. (2012 Oct-Dec). Effects of eight-week supplementation of ashwagandha on cardiorespiratory endurance in elite Indian cyclists. *J Ayurveda Integr Med.* 3(4): 209-214. doi: 10.4103/0975-9476.104444 PMCID: PMC3545242PMID: 23326093

Singh, RS. (1983). Ashwagandha, vanaushadhi nidharsika *(Ayurvedic Pharmacopia) UP Sansthan:* pp. 30-31. [Ref list]

Yang, H., Shi, G., & Dou, QP. (2007). The tumor proteasome is a primary target for the natural anticancer compound Withaferin An isolated from "Indian winter cherry" *Mol Pharmacol.* 71:426-437. [PubMed]

## CHAPTER THREE: RECOMMENDED WEBSITES

http://balconygardenweb.com/how-to-grow-ashwagandha-cultivation-and-growing-ashwagandha/

http://www.toddcaldecott.com

https://food.ndtv.com/ayurveda/ashwagandha-the-powerful-health-benefits-and-beauty-benefits-you-need-to-know-1220328

https://sunrisechildrenshospital.com/hl/?/21532/Ashwagandha

https://www.curejoy.com/content/ashwagandha-for-insomnia-and-dosage-for-better-sleep

https://www.curejoy.com/content/ashwagandha-recipes-tea-tincture-smoothie

https://www.theayurvedaexperience.com/blog/what-is-ashwagandha-benefits-usage

https://www.webmd.com/vitamins/ai/ingredientmono-953/ashwagandha

https://www.youtube.com/watch?v=FNSCI15XG0M

## CHAPTER FOUR: GINGER

Benzie, BAM., Dong, Z. (2011). Wachtel-Galor S, The amazing and mighty ginger. *Herbal Medicine: Biomolecular and Clinical Aspects.* 2nd edition/. Boca Raton (FL): CRC Press/Taylor & Francis;. Chapter 7

Chen, CY., Liu, TZ., & Liu, YW., et al. (2007). "6-shogaol (alkanone from ginger) induces apoptotic cell death of human hepatoma p53 mutant mahlavu subline via an oxidative stress-mediated caspase-dependent mechanism." *Journal of Agricultural and Food Chemistry,* vol. 55, no. 3, pp. 948-954

Citronberg, J., Bostick, R., Ahearn, T., Turgeon, DK., Ruffin, MT., Djuric, Z., & Zick, SM. (2013 ). Effects of ginger supplementation on cell-cycle biomarkers in the normal-appearing colonic mucosa of patients at increased risk for colorectal cancer: results from a pilot, randomized, and controlled trial. *Cancer Prev Res* (Phila). Apr;6(4):271-81. doi: 10.1158/1940-6207.CAPR-12-0327

Eun, MK., Hye Jin, K., Sohee, Kim., Woo, Hyuck Choi., & Young, Park. (2009). Modulation of macrophage functions by compounds isolated from zingiber officinale. *Planta Med,* 75(2): 148-151 DOI: 10.1055/s-0028-1088347

Daily, JW., Zhang, X., Kim, DS., & Park S. (Epub 2015 Jul 14). Efficacy of ginger for alleviating the symptoms of primary dysmenorrhea: a systematic review and meta-analysis of randomized clinical trials. pain med.;16(12):2243-55. doi: 10.1111/pme.12853

Grøntved, A., Brask, T., Kambskard, J., & Hentzer, E. (1988 Jan-Feb). Ginger root against seasickness. A controlled trial on the open sea. *Acta Otolaryngol,* ;105(1-2):45-9

Ishiguro, K., Ando, T., Maeda, O., et al., (2007). "Ginger ingredients reduce viability of gastric cancer cells via distinct mechanisms," *Biochemical and Biophysical Research Communications,* vol. 362, no. 1, pp. 218-223,

Karna, P., Chagani, SRSG., Padmashree, C., Rida, G., Asif, G., Sharma, V., Gupta, M., & Aneja R. (2013 Feb 13). Benefits of whole ginger extract in prostate cancer. *Br J Nutr. Author manuscript; available in PMC.* Published in final edited form as: Br J Nutr. 2012 Feb; 107(4): 473-484. Published online 2011 Aug 18. doi: 10.1017/S0007114511003308 PMCID: PMC3426621 NIHMSID: NIHMS399876 PMID: 21849094

Mashhadi, NS., Ghiasvand, Reza, Askari, Gholamreza, Darvishi, L., & Reza, M. (2013 Apr). Anti-oxidative and anti-inflammatory effects of ginger in health and physical activity: review of current evidence. *MofidInt J Prev Med4* (Suppl 1): S36-S42. PMCID: PMC3665023PMID: 23717767

Nicoll, R. and Henein, MY. (2009). Ginger (zingiber officinale roscoe): a hot remedy for cardiovascular disease? *Int J Cardiol.* ;131(3):408-9. [PubMed: 18037515] [Reference list]

Park,YJ., Wen, J., Bang, S., Park, SW., & Song, SY. (2006). "[6]- Gingerol induces cell cycle arrest and cell death of mutant p53 expressing pancreatic cancer cells". *Yonsei Medical Journal,* vol. 47, no. 5, pp. 688-697

Parsa, YZ., Meisam, ES., Hosseini, M., Nikbakht, NA., Sedighi, S., Salehi, SMH., & Madani, H. (2012 Jul-Aug). Ginger as a miracle against chemotherapy-induced vomiting *Iran J Nurs Midwifery Res.* 17(5): 325-329. PMCID: PMC3703071PMID: 23853643

Ryan, JL., Heckler, CE., Roscoe, JA., Dakhil R, Kirshner, J., Flynn, PJ., & Morrow, GR. (2011 Aug 5). Ginger (Zingiber officinale) reduces acute chemotherapy-induced nausea: A URCC CCOP study of 576 patients Published online. doi: 10.1007/s00520-011-1236-3 PMCID: PMC3361530 NIHMSID: NIHMS358570 PMID: 21818642 *Support Care Cancer.* 2012 Jul; 20(7): 1479-1489.

Stanisiere, J., Mousset, PY., & Lafay, S. (2018 Apr 1). How safe is ginger rhizome for decreasing nausea and vomiting in women during early pregnancy? ;7(4). pii: E50. doi: 10.3390/foods7040050.

Young, HY., Luo,YL., Cheng, HY., Hsieh, WC., Liao, JC., & Peng, WH. (2005). Analgesic and anti-inflammatory activities of [6]-gingerol. J Ethnopharmacol. 96(1-2):207-10. [PubMed: 15588672] [Reference list]

Zhu, J., Chen, H., Song, Z., Wang, X., & Sun, Z. (2018 Jan 9). Effects of ginger (zingiber officinale roscoe) on type 2 diabetes mellitus and components of the metabolic syndrome: a systematic review and meta-analysis of randomized controlled trials. *Evid Based Complement Alternat Med,* 2018; 2018: 5692962. Published online. doi: 10.1155/2018/5692962 PMCID: PMC5818945 PMID: 29541142

## CHAPTER FOUR: RECOMMENDED WEBSITES

https://veggieharvest.com/herbs/ginger.htmls

https://www.livestrong.com/article/232697-how-to-dry-ginger-root

http://muditainstitute.com/blogs/happybelly/ginger.html

https://www.medicalnewstoday.com/articles/265990.php

https://www.wellness.com/reference/herb/ginger-zingiber-officinale-roscoe/dosing-and-safety

https://draxe.com/10-medicinal-ginger-health-benefits/

https://examine.com/supplements/ginger

## CHAPTER FIVE: CINNAMON

Akilen, R., Pimlott, Z., Tsiami, A. & Robinson, N. (2013). Effect of short-term administration of cinnamon on blood pressure in patients with prediabetes and type-2 diabetes. *Nutrition,* 29:1192-6 [PubMed]

Allen, RW., Schwartzman, E., Baker, WL., Coleman, CI., & Phung, OJ. (2013). Cinnamon use in type-2 diabetes: an updated systematic review and meta-analysis. *Ann Fam Med,* 11:452-9 [PMC free article] [PubMed]

Alqasoumi, S. (2012). Anti-secretagogue and antiulcer effects of cinnamon (cinnamomum zeylanicum) in rats. *J Pharmacog Phytother,* 4:53-61

Ghosh, RM., Ganapathy, WL., Alworth, DC., Chan., & Kumar, AP. (2009). "Combination of 2-methoxyestradiol (2-ME2) and eugenol for apoptosis induction synergistically in androgen independent prostate cancer cells." *The Journal of Steroid Biochemistry and Molecular Biology,* vol. 113, no. 1-2, pp. 25-35

Hong, JW., Yang, GE., Kim, YB., Eom, SH., Lew, JH., & Kang, H. (2012). Anti-inflammatory activity of cinnamon water extract in vivo and in vitro LPS-induced models. BMC Complement Altern Med, 12:237 [PMC free article] [PubMed]

Jaganathan, SKA., Mazumdar, D., Mondhe & Mandal. (2011). "Apoptotic effect of eugenol in human colon cancer cell lines." *Cell Biology International,* vol. 35, no. 6, pp. 607-615

Javed, I., Faisal, I., Rahman, Z., Khan, MZ., Muhammad, F., Aslam, B., et al. (2012). Lipid lowering effect of cinnamomum zeylanicum in hyperlipidaemic albino rabbits. *Pak J Pharm Sci,* 25:141-7[PubMed]

Koppikar, SJ., Choudhari, AS., Suryavanshi, SA., Kumari, S., Chattopadhyay, S., Kaul-Ghanekar,R. (2010). "Aqueous cinnamon extract (ace-c) from the bark of cinnamomum cassia causes apoptosis in human cervical cancer cell line (siha) through loss of mitochondrial membrane potential." *BMC Cancer,* vol. 10, article no. 210

Kwon, HK., Hwang, JS., So, JS., Lee, CG., Sahoo, A., Ryu, JH., et al. (2010). Cinnamon extract induces tumor cell death through inhibition of NFkappaB and AP. *BMC Cancer.* 10:392, [PMC free article] [PubMed]

Mancini-Filho, J., Van-Koiij, A., Mancini, DA., Cozzolino, FF. & Torres, RP. (1998). Antioxidant activity of cinnamon (Cinnamomum zeylanicum, Breyne) extracts. *Boll Chim Farm,* 137:443 [PubMed]

Muthuswamy, S., Rupasinghe, HP., & Stratton, GW. (2008). Antimicrobial effect of cinnamon bark extract on Escherichia coli O157: H7, listeria innocua and fresh-cut apple slices. *J Food Saf,* 28:534-49

Nyadjeu, P., Dongmo, A., Nguelefack, TB., & Kamanyi A. (2011). Antihypertensive and vasorelaxant effects of cinnamomum zeylanicum stem bark aqueous extract in rats. *J Complement Integr Med.* :8 [PubMed]

Park, KRD., Nam, HM., & Yun et al., (2011). "Caryophyllene oxide inhibits growth and induces apoptosis through the suppression of PI3K/AKT/mTOR/S6K1 pathways and ROS-mediated MAPKs activation." *Cancer Letters,* vol. 312, no. 2, pp. 178-188

Schoene, NW., Kelly, MA., Polansky, MM., & Anderson, RA. (2005). "Water-soluble polymeric polyphenols from cinnamon inhibit proliferation and alter cell cycle distribution patterns of hematologic tumor cell lines." *Cancer Letters,* vol. 230, no. 1, pp. 134-140

Song, F., Li, H., Sun, J., Wang, S. (2013). Protective effects of cinnamic acid and cinnamic aldehyde on isoproterenol-induced acute myocardial ischemia in rats. *J Ethnopharmacol,* 150:125-30 [PubMed]

Wainstein, J., Stern, N., Heller, S., & Boaz, M. (2011). Dietary cinnamon supplementation and changes in systolic blood pressure in subjects with type-2 diabetes. *J Med Food,* 14:1505-10 [PubMed]

Wu, SJ., Ng, LT., & Lin, CC. (2005). "Cinnamaldehyde-induced apoptosis in human PLC/PRF/5 cells through activation of the proapoptotic Bcl-2 family proteins and MAPK pathway." *Life Sciences,* vol. 77, no. 8, pp. 938-951

Yoo, CB., Han, KT., Cho, KS., et al. (2005). "Eugenol isolated from the essential oil of Eugenia caryophyllata induces a reactive oxygen species-mediated apoptosis in HL-60 human promyelocyticleukemia cells." *Cancer Letters,* vol. 225, no. 1, pp. 41-52

## CHAPTER FIVE: RECOMMENDED WEBSITES

https://www.motherearthliving.com/gardening/growing-tropical-cinnamon-ze0z1101zdeb

## CHAPTER SIX: GARLIC

Aggarwal, BB., Ichikawa, H., Garodia, P., et al., (2006). From traditional ayurvedic medicine to modern medicine: identification of therapeutic targets for suppression of inflammation and cancer. *Expert Opin Ther Targets,* 10:87-118.

Ashraf, Rizwan, Khan, Rafeeq, & Ashraf, I. (2011). Garlic (Allium sativum) supplementation with standard antidiabetic agent provides better diabetic control in type 2 diabetes patients. *Pakistan Journal of Pharmaceutical Sciences.* 24. 565-70

Banerjee, SK. and Maulik, SK. (2002). Review effect of garlic on cardiovascular disorders: a review. *Nutrition Journal*

Budoff, MJ., Ahmadi, N., Gul, KM., Liu ST., Flores FR., Tiano J., et al. (2009). Aged garlic extract supplemented with B vitamins, folic acid and L-arginine retards the progression of subclinical atherosclerosis: a randomized clinical trial. *Prev Med,* 49:101e7

Das, A., Banik, NL., & Ray, SK. (20 August 2007). Garlic compounds generate reactive oxygen species leading to activation of stress kinases and cysteine proteases for apoptosis in human glioblastoma T98G and U87MG cells. *Cancer,* First published: https://doi.org/10.1002/cncr.22888

Dhawan, V. and Jain, S. (2004). Effect of garlic supplementation on oxidized low density lipoproteins and lipid peroxidation in patients of essential hypertension. *Mol Cell Biochem,* 266:109e15

Duda, G., Suliburska, J., & Pupek-Musialik, D. (2008). Effects of short term garlic supplementation on lipid metabolism and antioxidant status in hypertensive adults. *Pharmacol Rep* ;60:163e70

Durak, L. (2004). Effects of garlic extract consumption on blood lipid and oxidant/antioxidant parameters in humans with high blood cholesterol. *J Nutr Biochem,* 15:373e7

Fleischauer, AT. and Arab, L. (2001 Mar). Garlic and cancer: a critical review of the epidemiologic literature. *J Nutr*

Frances, MK., Williams, Jane, S., Tim, DS., Aedin, C., Ian, MC., & MacGregor, AJ. (2010). Dietary garlic and hip osteoarthritis: evidence of a protective effect and putative mechanism of action. *BMC Musculoskeletal Disorders,* 11 (1): 280 DOI: 10.1186/1471-2474-11-280

Kim, JY. and Kwon, O. (2009). Garlic intake and cancer risk: an analysis using the food and drug administration's evidence-based review system for the scientific evaluation of health claims. *Am J Clin Nutr,* 89:257e64

Li, H., Li, HQ., Wang, Y., Xu, HX., Fan, WT., & Wang, ML., et al. (2004). An intervention study to prevent gastric cancer by microselenium and large dose of allitridum. *Chin Med J* (Engl);117:1155e60

Mahmoodi, M., Islami, MR., Asadi, Karam, GR., Khaksari, M., Sahebghadam, LA., & Hajizadeh, MR. (2006). Study of the effects of raw garlic consumption on the level of lipids and other blood biochemical factors in hyperlipidemic individuals. *Pak J Pharm Sci,*19:295e8.

Sahdeo, P. and Aggarwal, BB. (2011). From *Traditional Medicine to Modern Medicine Herbal Medicine.*

Setiawan, VW., Yu, GP., Lu, QY., Lu, ML., Yu, SZ., & Mu, L. (2005). Allium vegetables and stomach cancer risk in China. *Asian Pac J Cancer Prev* 6:387e95

Sobenin, IA., Pryanishnikov, VV., Kunnova, LM., Rabinovich, YA., Martirosyan, DM., & Orekhov, AN. (2010). The effects of time-released garlic powder tablets on multifunctional cardiovascular risk in patients with coronary artery disease. *Lipids Health Dis,* 9:119

Tanaka, S., Haruma, K., Yoshihara, M., Kajiyama, G., Kira, K., & Amagase, H., et al. (2006). Aged garlic extract has potential suppressive effect on colorectal adenomas in humans. *J Nutr,* 136:821Se6S

Tattleman, E. (2005). Health effects of garlic. Albert Einstein College of Medicine of Yeshiva University, Bronx, New York (*Am Fam Physician,* 72:103-6. 2005 American Academy of Family Physicians

Tsai, CW., Chen, HW., Sheen, LY., Lii, CK., (2012). Review article garlic: health benefits and actions. *Biomedicine*

Zi-Yi, J., Ming, W., Ren-Qiang, H., Xiao-Feng, Z., Xu-Shan, W., Ai-Ming, L., Jin-Kou, Z. ( July 2013). Raw garlic consumption as a protective factor for lung cancer, a population-based case-control study in a chinese population. *Cancer Prev Res* (Phila), DOI: 10.1158/1940-6207.CAPR-13-0015

## CHAPTER SIX: RECOMMENDED WEBSITES

*Spice Board of India:* http://www.indianspices.com/spices-development/properties/medicinal-other-values-spices

https://www.thespruceeats.com/all-about-garlic-995693

file:///C:/Users/Owner/AppData/Local/Microsoft/Windows/INetCache/IE/V2KBHHUE/grow-save-garlic.pdf

https://growagoodlife.com/homemade-garlic-powder

https://www.thespruceeats.com/all-about-garlic-995693

## CHAPTER SEVEN: PEPPERS

Ahuja, KD. and Ball, MJ. (2006 Aug ). Effects of daily ingestion of chilli on serum lipoprotein oxidation in adult men and women. *Br J Nutr,* 96(2):239-42. PMID:16923216

Ahuja, KD., Robertson, IK., Geraghty, DP., & Ball, MJ. (2006 July). Effects of chili consumption on postprandial glucose, insulin, and energy metabolism. *Am J Clin Nutr,* (1):63-9. PMID:16825682

Bernstein, JE., Bickers, DR., Dahl, MV., & J.Y. Roshal. (1987). Treatment of chronic postherpetic neuralgia with topical capsaicin. A preliminary study. *J Am Acad Dermatol* 17(1):93-96

Bernstein, JENJ., Korman, DR., Bickers, MV., Dahl., & Millikan., LE. (1989). Topical capsaicin treatment of chronic postherpetic neuralgia. *J Am Acad Dermatol* 21(2 Pt 1):265-270

Chang, HC., Chen, ST., Chien, SY., Kuo, SJ., Tsai, HT., & Chen, DR. (2011). Capsaicin may induce breast cancer cell death through apoptosis-inducing factor involving mitochondrial dysfunction. *Hum. Exp. Toxicol,* 30,1657-1665. [CrossRef] [PubMed]

Deal, CL., Schnitzer, TJ., Lipstein, E., Seibold, JR., Stevens, RM., Levy, MD., & Renold, F. (1991 May-Jun ).Treatment of arthritis with topical capsaicin: a double-blind trial. Case Western Reserve University, Cleveland, *Ohio Clin Ther,* 13(3):383-95

Deutsches, A. (1997). Stuttgart: Deutscher Apotheker Verlag.

Ellis, CN. and Berberian, B. (1993). A double-blind evaluation of topical capsaicin in pruritic psoriasis. *J Amer Acad Dermatol* 29:438-42 1993

Garrett, NE., SC., Cruwys, BL., Kidd, DR., & Tomlinson. (1997). Effect of capsaicin on substance P and nerve growth factor in adjuvant arthritic rats. *Neurosci Lett,* 230(1):58

Gaubitz, M., Schiffer, T., Holm, C., Richter, E., Pisternick-Ruf, W., & Weiser, T. (2016). Efficacy and safety of nicoboxil/nonivamide ointment for the treatment of acute pain in the low back — a randomized, controlled trial. *Eur. J. Pain,* 20, 263-273. [CrossRef] [PubMed]

Gupta, D., Kishore, K., Rastogi, S., Singh, PK., Agarwal, A., & Singh, U. (Epub 2013 Feb 11). A comparative evaluation of local application of the combination of eutectic mixture of local anesthetics and capsaicin for attenuation of venipuncture pain. *Anesth Analg,* 116(3):568-71. doi: 10.1213/ANE.0b013e3182788376

Lembeck, FR., Aman. Capsaicin sensitive afferent neurons involved in neuroendocrine regulations.

Lo, YC., Yang, YC., Wu, IC., Kuo, F.C., Liu, CM., Wang, HWWu, DC. (2005,11). Capsaicin-induced cell death in a human gastric adenocarcinoma cell line. *World J. Gastroenterol,* 6254-6257 [CrossRef] [PubMed]

Lu, HF., Chen, YL., Yang, JS., Yang, YY., Liu, JY., Hsu, SC., & Chung, JG. (2010). Antitumor activity of capsaicin on human colon cancer cells in vitro and colo 205 tumor xenografts in vivo. *J. Agric. Food Chem,* 58, 12999-13005. [CrossRef] [PubMed]

McCarty, MF., DiNicolantonio, JJ., & O'Keefe, JH. (2017). Capsaicin may have important potential for promoting vascular and metabolic health, http://www.ncbi.nlm.nih.gov/pubmed/26113985

Mori, A., Lehmann, S., O'Kelly, J., Kumagai, T., Desmond, J.C., Pervan, Kizaki, M. (2006). Mutant prostate cancer cells. *Cancer Res.* 66, 3222-3229. [CrossRef] [PubMed]

Palevitch, D. and Craker, LE. (1995). Nutritional and medical importance of red pepper (Capsicum spp.). *J Herbs Spices Med Plants* 3(2):55-83.

Shih-Chen, L., Smith, FP., & Stuart, GA., 1973. *Chinese Medicinal Herbs.* San Francisco, CA: Georgetown Press.

Ternesten-Hasséus, E., Johansson EL., Millqvist E. Respir Med. (2015). Cough reduction using capsaicin. *Substance P and Neurokinins* pp 251-253| http://www.ncbi.nlm.nih.gov/pubmed/25468411

Whiting, S., Derbyshire, E., & Tiwari, BK. (2013). Could capsaicinoids help to support weight management? A systematic review and meta-analysis of energy intake data. http://www.ncbi.nlm.nih.gov/pubmed/24246368

Whiting, S., Derbyshire, E., & Tiwari, BK. ( 2012). Capsaicinoids and capsinoids. A potential role for weight management? A systematic review of the evidence. http://www.ncbi.nlm.nih.gov/pubmed/22634197

Yuan, LJ., Qin, Y., Wang, L., Zeng, Y., Chang, H., Wang, J., & Mi, MT. (2016). Capsaicin-containing chili improved postprandial hyperglycemia, hyperinsulinemia, and fasting lipid disorders in women with gestational diabetes mellitus and lowered the incidence of large-for-gestational-age newborns. *Clin Nutr,* ( http://www.ncbi.nlm.nih.gov/pubmed/25771490

Zhang, R., Humphreys, I., Sahu, RP., Shi, Y., & Srivastava, SK. (2008). In vitro and in vivo induction of apoptosis by capsaicin in pancreatic cancer cells is mediated through ros generation and mitochondrial death pathway. *Apoptosis,* 13, 1465-1478. [CrossRef] [PubMed]

## CHAPTER SEVEN: RECOMMENDED WEBSITES

http://www.whfoods.com/genpage.php?tname=foodspice&dbid=29https://www.avacare.in/blog/navara-rice

https://www.yinovacenter.com/blog/some-like-it-hot-the-healing-power-of-peppers-2

https://www.whiterabbitinstituteofhealing.com/herbs/cayenne

https://www.globalhealingcenter.com/natural-health/what-is-capsaicin/Introduction

https://en.wikipedia.org/wiki/Capsaicin

*International Journal of Ayurveda and Pharma Research* https://www.anniesremedy.com/capsicum-minimum-cayenne-pepper.php?gc=122&gclid=CjwKCAjwlujnBRBlEiwAuWx4LRklpoitTgBaTqTRqH1DFuhYYD86wByvCpMKqv1muJOk0TzKza7YPBoC-b0QAvD_BwE

https://www.youtube.com/watch?v=bFvimRuxeto

## CHAPTER EIGHT: OREGANO

Dhaheri, ALY., Attoub, S., Arafat, K., AbuQamar, S., & Viallet, J., et al. (2013). Anti-metastatic and anti-tumor growth effects of Oreganum majorana on highly metastatic human breast cancer cells: inhibition of nfκb signaling and reduction of nitric oxide production anti-metastatic and anti-tumor growth effects of Oreganum majorana on highly metastatic human breast cancer cells: inhibition of nfκb signaling and reduction of nitric oxide production. *PLOS ONE,* 8(7): e68808. https://doi.org/10.1371/journal.pone.0068808

Erenler, R., Sen, O., Aksit, H.,Demirtas, I.; Yaglioglu, AS.; Elmastas, M., & Telci, I. (2016). Isolation and identification of chemical constituents from Oreganum majorana and investigation of antiproliferative and antioxidant activities. *J. Sci. Food Agric,* 96, 822-836. [CrossRef] [PubMed]

García-Pérez, E., Noratto, G.D., García-Lara, S., Gutiérrez-Uribe, JA., Mertens-& Talcott, SU. (2013). Micropropagation effect on the anti-carcinogenic activitiy of polyphenolics from mexican oregano (Poliomintha glabrescens Gray)in human colon cancer cells HT-29. *Plant Foods Hum Nutr,* 68, 155-162. [CrossRef] [PubMed

Gilling, DH., Kitajima, M., Torrey, JR., & Bright, KR. (Epub 2014 Feb 12.). Antiviral efficacy and mechanisms of action of oregano essential oil and its primary component carvacrol against murine norovirus. *J Appl Microbiol,*116(5):1149-63. doi: 10.1111/jam.12453

Gutiérrez-Grijalva, EPID., Picos-Salas, MA., López Nayely, Leyva, ID., Marilyn, S., Criollo-Mendoza, Gabriela, Vazquez-Olivo, ID., & Basilio Heredia. (2017 Dec). Flavonoids and phenolic acids from oregano: occurrence, biological activity and health benefits. *Plants (Basel),* 7(1). pii: E2. doi: 10.3390/plants7010002

Kolda, S., Demirtas, I., Ozen, T., Demirci, M.A., & Behçet, L. (2015). Phytochemical screening, anticancer and antioxidant activities of Oreganum vulgare l. Ssp. Viride (boiss.) Hayek, a plant of traditional usage. *J. Sci. Food* Agric, 95, 786-798 [PubMed

Marrelli, M., Cristaldi, B., Menichini, F., & Conforti, F. (2015). Inhibitory effects of wild dietary plants on lipid peroxidation and on the proliferation of human cancer cells. *Food Chem Toxicol,* 86, 16-24. [CrossRef] [PubMed]

Mitropoulou, G., Fitsiou, E., Stavropoulou, E., Papavassilopoulou, E., Vamvakias, M., Papp, A., & Kourkoutas, Y. (online 2015 May 6). Composition, antimicrobial, antioxidant, and antiproliferative activity of Oreganum dictamnus (dittany) essential oil microbial ecology in health and disease. *Microb Ecol Health Dis,* 26: 10.3402/mehd.v26.26543. doi: 10.3402/mehd.v26.26543

Silva, FV., Guimarães, AG., Silva, ER., Sousa-Neto, BP., Machado, FD, Quintans-Júnior, LJ., & Oliveira, RC. (2012 Nov 15; Epub 2012 Aug 14). Anti-inflammatory and anti-ulcer activities of carvacrol, a monoterpene present in the essential oil of oregano. *J Med Food,* (11):984-91. doi: 10.1089/jmf.2012.0102

## CHAPTER EIGHT: RECOMMENDED WEBSITES

http://www.whfoods.com/genpage php?tname=foodspice&dbid=73

https://draxe.com/essential-oils/oregano-oil-benefits-superior-prescription-antibiotics

http://ayurvedicoils.com/tag/ayurvedic-health-benefits-of-oregano-oil

https://www.medicalnewstoday.com/articles/266259.php

https://articles.mercola.com/sites/articles/archive/2014/02/01/oregano-health-benefits.aspx

https://www.gardeningknowhow.com/edible/herbs/oregano/drying-oregano.htm

## CHAPTER NINE: SAFFRON

Abdullaev, FL. and Espinosa-Aguirre, JJ. (2004). Biomedical properties of saffron and its potential use in cancer therapy and chemo prevention trials. *Cancer Detect* PRev, 28:426-32. [PubMed] [Google Scholar]

Abe, K. and Saito, H. (2000). Effects of saffron extract and its constituent crocin on learning behaviour and long-term potentiation. *Phytother Res,* 14:149-52. [PubMed] [Google Scholar]

Abrishami, MH. and Mashhad. (1997). Iranian saffron. Historic, cultural and agronomic prospects: pp 1-10. *Iran: Astan Ghods Razavi Publication,* [Google Scholar]

Akhondzadeh, SMS., Sabet, MH., Harirchian, M., Togha, H., & Cheraghmakani, et al. (2010). A 22-week, multicenter, randomized, double-blind controlled trial of crocus sativus in the treatment of mild-to-moderate Alzheimer's Disease. *Psychopharmacology* (Berl), 207(4):637-43. doi: 10.1007/s00213-009-1706-1

Akhondzadeh, S., Fallah-Pour, H., Afkham, K., Jamshidi AH., & Khalighi-Cigaroudi, F. (2004). Comparison of Crocus sativus L. and imipramine in the treatment of mild to moderate depression: a pilot double-blind randomized trial. *BMC Complement Altern Med.* ;4:12. [PMC free article] [PubMed] [Google Scholar] *Psychopharmacology* 207(4):637-643 [ISRCTN45683816]

Aung, HH., Wang, CZ., NiM, Fishbein, A., Mehendale, SR., Xie, JT., Shoyama, CY., & Juan, CS. (2007). Crocin from Crocus sativus possesses significant anti-proliferation effects on human colorectal cancer cells. *Exp. Oncol.*; 29:175-180. [PMC free article] [PubMed] [Google Scholar]

Blumenthal M. Boston; (1998). The complete german commission E monographs: *American Botanical Council* [Google Scholar]

Brown, AC., Hairfield, M., Richards, DG., McMillin, DL., Mein, EA., & Nelson, CD.. (2004). Medical nutrition therapy as a potential complementary treatment for psoriasis: Five case reports. *Altern Med Rev.* ;9:297-307. [PubMed] [Google Scholar]

Chatterjee, S., Poduval, TB., Tilak, JC., & Devasagayam, TP. (2005.) A modified, economic, sensitive method for measuring total antioxidant capacities of human plasma and natural compounds using Indian saffron (Crocus sativus) *Clin Chim Acta,* 352:155-63. [PubMed] [Google Scholar]

Chryssanthi, DG., Lamari, FN., Iatrou, G., Pylara, A., Karamanos, NK., Cordopatis, P. Inhibition of breast cancer cell proliferation by style constituents of different crocus species. Anticancer Res, 2007;27:357-362. [PubMed] [Google Scholar]

Dhar, A., Mehta, S., Dhar, G., Dhar, K., Banerjee, S., Van Veldhuizen, P., & Banerjee, SK. ( 2009). Crocetin inhibits pancreatic cancer cell proliferation and tumor progression in a xenograft mice model. *Mol. Cancer Ther,* 8:315-323 [PubMed] [Google Scholar]

Evans, WC. (1997). 14th ed. London: WB Saunders Company Ltd; Trease and Evans' *Pharmacognosy*; p. 438. [Google Scholar]

Fatehi, M., Rashidabady, T., & Fatehi-Hassanabad, Z. (2003 Feb). Effects of Crocus sativus petals' extract on rat blood pressure and on responses induced by electrical field stimulation in the rat isolated vas deferens and guinea-pig ileum. *J Ethnopharmacol,* 84(2-3):199-203

Gainer, JL. and Jones, JR. (1975). The use of crocetin in experimental atherosclerosis. *Experientia.* ;31:548-9. [PubMed] [Google Scholar]

Gainer, JL., Wallis, DA., & Jones, JR. (1976). The effect of skin papilloma and rous sarcoma. *Oncology,* 33:222-224. [PubMed] [Google Scholar]

Gohari, AR., Soodabeh, S., & Mahdie, KM. (2013 Jan-Jun). An overview on saffron, phytochemicals, and medicinal properties. *Pharmacogn Rev,* 7(13): 61-66.doi: 10.4103/0973-7847.112850 PMCID: PMC3731881PMID: 23922458

Harper, D. (2001. Online, Last accessed on 2006 Jan 10). *Etymology Dictionary,* [Availabe from:www.etymonline.com/index.php?search=saffron

Hossein, H. and Hani, MY. (2002). Antinociceptive and anti-inflammatory effects of crocus sativus L. stigma and petal extracts in mice BMC. *Pharmacology,* Volume 2, Article number: 7 Published: 15 March 2002

Hosseinzadeh, H. and Younesi, HM. (2002). Antinociceptive and anti-inflammatory effects of Crocus sativus L. stigma and petal extracts in mice. *BMC Pharmacol,* 2:7. [PMC free article] [PubMed] [Google Scholar]

Kianbakht, S. and Hajiaghaee, R. (2011. Anti-hyperglycemic effects of saffron and its active constituents, crocin and safranal, in alloxan-induced diabetic rats. J. Med. Plants, 10(39):82-89

Maccarone, R., Di Marco, S., & Bisti S. (2008). Saffron supplement maintains morphology and function after exposure to damaging light in mammalian retina. *Invest Ophthalmol Vis Sci,* 49:1254-61. [PubMed] [Google Scholar]

Magesh, V., Singh, JP., Selvendiran, K., Ekambaram, B., & Sakthisekaran, D. (2006). Anti-tumor activity of crocetin in accordance to tumor incidence, antioxidant status, drug metabolizing enzymes and histopathological studies. *Mol. Cell. Biochem,* 287:127-135. [PubMed] [Google Scholar

Mathews-Roth, M., Anti-tumor activity of beta-carotene, canthaxanthin and phytoene. *Oncology,* 1982;39:33-37. [PubMed] [Google Scholar]

Modaghegh, MH., Shahabian, M., Esmaeili, HA., Rajbai, O., & Hosseinzadeh, H. (2008). Safety evaluation of saffron (Crocus sativus) tablets in healthy volunteers. *Phytomedicine.*;15:1032-7. [PubMed] [Google Scholar]

Modabbernia, AH., Sohrabi, AA., Nasehi, F., Raisi, S., & Saroukhani, et al. (2012). Effect of saffron on fluoxetine-induced sexual impairment in men: randomized double-blind placebo-controlled trial. *Psychopharmacology,* 223(4):381-388.

Modaghegh, MH., Shahabian, M., Esmaeili, HA., Rajbai, O., & Hosseinzadeh, H. (2008). Safety evaluation of saffron (Crocus sativus) tablets in healthy volunteers. *Phytomedicine.* ;15:1032-7. [PubMed] [Google Scholar]

Mozaffarian, V. (1996). Tehran: Farhang Moaser Publisher; *A dictionary of Iranian plant names;* p. 165. [Google Scholar]

Rechinger, KH. (1975). Graz, Austria: Academische Druck-U-Verganstalt;. Flora Iranica, Iridaceae; pp. 1-79. [Google Scholar]

Sarris, J. (2007). Herbal medicines in the treatment of psychiatric disorders: A systematic review. *Phytother Res,* 21:703-6 [PubMed] [Google Scholar]

Schmidt, M., Betti, G., & Hensel, A. (2007). Saffron in phytotherapy: pharmacology and clinical uses. W*ien Med Wochenschr,* 157:315-9. [PubMed] [Google Scholar]

Tarantilis, PA., Morjani, H., Pollissiou, M., & Manfeit, M. (1994). Inhibition of growth and induction of differentiation of promyelocytic leukemia (HL-60) by caratenoids from Crocus sativus *L. Anticancer Res,* 14:1913-1918. [PubMed] [Google Scholar]

Tavakkol-Afshari, J., Brook, A., & Mousavi, SH. Study of cytotoxic and apoptogenic properties of saffron extract in human cancer cell lines. *Food Chem. Toxicol.* 2008;46:3443-3447. [PubMed] [Google Scholar]

Thachil, AF., Mohan, R., & Bhugra, D. The evidence base of complementary and alternative therapies in depression. *J Affect Disord,* 2007;97:23-35. [PubMed] [Google Scholar]

USDA N. (Last accessed on 2009 Sep 17). *The PLANTS database.* Available from: http://plants.usda.gov/java

Verma, S. and Bordia, A. (1998). Antioxidant property of saffron in man, *Indian J. Med. Sci,* 52(5) 205-207

Wang, CJ., Shiah, HS., & Lin, JK. (1991). Modulatory effect of crocetin on aflatoxin B1 cytotoxicity and DNA adduct formation in C3H10T1/2 fibroblast cell. *Cancer Lett,* 56:1-10. [PubMed] [Google Scholar]

## CHAPTER NINE: RECOMMENDED WEBSITES

https://en.wikipedia.org/wiki/Saffron

*Spice Board of India:* http://www.indianspices.com/spices-development/properties/medicinal-other-values-spices

http://www.whfoods.com

https://www.gardeningknowhow.com/edible/herbs/saffron/growing-saffron-crocus.htm

## CHAPTER TEN: SALT

Balci, AK., Koksal, O., Kose, A., Armagan, E., Ozdemir, F., & Oner, N. (2013). General characteristics of patients with electrolyte imbalance admitted to emergency department. *World Journal of Emergency Medicine,* 4(2), 113-116. https://doi.org/10.5847/wjem.j.1920-8642.2013.02.005

Fatima, R., Aziz, M. & Achlorhydria. (Updated 2019 Jun 12). In: StatPearls [Internet]. *Treasure Island (FL): StatPearls Publishing;* 2020 Jan-. Available from: https://www.ncbi.nlm.nih.gov/books/NBK507793/

Giuliani, C. and Peri, A. (2014). Effects of Hyponatremia on the Brain. *Journal of Clinical Medicine,* 3(4), 1163-1177. https://doi.org/10.3390/jcm3041163

Perez, V. and Chang, ET. (2014). Nov 14;5(6):712-41. doi: 10.3945/an.114.006783. Print 2014 Nov. Sodium-to-potassium ratio and blood pressure, hypertension, and related factors. *Adv Nutr*

## CHAPTER TEN: RECOMMENDED WEBSITES

https://modernfarmer.com/2019/07/how-to-make-fresh-sea-salt

https://www.healthline.com/nutrition/sendha-namak

https://draxe.com/nutrition/10-benefits-celtic-sea-salt-himalayan-salt

https://www.ncbi.nlm.nih.gov/pmc/articles/PMC3331422/pdf/ASL-6-217.pdf

https://www.medicalnewstoday.com/articles/146677#effects

# About the Authors

**Dr. Ed Bauman** has been at the forefront of the holistic health renaissance for the past 50 years. He has earned a Masters in Education from the University of Massachusetts, and a Ph.D. in Health Education from the University of New Mexico. He is the founder and president of **Bauman College: Holistic Nutrition and Culinary Arts.** After studying traditional health systems for more than 30 years, Dr. Bauman created the *Eating for Health*™ approach, which forms the basis of his programs and wellness retreats. At **Bauman Wellness**, Dr. Bauman consults with individuals, companies and teams on how to overcome chronic illness and achieve optimal well being. Dr. Bauman is a co-founder of the *National Association of Nutrition Professionals.*

In the 1970's Dr. Bauman lived on an organic farm in Western Massachusetts where he grew food and preserved food, cooked on a wood stove, started a natural food coop and the *Home Comfort Restaurant*, an all organic farm to table restaurant. Thereafter, Dr. Bauman moved to California where he co-founded and directed the *Berkeley Holistic Health Center,* a landmark integrative health clinic. For over 30 years, Dr. Bauman has facilitated *Vitality Rejuvenation Retreats* for groups in pristine natural settings. On retreat, folks practiced juice fasting, colon cleansing, yoga, meditation, sharing and living consciously in community.

More recently, Dr. Bauman developed the highly acclaimed *Affordable Nutrition Program* taught by his graduates to people in transition, recovering from illness, addiction, poverty, abuse and low food making skills. *Affordable Nutrition* teaches people how to source, prepare and share local food, and eat well on a modest budget. Dr. Bauman is the co-author of the best-selling *Holistic Health Handbook, Holistic Health Lifebook, Whole Food Guide for Breast Cancer Survivors, Foundations of Nutrition Textbook, Therapeutic Nutrition Textbook, Flavors of Health Cookbook, Affordable Nutrition Workbook,* and *Spice for Life: Self-Healing Research, Remedies and Recipes.*

**Shiela Moorthy** received her Master's in Business Administration with a major in Marketing from the University of Mumbai, India and a Master's in Economics from Bhopal University, India. She has worked in the Philadelphia area for 25 plus years, starting in market research and transitioning to marketing.

Moorthy is now dedicated to helping people regain and maintain health and vitality through whole foods nutrition, custom supplementation and wellness coaching. She received her Nutrition Consultant certificate through California state-certified Bauman College: Holistic Nutrition and Culinary Arts, graduating with honors. Subsequently, she founded **Vitalify Nutrition, Inc.** (**www.vitalifynutrition.com**) to educate and empower individuals to take control of their health and wellness.

Shiela offers comprehensive support, one-on-one consultations that include custom diet analysis and recommendations, and group wellness programs. She has been practicing yoga much of her life and recently became a certified yoga instructor. She teaches vinyasa flow, pranayama, and meditation around the Philadelphia area.

# About the Photographer

I am a professional photographer specializing in food and travel photography. Photographing fresh foods artistically styled into tantalizing visuals is my art form and a challenge I love.

I have worked as an editorial photographer capturing high-quality compelling imagery of food, cooking, and people used in cookbooks, magazines and websites in the San Francisco Bay Area for 26 years.

My photos have been featured in books including the *Flavors of Health Cookbook, Affordable Nutrition, Two Hearts, Four Hands, Eating for Health* and the award-winning *New Mexico's Living Landscapes: A Roadside View.*

Taking photos for *Spice for Life* has been my favorite project to date. The process of tuning my camera's settings to the play of light on these beautiful dishes has been very gratifying. It was also satisfying to sample the dishes made for photo sessions! Below are some photos from our trip in India.

— Christine Bauman

Made in the USA
Middletown, DE
10 July 2020